THE RAMAN EFFECT

IN TWO VOLUMES

Volume 1: Principles

Edited by A. Anderson

University of Waterloo
Waterloo, Ontario, Canada

MARCEL DEKKER, INC., New York   1971

COPYRIGHT © 1971 BY MARCEL DEKKER, INC.

MARCEL DEKKER, INC.
95 Madison Avenue, New York, New York 10016

LIBRARY OF CONGRESS CATALOG CARD NUMBER 77-134788
ISBN 0-8247-1014-2

PRINTED IN THE UNITED STATES OF AMERICA

The Raman Effect

IN TWO VOLUMES

Volume 1: Principles

Sir Chandrasekhara Raman

1888-1970

Preface

> The universality of the phenomenon, the convenience of the experimental technique, and the simplicity of the spectra obtained enable the effect to be used as an experimental aid to the solution of a wide range of problems in physics and chemistry. Indeed, it may be said that it is this fact which constitutes the principal significance of the effect. The frequency-differences determined from the spectra, the width and character of the lines appearing in them, and the intensity and state of polarization of the scattered radiations enable us to obtain an insight into the ultimate structure of the scattering substance.

These words, taken verbatim from Sir C. V. Raman's Nobel Lecture delivered at Stockholm in 1930, are, astonishingly, just as relevant today as 40 years ago. They indicate clearly the insight and perception of the discoverer of the Raman effect, but during most of this period such claims would have been greeted with skepticism, because infrared spectroscopy had proved more convenient and useful for most problems. In recent years, however, Raman spectroscopy has enjoyed a spectacular resurgence in popularity and has attracted many new research workers and students. This "Raman Renaissance," as it has been aptly named, has embraced the disciplines of both physics and chemistry, and although the prime motivator of the revival has been the dramatic experimental advantages afforded by the laser, the many new discoveries have also stimulated intensive theoretical activities.

The aim of this book is to provide a basic coverage of the theoretical and experimental principles of Raman spectroscopy and discussions of some of its important applications in physics and chemistry. It is hoped that it will prove useful to students and research workers entering this exciting field or related areas, and to those in other subjects, where Raman results are

iii

providing complementary information to that obtained from different techniques.

The three main problems encountered in the compilation of any multi-authored volume appear to be those of meeting a common deadline, reaching a uniform level of presentation, and avoiding serious overlap. A few comments on each of these, as they affected this book, may be in order. There have been some inevitable delays in obtaining manuscripts from some authors, but fortunately these occurred at a time when there appeared to be a slight slackening of pace in the sometimes frantic activity in this field. The authors were, of course, aware of the dangers of obsolescence in a rapidly developing area, and have tried to emphasize those aspects they believe to have more than transient value. Each author was asked to write at a level suitable for a "typical graduate student," and was reminded that readers would be from the disciplines of physics or chemistry. Nevertheless, some differences in depth of coverage and amount of rigor are inevitable, considering the variety of backgrounds and nationalities represented. Contributors were encouraged to provide references when their own coverage of a particular topic was cursory, and to insert descriptive physical interpretations into long detailed theoretical developments, to minimize these problems. From the chapter outlines submitted by the authors, changes to avoid major regions of overlap were suggested. In a few instances, minor duplications occurred, although usually at different levels or from different viewpoints. Retention of these was preferred to making further changes and possibly breaking the continuity of a particular author's contribution.

I would like to express my thanks to all the authors for their cooperation and efforts during the preparation of this book. I am also grateful to several of my colleagues at the University of Waterloo: Drs. Bruce Torrie, Don Irish, Neil Isenor, and Mike Hutley, for reading several chapters and making valuable suggestions, and Miss Sylvia MacQuarrie for her skilful secretarial help.

Waterloo, Ontario, Canada   A. ANDERSON

Contributors to Volume 1

G. W. CHANTRY, National Physical Laboratory, Teddington, Middlesex, United Kingdom

R. A. COWLEY,* Chalk River Nuclear Laboratories, Chalk River, Ontario, Canada

C. E. HATHAWAY, Department of Physics, Kansas State University, Manhattan, Kansas

R. S. KRISHNAN,† Indian Institute of Science, Bangalore 12, India

P. LALLEMAND, Ecole Normale Supérieure, University of Paris, Paris, France

  * Present address: Department of Natural Philosophy, University of Edinburgh, Scotland.

  † Present address (until March 31, 1972): Department of Physics, North Texas State University, Denton, Texas 76203.

Contents

6. Brillouin Scattering 343

R. S. Krishnan

Contents of Volume 2

CHAPTER 1

Historical Introduction

R. S. KRISHNAN

INDIAN INSTITUTE OF SCIENCE
BANGALORE 12, INDIA

I. EARLY HISTORY

A. Discovery

In 1921, Prof. C. V. Raman began a series of experimental studies on the scattering of light by transparent media of all kinds. These investigations by Raman and his students, besides establishing the various laws connected with scattering, revealed the presence of a feeble type of secondary radiation of altered wavelength in liquids (*1*); this was found to persist even after chemical purification and repeated slow distillation in vacuum. Sunlight was used as the primary exciting radiation and a pair of complementary filters, one kept in the path of the incident beam, the other in the path of the transversely scattered beam from the liquid under investigation, constituted the apparatus; observations were made visually. The intensity of the secondary radiation was found to depend on the wavelength of the incident radiation, and it was also strongly polarized (*2*). The new phenomenon was observed not only in liquids but also in crystals and glasses (*3*). It was recognized immediately by Raman that he was dealing with a new phenomenon of a fundamental character in light scattering, something analogous to the Compton effect. In order to establish its identity, Raman employed a mercury arc and a spectrograph to record the spectrum of the scattered light. He then made the startling observation that when any transparent substance (be it solid, liquid, or gas) was illuminated by a mercury arc lamp, and the light scattered by the medium was analyzed with the aid of a spectrograph (preferably in the transverse direction) the spectrum of the scattered light exhibited over and above the lines present in the spectrum of the mercury arc light, either new lines, or in some cases, bands and generally also unresolved continuous radiation shifted from the parent line to different extents. The unmodified radiation constituted the Rayleigh scattering.

The first announcement of the discovery of this phenomenon, namely the appearance of modified radiation in scattering, was made by Professor C. V. Raman on March 16, 1928, at a meeting of the South Indian Science Association at Bangalore (4). In Fig. 1(a) the Raman spectrum of carbon

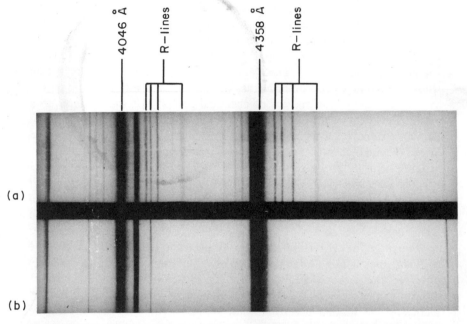

Fig. 1. (a) The Raman spectrum of CCl₄ taken by C. V. Raman. (b) Comparison mercury spectrum.

tetrachloride taken by him is shown. In the very first announcement Raman drew special attention to the universality of the phenomenon and its importance for the elucidation of the structure of matter. He further showed that each line of the incident radiation, provided it was of sufficient intensity, gave rise to its own modified scattering, and the frequency shifts, the relative intensities, the state of polarization, and other features of the new lines and bands were independent of the exciting radiation. The new lines were shown to be characteristic of the substance under investigation. In a series of papers (5,6,7), C. V. Raman and K. S. Krishnan reported the results obtained with many liquids, some gases, crystals, and amorphous substances like glass. They reported the appearance of modified lines on either side of the exciting line, the lines appearing on the longer wavelength (Stokes) side being more numerous and intense than the ones appearing on the shorter wavelength (anti-Stokes) side. They showed that the differences between the frequencies of the emitted radiations and the frequency of the exciting radiation, closely agreed in many cases with the frequencies of infrared absorption bands of the same substances. Thus the frequency shifts observed in scattering are the frequencies of oscillation of the chemically bonded atoms of a molecule; the latter being dependent on the geometry of the molecule and the forces of chemical affinity. The Raman scattering method of investigation thus afforded an extraordinarily easy and convenient way of mapping the vibration and rotation spectra of chemical compounds and opened up a wholly new field of the study of molecular structure. The importance of Raman's discovery was immediately recognized by Pringsheim (8) and Wood (9) and their subsequent work confirmed Raman's findings.

Pringsheim (8) christened the new scattering phenomenon the Raman effect and the spectrum of new lines, the Raman spectrum. By comparing it with the Tyndall effect (Rayleigh scattering), fluorescence, and Compton effect, he showed that the Raman effect was an entirely new phenomenon which enabled one to record the characteristic molecular frequencies more conveniently in the visible region. While investigating the scattering of light in crystals, Landsberg and Mandelstam (10) independently observed the same effect in quartz. Their first paper on this subject appeared a couple of months after Raman's announcement. Besides recording the Raman spectrum, they investigated also the temperature variation of the intensities of Raman lines. After the announcement of Raman's discovery, investigations were carried out by many workers over the world, notably by Wood in the United States, Menzies in England, Cabannes and Daure in France, Rasetti in Italy, Schaefer and Kohlrausch in Germany, Mizushima in Japan, Mclennan in Canada, and Placzek, and Gross et al. in Russia.

B. Significance

The simplest picture of the mechanism of the Raman effect is furnished by considering the interaction between a light quantum ($h\nu$) and a molecule, as a collision satisfying the law of conservation of energy. If the incident light quantum suffers a loss of energy as a result of the encounter, it appears in the spectrum as a radiation of increased wavelength, i.e., as a Stokes line, while the molecule which takes up the energy is transported to a higher level of rotation or vibration. It is also possible to conceive of collisions in which the molecule, already in an excited state, gives up its energy to the light quantum and comes down to a lower energy level. The scattered radiation will then appear in the spectrum as a line of diminished wavelength or of increased frequency, i.e., as an anti-Stokes line. In either case the spectral shifts of the modified radiations from the parent line give us a measure of the rotational or vibrational frequencies of the molecule.

While discussing the interaction of radiation with matter on the basis of the quantum theory, the possibility of the occurrence of a process of the type described above was envisaged by Smekal (11) as early as in 1923. He pointed out that scattering might be accompanied by a change in the energy of the scattering system, with the scattered radiation differing from the incident radiation by the frequencies characteristic of the system. This idea was further developed by Kramers and Heisenberg (12) in their treatment of the quantum theory of dispersion and also by Dirac (13) in his radiation theory. Although the modified lines were implicit in the dispersion formula, the existence of the effect remained obscure and their significance was not understood until they were discovered quite independently by Raman in 1928. It is only after Raman's discovery that the full implications of the dispersion theory came to be recognized.

C. Important Observations

The important parameters obtained from Raman spectroscopy are the frequency shifts, the state of polarization, and the intensities of the Raman lines. The frequency shifts are expressed in wave numbers (cm^{-1}), and are obtained as the differences of the wave numbers of the incident exciting line and the corresponding Raman lines. If these are multiplied by 3×10^{10} cm/sec (velocity of light) one gets the actual frequencies of the different modes of vibration. The observed range of frequencies in any Raman spectrum extends from a few cm^{-1} to about 3800 cm^{-1}. The state of polarization is often expressed as the ratio of the intensities of the horizontal component to the vertical component of the Raman line. If the value is less than 0.1, the line is considered as polarized and if it is more than 0.5, it is considered as depolarized.

Immediately after the discovery of the effect, studies on the effect of temperature on the Raman lines were carried out by Krishnan (*14*), Brickwedde and Peters (*15*), Landsberg and his group (*16*), and Fujioka (*17*). The principal observations reported were the increase of intensity of the anti-Stokes Raman lines, a slight decrease of intensity of the Stokes Raman lines and increase in the width of the lines with increase of temperature.

It may not be out of place here to mention two important features of the Raman spectrum of any substance. The intensity of Raman scattering increases as the fourth power of the incident frequency except in the neighborhood of an absorption band. The ratio of the intensities of the corresponding Stokes and anti-Stokes Raman lines is proportional to the ratio of the population of states in terms of the Boltzmann distribution.

II. THEORY OF THE EFFECT

A. Basic Theory

While infrared absorption involves only one transition, namely the direct transition between the two states, the Raman effect is the result of a double transition involving three stationary levels. The Raman line corresponding to the transition from the initial level k to the final level n of the system can appear only when there is an intermediate level r (also called the virtual level) which can combine with k and n in absorption or emission. If there is no such intermediate state r at all, the corresponding transition $k \rightarrow n$ is forbidden in the Raman effect. The quantity which determines the spontaneous transition probability between k and n in infrared absorption has, however, no influence on the intensity of Raman scattering. The selection rules governing the appearance of a Raman line have been worked out exhaustively by Placzek (*18*) who has shown that the vibrations of a molecule which produce changes in the induced electric moment (i.e., polarizability) of the molecule are active in the Raman effect. The symmetrical oscillations of the molecule which are usually missed in the infrared, come out most prominently in Raman scattering, while the antisymmetric vibrations generally show the opposite behavior. Thus the Raman spectra and the infrared absorption spectra are not identical but complementary in character. The frequency shift, the intensity which depends upon the change in the polarizability of the molecule during the vibration, the state of polarization of the Raman line which depends on the symmetry character of a particular vibration, and the appearance or nonappearance in infrared absorption are the four features that are necessary for the identification of the mode of vibration responsible for any particular Raman line.

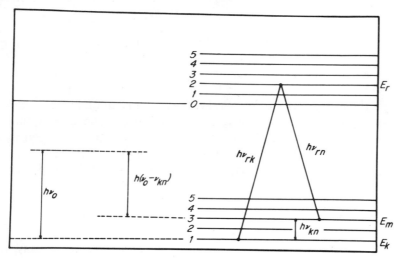

Fig. 2. Schematic diagram for Raman scattering process.

B. Polarizability Theory

The theory of light scattering is based on the fact that the incident light wave induces an oscillating dipole moment $[\mathbf{M} = [\alpha]\mathbf{E}_0 \cos (2\pi v t)]$ in the molecules, where $[\alpha]$ represents the polarizability and $\mathbf{E}_0$ the electric vector. If the atoms execute periodic motion, α is given by $\alpha = \alpha_0 + \alpha_1 \cos 2\pi v_1 t$ where α_0 is the polarizability in the equilibrium configuration and α_1 the maximum change of polarizability when the atoms vibrate.

$$\mathbf{M} = (\alpha_0 + \alpha_1 \cos 2\pi v_1 t)[\mathbf{E}_0 \cos (2\pi v t)] \tag{1}$$

The induced electric moment can, therefore, be regarded as the superposition of three periodically changing moments having frequencies v, $(v + v_1)$, and $(v - v_1)$ respectively. They radiate light of corresponding frequencies which constitute the Rayleigh line, the anti-Stokes Raman line and the Stokes-Raman line respectively. It is thus clear that, while the polarizability of a molecule gives rise to Rayleigh scattering, it is the changes of polarizability during molecular motions that are responsible for the Raman effect. In the most general case of any asymmetrical molecule, the induced dipole moment need not point in the same direction as the incident electric vector. The components of the induced moment vector are related to the electric vector as follows:

$$\mathbf{M}_x = \alpha_{xx}\mathbf{E}_x + \alpha_{xy}\mathbf{E}_y + \alpha_{xz}\mathbf{E}_z$$

$$\mathbf{M}_y = \alpha_{yx}\mathbf{E}_x + \alpha_{yy}\mathbf{E}_y + \alpha_{yz}\mathbf{E}_z \qquad (2)$$

$$\mathbf{M}_z = \alpha_{zx}\mathbf{E}_x + \alpha_{zy}\mathbf{E}_y + \alpha_{zz}\mathbf{E}_z$$

where the coefficients α_{xx}, α_{xy}, etc., are the components of the polarizability tensor and $\alpha_{xy} = \alpha_{yx}$, $\alpha_{xz} = \alpha_{zx}$, $\alpha_{yz} = \alpha_{zy}$. The Raman transition is allowed and the observed Raman line usually has an appreciable intensity, if one or more of the six components of the polarizability tensor α_{xx}, α_{xy}, etc. is different from zero. If the polarizability of a molecule is not spherically symmetric the induced moment will depend on the orientation of the molecule. If such a molecule rotates with a frequency v_r, the Raman scattering will consist of sums and differences of the light frequency and rotational frequency and the new lines are rotational Raman lines. The anisotropic part of the polarizability is alone responsible for the rotational Raman effect. In the case of molecules like H_2, O_2, etc., the polarizability is represented by a rotation ellipsoid. During the rotation of the molecule, the polarizability will change with a frequency which is twice as great as the frequency of rotation. In the Raman spectrum, therefore, the frequency shifts of the rotational lines will be twice the rotational frequency of the molecule. This corresponds to the quantum mechanical selection rule $\Delta J = \pm 2$.

If a vibration of the atoms which constitute a molecule introduces a corresponding periodic change in its polarizability, the scattered radiation will contain the sum and difference of the incident frequency and the molecular vibration frequency. This is the vibrational Raman effect. If the vibrations of the molecule are purely harmonic, each vibration will contribute independently to the electric moment and will appear in the Raman effect. The intensity of any vibrational Raman line is determined by the displacement belonging to the corresponding normal vibration. Besides the fundamental frequencies of vibrations, octaves, and combinations of these often appear in the Raman effect. Although some of the infrared active modes are forbidden to appear in the Raman effect as fundamentals, their octaves are often recorded in the Raman spectrum.

C. Anharmonicity of Vibrations

If one restricts oneself to the harmonic approximation, the amplitudes of vibration being assumed to be small and the potential energy being restricted to quadratic terms, only the fundamental frequencies can appear in the Raman effect. In an actual case, the vibrations are not strictly harmonic and one has to consider higher terms than the quadratic ones in the potential energy function. The vibrational energy of a molecule is then no longer a sum of independent terms, corresponding to the different normal vibrations, but also has cross terms containing the vibrational quantum numbers of two or more normal vibrations, resulting in the appearance of overtones and combinations in the Raman spectrum. It is often noticed that the Raman frequency of the first overtone is not equal to twice the Raman frequency of the fundamental. In a similar way, a combination tone is not exactly the sum or the difference of the two fundamental frequencies. This arises from the fact that the vibrational levels are not spaced uniformly as in the case of a harmonic oscillator. Knowing the actual spacing of the energy levels, one can evaluate the anharmonicity constants.

D. Fermi Resonance

In the case of a polyatomic molecule, it is possible that two vibrational levels belonging to two different vibrations or combinations of vibrations may have nearly the same energy, i.e., may be accidentally degenerate. This was first recognized by Fermi (19) in the case of CO_2; such a resonance leads to a perturbation of the energy levels. One of the sublevels of the second excited state of the degenerate vibrations of CO_2 happens to coincide with the first excited level of the symmetric vibration and has the same symmetry, thus leading to a Fermi resonance. Because of the quantum mechanical resonance a splitting takes place and there arise two levels none of which corresponds to the first level of the symmetric vibration or the second level of the degenerate vibration. Both the levels contain something of the properties of the two original levels. Two Raman lines therefore appear in the scattered spectrum. These are at 1285.5 and 1388.5 cm^{-1} in the case of carbon dioxide. Fermi resonance has also been observed in carbon tetrachloride and in many other molecules, especially in large molecules of low symmetry. In almost all of them, a fundamental has nearly the same frequency as a first overtone or a binary combination.

III. TECHNIQUES OF RAMAN SPECTROSCOPY

A. Experimental Setup

Before discussing the results of Raman effect studies from various angles, a short account of the techniques of Raman spectroscopy is given here. The three main items of equipment necessary for recording the Raman spectrum of any substance are (1) a convenient source of illumination giving at least a line spectrum, if not monochromatic light; (2) a container for the substance with transparent windows for illumination and observation; and (3) a spectrograph for recording the spectrum. In the case of solids in the form of single crystals, the container can be dispensed with. Auxiliary devices such as light filters, condensing lenses, heating and cooling systems, reflectors, polarizers, and analysers have to be used for special purposes.

The simplest experimental arrangement in pre-laser Raman work was to illuminate the substance in the horizontal plane by the light from a mercury arc. The light scattered from it in the transverse horizontal direction is focussed on the slit of a spectrograph of high light gathering power by means of a condensing lens. The transverse direction of observation is generally used mainly to eliminate all stray light and also to facilitate the interpretation of intensity and polarization data.

B. Sources

In the very first experiment, Raman used sunlight and a pair of complementary filters having fairly narrow regions of transmission. Later he used the conventional mercury arc which is being used even today as the most common light source for Raman spectroscopy. Mercury arcs are relatively easy to make and operate. The mercury spectrum contains several intense lines which are suitable for scattering experiments. Those used most frequently arc 2536.5 Å, 4046.6 Å, and 4358.3 Å. Of these, the last two are more often used and are particularly suited for Raman effect studies because they lie in the violet and blue regions of the spectrum, and the regions from 4046 Å to 4358 Å and from the latter to 4916 Å are almost free of lines.

The ordinary mercury arc lamp takes a current of a few amperes for normal running. If the electrodes are water cooled, higher currents could be passed with a consequent gain in intensity. Special lamps of this type with water cooled mercury pool electrodes have been developed by

Welsh et al. (*20*) for investigating the Raman spectra of gases. The cooling permits the use of higher currents up to 15 A; such lamps are now known as "Toronto" arcs. Mercury lamps with external water cooling (entire lamp being water cooled) have also been developed using currents up to 50 A (Stoicheff, *21*).

Rasetti (*22*) was the first to use 2537 Å radiation of the quartz mercury arc for exciting the Raman spectra of gases and also crystals. This radiation of mercury was chosen for two reasons: first, this line has a high intrinsic intensity; second, this line is a resonance line and can be reabsorbed by

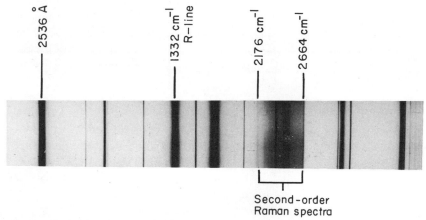

Fig. 3. The Raman spectrum of diamond taken by the author using 2537 excitation, showing the first order spectrum at 1332 cm⁻¹ and second order spectrum extending from 2176 cm⁻¹ to 2664 cm⁻¹.

mercury vapor. A cell containing a small quantity of mercury placed between the Raman cell and the spectrograph would completely absorb the exciting radiation (scattered or stray) and thereby give a clear background on which weak low frequency Raman lines could be easily recorded. The advantages of using the 2537 Å radiation from a water cooled magnet controlled mercury arc especially for crystals have been pointed out by this author (*23*). The enormously increased scattering power of the resonance radiation arising from its exceptional intensity as compared with the other mercury radiations and the λ^{-4} law have made it an ideal source for Raman effect studies in the case of gases at ordinary pressures and in the case of crystals that are transparent to the ultraviolet and are not damaged by it. The 2537 Å excitation was successfully used by the author (*24*) to record the second order spectra of diamond and alkali halides (Figs. 3 and 4).

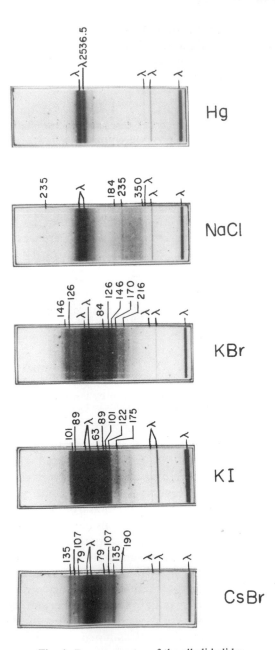

Fig. 4. Raman spectra of the alkali halides.

The shape of the lamp to be used depends very much on the nature of the investigation and also on the size and shape of the container (Raman cell). Straight lamps for horizontal and vertical use (both long and short ones), capillary lamps, spiral arcs, annular arcs, etc., have been used. Often more than one lamp is employed with suitable mirrors in order to have higher intensity of excitation.

Wood (25) employed the 3888 Å radiation of a helium discharge lamp for exciting the Raman spectrum, the main advantage being that the lamp could be obtained in the form of a helical coil and the specimen tube could be kept along its axis. In the case of colored crystals, Krishnamurti (26) used the 4800 Å and 5086 Å of a cadmium arc. The yellow radiation of a sodium lamp was used by Venkateswaran (27) for recording the Raman spectrum of sulfur. Microwave powered rubidium, potassium, and caesium lamps (28) have also been used in recent years. As the manipulation and the construction of these sources are more difficult than in the case of a mercury lamp, their use has been very much restricted.

Since the development of the laser in recent years, there has been a renaissance in the progress of Raman spectroscopy. Because the light coming from a laser is highly monochromatic, plane polarized, highly directional, and of exceptionally high specific intensity, it is an ideal source for Raman effect studies. The radiations normally used are the 6943 Å from a ruby laser, 6328 Å from a helium neon laser, the 4880 Å and 5145 Å from an argon ion laser, the 4416 Å from a He—Cd laser, and the 8400 Å from a Ga As semiconductor laser. The use of a laser has considerably widened the scope of investigations on the Raman effect. If a giant pulsed laser is used, entirely new phenomena are observed (29), such as the stimulated Raman effect and hyper-Raman effect. These will be dealt with in some detail later.

C. Spectrographs

The Raman effect being a feeble phenomenon, it is often necessary to employ spectrographs of good dispersion and of high light gathering power. Photography is still commonly used to record the Raman spectra; however, with the advent of the laser as the source of excitation, photography is being replaced by continuous photoelectric recording techniques. These techniques are all the more essential since the exciting lines from the commonly used helium-neon or ruby lasers lie near the red region of the spectrum where the photographic plate is not so sensitive. Also, because of the smaller dispersion in this region, prism spectrographs are replaced by monochromators with grating optics. Double monochromators with photomultiplier recorder assembly are widely used now.

D. Containers

In Raman's earlier experiments he used a flask as the container for the liquid. This had a very poor geometry. For liquids the ideal container is a cylindrical tube of special design first described by Wood (30), known as the Wood's tube. One end of this tube is closed with an optically flat window, while the other end is drawn out in the form of a horn. The tube is illuminated from the side by placing it parallel to a long tubular mercury arc almost touching it, and the light scattered by the liquid along the axis of the tube is taken out of the flat end and focused on to the slit of a spectrograph. The tube could be suitably cooled by passing ordinary water or a filter solution through a jacket surrounding it. Depending on the quantity of liquid available, the Wood's tube can be of any size. Continuous distillation apparatus has also been used for liquids which become colored during an exposure.

For gases under high pressures, special containers were used by Rasetti (31). In order to increase the efficiency, especially when working with gases at one atmosphere pressure, mirror-type Raman tubes for gases have been developed. The most efficient among these is the four mirror arrangement described by Stoicheff (32) and by Welsh (33).

Different types of containers for crystal powders have been developed from time to time (34). Depending upon the proximity of the lamp to the container and on the number of lamps used, the container has to be effectively cooled.

E. Light Filters

It is necessary to use suitable light filters between the lamp and the container in order to remove the high energy light which might cause photodecomposition and to isolate a particular line from the source and to suppress all the other lines. An aqueous solution of sodium nitrite is used to absorb 4046 Å and a saturated solution of iodine in carbon tetrachloride to absorb 4358 Å. Filters have also been used to eliminate the continuous spectrum present in the region occupied by the Raman lines. Ananthakrishnan (35) employed the technique of complementary filters for obtaining the Raman spectra from crystal powders. As already mentioned, in the case of 2537 Å excitation, a filter of mercury vapor is used to suppress the exciting line from the scattered light.

For determining the state of polarization of the Raman lines, suitable polarizers should be employed in the path of the incident beam before its entry into the specimen and in the path of the scattered beam before its entry into the spectrograph. Appropriate corrections will have to be applied, for the convergence of the incident beam, lack of transversality between the incident and scattered beams, and also for the polarization arising from the oblique refraction at the prism surface or diffraction at the grating.

For estimating the intensities of Raman lines, various methods have been employed. When the photographic technique is used for recording the Raman spectrum, a series of graded intensity marks are taken on the same photographic negative and with the aid of a microphotometer, density–log intensity curves are plotted for the different regions of the spectrum, and from the microphotometer tracings of the Raman lines the relative intensities of the lines are evaluated using the calibration curve. When a photoelectric recording is employed, the relative intensities of the lines are directly obtained from the tracings knowing the characteristic response curve of the photomultiplier for the different wavelengths. The latter technique is now more frequently used in many laboratories.

IV. THE PERIOD FROM 1928 TO 1940

The progress of Raman studies since its discovery in 1928 can be classified under three periods: (1) 1928—1940, (2) 1940—1960, and (3) from 1960 onwards. The review of the progress will be discussed separately for the three periods.

During the twelve years after the discovery of the Raman effect, the number of papers published on various aspects of the phenomenon was more than 1800. In the early stages, the interest changed from an explanation of the Raman effect to the correlation of the effect with the modes of atomic vibration, and both physicists and chemists began to realize more and more the applicability of the Raman effect to structural and constitutional problems. During the same period, more than 2500 different substances were investigated. The number of papers published on simple substances like water, carbon tetrachloride, and benzene is quite considerable; nearly 100 have been published on each substance. In the paragraphs which follow the main contributions to the various aspects of the Raman effect are briefly reviewed.

A. Molecular Rotation

.The rotational frequencies of molecules are of much lower order of magnitude compared to the vibrational, so that they appear in light-scattering as closely grouped lines or as unresolved wings on either side of the exciting line. In the case of gases and vapors at moderate pressures, the rotational spectrum is capable of being resolved into discrete lines by employing instruments of sufficiently high dispersion and resolving power. In liquids and highly compressed gases, there is presumably greater hindrance to molecular rotation, and the rotational scattering comes out only in the form of a diffuse halo or wing spreading out on either side of the Rayleigh lines. It has also been found that when a gas is subjected to greater and greater pressures, the distribution of intensity in the rotational wing undergoes a progressive modification tending more and more towards that found in the case of the liquid. The principal features of the distribution of intensity in the rotational wing of a gas at moderate pressures are that the wing starts with zero intensity at the center of the Rayleigh or unmodified line, reaching a maximum of intensity at a definite distance, and falling off again to zero intensity. The intensity distribution curve is governed by the well-known Maxwell-Boltzmann distribution law. When we pass on to a liquid, the intensity distribution curve in the wing undergoes a profound modification. The wing which starts with maximum intensity at the center of the Rayleigh line falls off in intensity, at first rapidly and then slowly, and it attains zero value at a distance far greater than that anticipated by theory. These peculiar features exhibited by the rotational wings of liquids have been the subject matter of extensive experimental investigation and theoretical analysis.

When liquids are solidified the extended portions of the wings, which appear prominently in the liquid state, are replaced by a set of discrete lines in the solids and are attributed to the vibrations characteristic of the crystal lattice. In the case of molecular crystals like benzene, naphthalene, etc., some of the low frequency Raman lines are attributed to the small angular oscillations of the molecules about their equilibrium positions.

B. Vibrational Raman Scattering

The molecular vibrations in solids, liquids, and gases manifest themselves in light scattering as distinct lines or bands displaced by large frequency shifts from the exciting line of the incident radiation. The measurement of the spectral shifts of the modified lines from the parent line give us directly the vibrational frequencies of the molecules. Apart from its frequency shift, there are three other characteristic features of every vibrational Raman line which give an insight into the geometry of the particular mode of vibration which gives rise to it. These are its structure, intensity, and polarization. It is generally, though not always, true that a sharp and intense line is also well polarized, while a broad and diffuse line shows great imperfection of polarization.

The complete interpretation of the Raman spectrum of any substance would demand an explanation, qualitative as well as quantitative, of the diverse features of the modified lines that appear in it. Indeed, such a thorough understanding of the details of the Raman spectrum would no doubt tell us a vast deal more of the inner secrets of the chemical molecule. For a molecule containing N atoms, there are $3N$ degrees of freedom. Excluding three of these which are due to a rotation of the molecule as a whole and three which are due to a translatory motion of the molecule, there are $3N-6$ normal vibrations for a nonlinear polyatomic molecule. For a linear molecule there are only two degrees of freedom of rotation, hence, the number of normal vibrations is $3N-5$. Unfortunately in the most general case of a polyatomic molecule the problem of a theoretical analysis of the normal modes of vibration is beset with serious difficulties; excepting perhaps in the case of very simple molecules of high symmetry, we are nowhere near the complete solution. The diatomic molecule has, of course, only one vibrational frequency corresponding to the increase and diminution of the internuclear distance. A knowledge of this frequency and of the masses of the vibrating atoms enables us to estimate their binding strength. The vibration spectra of polyatomic molecules become increasingly complicated in proportion to the number and diversity of the atoms comprising them. However, considerable simplification is brought about in the spectra when the molecules possess certain elements of symmetry (e.g., the molecules NH_3, CH_4, SF_6, etc.), and the mathematical treatment of the vibrations of such molecules becomes comparatively easy. Considerable work has been done in such cases to correlate the results of theoretical calculation with the frequencies observed in the spectra of these molecules. In all such attempts the knowledge of the state of polarization of the Raman lines is always of great help in making exact assignments of the observed frequencies to specific vibrational modes.

C. Structure of Vibrational Raman Lines

The vibrational Raman lines are in general far from being sharp. There are several factors which tend to impart a finite width or structure to the Raman lines. The molecular rotation in the case of gases and liquids is, in fact, one of the most important of these causes. It has already been remarked that the pure rotational frequencies superposed on the frequency of the exciting radiation results in a broadening of the latter line in the modified spectrum. In a similar way, the molecular rotation superposed on the vibration manifests itself in a broadening of the vibrational Raman lines. In the case of molecules with low moments of inertia, the rotational components of the vibrational line can be resolved by employing suitable instruments as for the pure rotational spectrum itself.

In liquids, particularly those whose molecules are known to be associated or polymerized, the mutual influence of the neighboring molecules often has considerable influence on the vibrational frequencies. This point will be discussed at greater length in a later section.

The presence of isotopic atoms in one and the same molecule is another important factor which is responsible for the fine structure of some vibrational Raman lines in certain molecules. Since the frequencies of vibration are determined by the masses of the vibrating atoms, as well as by their mutual binding strength, it is evident that a change of mass without alteration in the binding strength (as happens when isotopic atoms occur in one and the same molecule) would produce a corresponding change in frequency. A beautiful illustration of this is the case of CCl_4 which has been studied in some detail by Langseth (36). He has found that the vibrational Raman line in the spectrum of CCl_4 which corresponded to the symmetrical radial motion of the four chlorine atoms actually consisted of a number of closely spaced components. Their origin was attributed by Wu and Sutherland (37) to the two isotopes of chlorine with masses 35 and 37. This was confirmed by Menzies (38) from intensity measurements.

D. Overtones and Combinations

The close relationship between Raman and infrared spectra has been mentioned in a previous section. Without laying undue emphasis, it is generally true that those vibrational frequencies of the molecule which come out most strongly in the Raman effect are either absent or feeble in the infrared and vice versa. One respect in which Raman spectra differ from the infrared is in regard to the overtones and combinational frequencies. The factors which govern their appearance in the Raman effect and in infrared absorption are discussed in detail by Herzberg (39). These are generally very intense and profuse in the infrared, when sufficiently thick specimens are used, but weak in Raman spectra. The order of intensity predicted by theory for overtones and combinational tones in Raman effect is vanishingly small compared to the intensity of the fundamental vibrations, so that the appearance of such lines in the Raman spectra, more appropriately called the second order Raman spectra, can happen only under exceptional circumstances.

E. Raman Spectra and Molecular Structure

As already pointed out in the previous sections, the Raman spectra of simple molecules were assigned to the normal modes of vibration of the atoms with ease. In the case of more complex molecules a rigorous treatment of the normal modes of vibration became impossible especially since electronic computers had not come into vogue at that time. An empirical way of approach was arrived at, which proved to be highly successful in the broad and general understanding of the Raman spectra of many polyatomic molecules. When one compared the Raman spectra of a large number of related compounds which possess analogous molecular geometry there was a fundamental similarity in their vibration spectra. Extensive investigations on a series of related compounds of similar structure and possessing the same groups like CH, CHO, COOH, etc., pursued largely by Kohlrausch and his coworkers in Europe and by Ganesan, Venkateswaran, and others, at Calcutta showed that it was possible to identify certain characteristic frequencies (now known as "group frequencies") in the Raman spectrum with the presence of specific groups of atoms or of characteristic chemical bonds in the molecule (12). The existence of characteristic vibrations with frequencies substantially independent of chemical constitution and the structure of the rest of the molecule was thereby demonstrated. As a typical example one can take a large number of molecules containing C—H groups. Their spectra exhibit a Raman line around 2900 cm^{-1} (due to C—H stretching) and another around 1450 cm^{-1} (due to C—H bending). In the same way there are frequencies characteristic of bonds C=O, C=C, C=N, C≡C, C≡N, etc. From a comparison of the spectra of a very wide variety of substances mainly in the liquid state, the frequencies characteristic of various groups and bonds have been completely analyzed and cataloged. The presence or absence of a particular group of frequencies in Raman effect or infrared absorption has been made use of in settling important problems regarding structure of complicated molecules.

A further refinement of this technique consisted in an isotopic substitution of atoms which enabled one to unambiguously identify the particular group frequencies. In this context, one should mention that the discovery of heavy hydrogen or deuterium opened up a new chapter in the book of Raman spectra. It is well known that the Raman frequencies depend on the masses of the vibrating atoms. Hydrogen and deuterium differ in a fundamental manner from the isotopes of other elements because of the high mass ratio of the two atoms $(1:2)$. If, therefore, we substitute the hydrogen atoms in a given molecule by means of atoms of the heavier isotope, the frequencies of those vibrations in which the hydrogen atoms are primarily involved will undergo a profound modification, while the remaining frequencies will be practically uninfluenced. Thus we have an elegant and unerring method of picking out the hydrogen frequencies from the multitude of lines exhibited by many organic molecules. From polarization measurements, one can easily identify the corresponding lines in their spectra. This method has already been employed with success in the case of a number of organic and inorganic compounds.

F. Force Constants

One of the important applications of Raman effect is the treatment of molecular vibrations. Attempts were made to analyze the vibration frequencies obtained from data on Raman effect and infrared absorption by the use of specific force fields involving bond stretching and valence angle deformations, appropriate to the various molecules. In a diatomic molecule there is only one force constant and this could be calculated easily and accurately from the vibration frequency. In a nonlinear polyatomic molecule consisting of N atoms, even in the harmonic oscillator approximation, there are $\frac{1}{2}(3N-6)(3N-5)$ potential constants which are mutually independent and all of them will be different from zero as long as the molecule has no symmetry. The number of constants is, therefore, usually large compared to the number of fundamental frequencies. For any practical application, it is, therefore, essential to make approximations by neglecting some of the interaction terms. The theoretical force constants obtained for polyatomic molecules depend upon the type of force field and interaction assumed. The commonly used force fields are the central force field, the valance force field, orbital valence force field, and Urey-Bradley force field. These simple force fields were found to be inadequate for a correct description of the fundamental vibrations of molecules; modified force fields which include the valence force fields plus a few judiciously chosen interaction constants have also been suggested and applied to the problem of molecular vibrations with partial success. In any actual evaluation one has to write down the expressions for the potential and kinetic energy in terms of the normal coordinates and obtain the secular equation. Assuming a central force field, Dennison (40), Manneback (41), and others, tried to evaluate the force constants from the observed Raman frequencies in the case of simple molecules. The procedure becomes more involved in the case of large and complicated molecules. In dealing with such cases the procedure is simplified to some extent by assuming that the force constants determined for a simple molecule can be transferred to more complex molecules, since a given bond has nearly the same force constant in many organic molecules. In the case of cross term constants a step by step method has been adopted. It is found that the procedure is applicable only to a limited number of organic molecules.

G. Physicochemical Problems

We may now pass on to the consideration of some of the physico-chemical problems which have been successfully elucidated with the aid of the Raman effect. Even from the very beginning it was realized that the potential value of the discovery was in the field of chemistry. From Raman effect data one obtains information concerning the frequencies and nature (symmetry type) of the vibrations and the derived bond polarizabilities. These in turn serve as an aid for the analysis of unknown structures of molecules and also for the identification and estimation of the quantity of the substance present in any permanent state or during any transient process. Thus a detailed study of the Raman effect would take us deep into the fundamental problems of chemistry. The various chemical problems that were successfully solved with the aid of Raman spectra are the composition and structure of molecules, molecular interaction, nature of the chemical bond, constitution, tautomerism, isomerism, electrolytic dissociation, association, polymerization, solvent effect, exchange interactions, hydrogen bonding, spectra-structure correlations, kinetics of fast reactions, etc.

V. THE PERIOD FROM 1940 TO 1960

During the period 1940—1960, considerable progress was made in our knowledge of the Raman spectra of crystals and their interpretation, lattice dynamics and the evaluation of the force constants using the F–G matrix method. In the case of gases more accurate data were obtained with gases under ordinary pressures using improved techniques such as Toronto arcs and mirror systems. Some of these aspects are described in detail below.

A. Crystal Spectra

The main difficulties of getting Raman effect data in the case of crystals were the lack of a proper exciting radiation and the nonavailability of good single crystals. Recently various techniques have been developed for growing single crystals of any substance. The first difficulty was overcome by the author (24) by the development of the Rasetti technique of using the 2537 Å radiations of the mercury arc as exciter. Using this technique, the author and his collaborators in India, Stekhanov and his collaborators in Russia, Menzies and Skinner in England, and Welsh and his group in Canada have accumulated a considerable volume of data on the Raman spectra of crystals. Mathieu, Couture, and Poulet in France have also extensively investigated the Raman spectra of crystals using the conventional techniques and have made valuable contributions. The data on crystals have been reviewed by Menzies (42) and by Loudon (43).

Raman spectra of crystalline substances reflect not only the structure of the molecular species present but also the nature and degree of interactions between molecules or ions as well as the structure of the crystal itself. The interpretation of the observed data in the case of crystals is very much more complicated than in the case of liquids and gases. It is not only necessary to know the vibration spectrum of a crystal lattice but also its interaction with radiation as manifested in light scattering. The foundation of the theory of vibrations of ionic lattices was laid by Born and von Karman (*44*) long ago. But it could not be developed in detail even for simple crystals for want of computation facilities. It remained dormant for quite a few years.

Semiempirical methods had, therefore, been adopted to interpret the results of many crystals exhibiting first order Raman spectra. As already indicated in an earlier section, the spectra of crystals containing complex ions like SO_4, NO_3, CO_3, etc., can be divided into two classes, those in which the relative motion of the atoms of the ions alone are involved and those involving oscillations of ionic units as a whole. The former type constitutes the internal vibrations, and the latter constitutes the external or lattice oscillations. As the intramolecular forces are much stronger than the crystalline forces, the internal frequencies of the complex ions or molecules usually lie in the region (400 to 4000 cm^{-1}) and are much higher than the external frequencies (usually below 200 cm^{-1}). This distinction, however, is quite arbitrary and sometimes the two regions overlap. But the above classification helps the interpretation of the Raman spectra of crystals. Excellent theoretical treatments of this problem have been given by Saksena (*45*), Bhagavantam and Venkatarayudu (*46*), Halford (*47*), Hornig (*48*), and Mathieu (*49*). Saksena has tabulated the theoretical depolarization ratios for many crystal symmetries and for three different states of polarization of the incident light propagated along the principal axes and for longitudinal and transverse scattering. Nedungadi (*50*) and Couture and Mathieu (*51*) have also given the symmetry types of the Raman lines of some crystals and the depolarization ratio of the lines for specific orientations.

Taking account of the fact that a unit cell is the repeating unit in the crystal, Bhagavantam and Venkatarayudu (*46*) suggested that the vibrational modes of the atoms in a unit cell are sufficient to account for the observed first order spectrum. They have applied group theoretical methods to enumerate the number of modes of the atoms in the unit cell and in a few simple cases, the theoretical predictions have been confirmed by the experimental findings. In some cases, fewer fundamental modes than those theoretically predicted have been detected experimentally; yet logical reasons were given for this discrepancy. However, this procedure becomes extremely cumbersome in cases where the unit cell contains a fairly large number of atoms. In such cases the above mentioned approach emphasizes certain distinctions which, with available experimental techniques, do not have any great significance.

Halford (*47*) suggested another plan of attack for this problem. He preferred to treat the vibration of one molecule or complex ion moving in a potential field reflecting the symmetry of the crystal. Equivalent ions in a unit cell are not expected to have appreciably different frequencies for the fundamental internal modes; therefore, the multiplicity of the spectra due to a number of equivalent ions might not be detected with available techniques. The resulting spectra owe their origin primarily to the vibration of the complex ion subject to selection rules operative for the actual symmetry of the ion in its site, which usually will be lower than that of free state symmetry. This will result in a splitting of some of the degenerate modes and activation of some, which in the free state would have been inactive. In addition, the crystalline field would affect the numerical value of the vibrational frequency to a certain extent. This approach has been found to be extremely useful in analyzing the spectra of crystals containing a large number of equivalent ions.

Hornig (48) put these ideas into a more quantitative form, and the results of his analysis show that if the vibrations in a crystal are regarded as strictly harmonic, its infrared absorption spectrum would consist of strictly monochromatic absorption lines corresponding to the fundamental modes. The presence of electrical as well as mechanical anharmonicity leads to a change in selection rules in the sense that overtones and combinations of internal and lattice modes can also become active and the monochromatic lines will change into broad bands. The anharmonicity is quite temperature sensitive and is expected to become smaller at lower temperatures. Thus the need for the study of spectra of crystals at low temperature is stressed, because the predictions based on the harmonic oscillator approximation become valid to a higher degree at lower temperatures. Besides, a study of the absorption spectra of crystals at low temperature helps in the assignment of the bands in the sense that summation and difference bands can be distinguished from the variation of their intensity with temperature. Also combination bands of the type v_i (internal) $\pm v_l$ (lattice) can be easily distinguished from the fundamentals (v), because the former will vary with temperature to a higher degree than the latter. Mathieu (49) has given a procedure of enumerating the vibrational modes of a unit cell utilizing the results of the vibration of a complex ion and introducing the idea of coupling of vibrations. In fact this approach is a connecting link between the site symmetry idea of Halford and unit cell approach of Bhagavantam. The prerequisite for this approach as also for the other two is a knowledge of the space group of the crystal The normal modes of the complex ion (having the site symmetry) can be worked out by the usual group theoretical methods. To obtain the internal vibrations of the unit cell, one need only couple the vibrations of the various equivalent ions, subject to symmetry restrictions imposed by the crystal structure. For example, if the crystal possesses a center of symmetry, the coupling has to be done in such a way that the resulting vibrations are either symmetric or antisymmetric with respect to the center of inversion. The external modes can, likewise, be obtained by coupling the translations and rotations of the ions subject to the same symmetry restrictions.

Using 2537 Å excitation, the Raman spectra of a large number of crystals belonging to different crystal systems have been recorded by the author and his associates at Bangalore. The results have been interpreted on the basis of the Bhagavantam and Venkatarayudu, and Halford and Hornig formalisms.

Mathieu and his associates (52) have suggested that some of the peculiarities of the Raman spectra of crystals may be explained by couplings of internal vibrations of the ions with the longitudinal and transverse vibrations of the crystals and by interionic vibrations. In this connection their work on zinc sulfide is very significant.

B. Born's Lattice Dynamics

Among crystals, the simple cubic crystals play an important role as the interpretation of Raman effect data of these crystals would be helpful in formulating the theory of lattice dynamics. We shall restrict ourselves to the case of cubic crystals with two atoms per unit cell whose lattice dynamical properties were first examined by Born and von Karman as early as in 1912 (44) and later applied by Blackman (53) for specific heat calculations (23).*

The theory of Born regards the crystals as an interacting mechanical system of "pN" particles where p is the number of particles in the unit cell and N is the number of unit cells in the lattice. The radiation with which the crystal interacts is regarded as being enclosed in a large box, very large compared with the size of the unit cell. Thus the crystal is considered as a large molecule and the Dirac theory of the particle radiation interaction as given by Placzek is applicable. In order to determine the frequency spectrum, the equations of motion for the lattice are set up in a classical way, and the solutions of the independent normal vibrations are plane waves. If the length of the parallellepiped of Np atoms along one direction is $2na$, where n is the number of cells in that direction and $2a$

---

*Text citations of the Bibliography are in parentheses in Roman type.

is the length of the unit cell in that direction, then all wavelengths $2na/r$ are permissible where r is an integer. Thus we get a continuum of frequencies in this model. These waves, therefore, have their phases continuously changing from cell to cell and according to Raman they cannot represent a normal mode.

C. Raman's Lattice Dynamics

To stress the importance of the smaller number of lines that were actually observed in the Raman and infrared spectra of alkali halides, Raman (54) put forward an atomistic theory of the vibrations of crystal lattices.

Raman's theory does not treat the lattice as a large mechanical system but focusses the attention on a "super cell" having eight times the volume of the ordinary Bravais cell. In other words, while the theory of Born assumes that the vibration pattern repeats itself in a unit consisting of $N = n \times n \times n$ cells where n is a very large number, the Raman theory considers n to be equal to 2. The basic postulate of Raman's theory is the definition of the normal mode as stated by Lord Rayleigh, i.e., "All particles in a normal vibration have at any instant the same or opposite phase of vibration." In a normal mode, the atoms in adjacent cells must vibrate either in the same or in opposite phase. Therefore, if the ratio of the amplitude of the atoms in adjacent cells along the three principal directions are α, β, γ, then these can take only the values $+1$ or -1. Also the values of α, β, γ must be the same for all the nonequivalent atoms in the unit cell. If the two nearest equivalent atoms have the same phase, the third must also have the same phase and the phase of the motion is pictured as $+ + + +$. If they have opposite phases, the motion must be like $+ - + -\ldots$. These two possibilities arise by translation along one of the primitive axes. The other two axes also have two such cases associated with each of them and the total number of discrete possibilities is 8. If there are "p" atoms in the unit cell, there are $3p$ equations for the modes for each case. Therefore, excluding the three translations, there are only $(24p - 3)$ modes out of which $(3p - 3)$ are invariant with respect to lattice translations, while the remaining $21p$ have opposite phases at least along one of the three axes and are therefore forbidden as fundamentals. On the basis of the Raman theory, the modes of oscillation of the 14 Bravais lattices have been worked out by Ramachandran (55). Qualitative rules governing the intensities of these modes and their activity in infrared and the Raman processes have been given by Raman (54).

According to Raman's theory, the vibrational spectrum of a crystal corresponding to the optical branch is discrete in character unlike the quasi-continuous frequency distribution obtained from the Born's dynamics. Accordingly, in the second order Raman spectra of cubic crystals one should observe a finite number of discrete frequency shifts.

D. Cubic Crystals

The only experimental data available in the literature at that time were the results on rock salt, first observed by Rasetti (56) and later discussed by Fermi and Rasetti (57). They had remarked about the feebleness and the peculiar nature of the spectrum which was attributed to the second order Raman effect. The author (23) attempted an interpretation of the spectrum of rocksalt on the basis of the Raman theory. The frequency shifts of the lines or peaks in the spectrum were accounted for as the octaves and combinations of the fundamental modes; but the feeble continuum superposed over the lines could not be accounted for in the Raman theory. In order to verify the theory further, the writer succeeded in recording for the first time the second order spectrum of diamond using the powerful 2537 Å radiation as exciter (24) (see Fig. 3). The second order spectrum of diamond extends from 2176 to 2664 cm^{-1} exhibiting a large number of prominent lines or peaks superposed over a feeble continuum. As in the case of NaCl, the frequency shifts of the peaks were accounted for on the basis of the Raman theory. Immediately thereafter a systematic study of the Raman spectra of alkali halides of NaCl and CsCl structures was taken up by the author and his coworkers (58).

The publication of the experimental results on diamond and rock salt prompted Born and his group to attempt a theoretical explanation of the observed second order spectra on the basis of the Born lattice dynamics. Born and Bradburn (59) were the first to work out quantitatively the intensity distribution in the second order Raman spectrum of NaCl. To simplify the problem they had to reduce the thirty six narrow maxima representing the density maxima of the combinations in pairs of the six branches of frequency (three optical and three acoustic) of the exact theory to sixteen and to assume the same selection rule at the point $L(\frac{1}{2} \frac{1}{2} \frac{1}{2})$ in the reduced zone to hold good for all the points. Their results show that the second order Raman spectrum of NaCl is of the nature of a continuum with superimposed peaks corresponding to high densities of frequencies in some narrow frequency regions of the vibration spectrum of the lattice. These high densities of frequencies according to Born and Bradburn lead to intensity maxima in the second order Raman spectrum. It is to be remarked here that the extreme sharpness of some of the lines found in the Raman spectra, such as the 235 cm^{-1} line of NaCl and their high intensity could not be satisfactorily explained by the Born–Bradburn theory or by the later refinements of the same. Smith (60) extended the theory to the case of diamond and tried to interpret the distribution of density in its second order spectrum in terms of a weighted density of two phonon processes. Yet the observed features of the spectrum were not satisfactorily explained.

Further experimental work on the Raman spectra of the alkali halides using the 2537 Å excitation was carried out by Menzies and Skinner (61) and by Gross, Stekhanov and their coworkers (62). Studies on the temperature dependence, polarization and intensity distribution were also carried out in some alkali halides. Those alkali halides in which the mass ratio of the cation and the anion is nearly unity, exhibit weak and completely polarized spectra with very few details. The other crystals belonging to the NaCl type exhibit one strong depolarized line, while the rest of the spectrum is polarized. Crystals belonging to the CsCl type of lattice possess intense and evenly distributed line spectra superposed over an extremely feeble continuum. Solutions of these crystal problems had to wait until a later period (see Section VI).

E. Group Theoretical Methods

When the classical treatment of the dynamics of a vibrating polyatomic molecule was found to be cumbersome and not capable of easy solution, simplifying procedures were employed which gave a partial, though not the complete solution to the problem. One such procedure was the application of the group theory initiated by Brester (63) and later developed by Wigner (64), Tisza (65), Wilson (66), Placzek (18), and Rosenthal and Murphy (67). The selection rules for the activity of the fundamental, overtones, and combinations of the normal modes of vibration depend on the symmetry of the structure and not on the types of forces that bind the atoms together. The nuclei of a molecule in its equilibrium configuration may possess certain symmetry elements such as reflection planes, rotation axes, center of inversion, etc. With each of these elements one can associate a symmetry operation. The complete set of such operations for any molecule forms a mathematical group and every molecule can, therefore, be assigned a point group, and an analysis of its normal modes can be carried out by standard group theoretical methods. The problem of finding the number and symmetry properties of normal vibrations of a given molecule is reduced to identifying its point group, symmetry operations, and irreducible representations and then finding out how many normal vibrations are associated with each irreducible representation. The total number of normal vibrations should come out as $3N-6$ for a general nonlinear polyatomic molecule. The notations used for vibrations are A = symmetric, B = antisymmetric, E = doubly degenerate, and F = triply degenerate. The group theoretical method outlined above has been extensively used to identify and assign the Raman frequencies of molecules to the corresponding modes of vibration.

F. F—G Matrix

After identifying the frequencies corresponding to the different symmetry types, the next step in the analysis of molecular vibrations is the setting up of the secular equation using a proper set of coordinates. Normal coordinates have been used in many cases. In some cases internal coordinates which are linear combinations of the Cartesian coordinates and which describe the internal configuration of the molecule have been used, thereby reducing the size of the secular equation. But these procedures are very involved in the case of molecules of even moderate size. One of the most powerful tools of simplifying the treatment of molecular vibrations is the group theoretical method developed by Wilson (68) for obtaining the normal frequencies by making use of symmetry coordinates which are linear combinations of internal coordinates. They allow the determinant of the secular equation to be factorized to the maximum extent. The method is called the F–G matrix method. In this method, the elements of the F and G matrices relating to the potential and kinetic energies respectively are obtained. These in turn call for the construction of symmetry coordinates that are subject to the conditions of normalization, orthogonality, and transformation according to the characters of the concerned vibration species. From these matrices the equations giving the normal frequencies in terms of the force constants are deduced. The chief advantages of the Wilson's F–G matrix method are (1) the method requires no separate coordinate system, but instead, makes use of the internal coordinates which are the changes in the bond distances and the interbond angles in a molecule; and (2) the solution of the secular equation in the form of an expanded algebraic equation becomes easier than in a determinental form. Numerous papers have been published on the evaluation of force constants and mean amplitude of vibrations and other thermodynamical properties using the F–G matrix method and the available data on the Raman and infrared frequencies.

G. Temperature Effects

Another important aspect of the Raman effect studies during the second period is the temperature variation. Although most of the investigations were confined to crystals, a few were related to liquids. As the temperature is raised, the frequency shift, the width and the intensity of any Raman line are affected. In no single investigation have the changes in all the three parameters been studied at the same time. While the data on the shift and width are available for some of the crystals studied in recent years, only isolated observations have been made on the intensity changes. This is mainly due to the difficulties inherent in the measurements of intensity. In this connection mention should be made to the work of Nedungadi (69) on quartz; Krishnan (70) on diamond; Narayanaswamy (71) on quartz, calcite, and barite; Shanthakumari (72) on anhydrite and sodium chlorate, and Srinivasan (73) on topaz. Their main observations can be summarized as follows:

1. The Raman lines shift towards the exciting line as the temperature is raised. The low frequency or lattice lines show a proportionately greater shift than the high frequency lines or lines arising from the internal oscillations of the groups of atoms. The χ value of a line, defined as $-(1/v)(dv/dt)$, is greater for the low frequency lines than for the high frequency ones.

2. The χ value for any line varies with temperature, its value increasing rapidly at high temperatures and approaching zero as the absolute zero is reached.

3. The χ values for the different lines in the same crystal are in general different. This value does not appear to depend on the symmetry class to which a vibration belongs.

4. In polymorphic transitions, the low frequency lines shift enormously and finally vanish before the transition point. Their width also increases enormously till the lines merge to form a continuum. Examples are the 207 cm^{-1} line of quartz, and the 185 cm^{-1} and 97 cm^{-1} lines of $NaNO_3$.

5. An increase in temperature causes an increase in the width due to anharmonicity of vibrations.
6. The width versus temperature curve runs parallel to the frequency shift versus temperature curve.
7. The width of the line is roughly proportional to the square root of absolute temperature.
8. The peak intensity of the Stokes line decreases as the temperature increases though an increase is to be expected on Placzek's theory.
9. The anti-Stokes lines increase in intensity with increase in temperature but not to the same extent as required in Placzek's theory.
10. The ratio of the aggregate intensities of the anti-Stokes to the Stokes lines for small frequency shifts at any temperature is roughly in accordance with the Placzek's theory.

Some of these features arising from temperature effects are yet to be satisfactorily accounted for.

During the period from 1945 to 1960, Raman spectroscopy was not so much used by analytical chemists as infrared spectroscopy. This was mainly due to the fact that for infrared spectroscopy only very small quantities of the sample are required and the time taken to record the absorption spectra are also very short. Besides, commercial infrared spectrometers were readily available at comparatively low cost.

VI. PERIOD FROM 1960 ONWARDS

A. Cubic Crystals

The important progress during this period has been the theoretical interpretation of the Raman data of alkali halides and other simple crystals.

Neutron scattering experiments have given an indication of the nature of dispersion (frequency versus wave vector) curves in the case of cubic crystals. The inability of the quasi-continuous frequency distribution to explain some of the finer details of the observed Raman spectra led to a recognition of the importance of the "critical points" in the density of states, $g(\omega)$ versus frequency, ω, curve, where the slope shows a discontinuity. Van Hove (74), who first pointed out these singularities, has shown that these singularities in the $g(\omega)$ function are consequences of the flatness in the dispersion curves at certain points in the symmetry directions. These singularities are designated as Γ, L, X, M, W, etc. Besides these, singularities can appear for general wave vectors also. Birman (75) and Loudon (76) have shown that the van Hove singularities in the frequency spectrum should be reflected in the multiphonon processes as slope discontinuities in the absorption coefficient in infrared or intensity in second order Raman scattering. In general, one should observe all the octaves and combinations of these critical points as allowed by the selection rules. The momentum conservation which arises on account of the periodicity of the lattice permits combinations of pairs of phonons of equal or equal and opposite wave vectors. The selection rules do not permit the appearance of all the overtones in infrared absorption. In this approach, the structure of the observed Raman and infrared bands are explained as the overtones and combinations of the phonon branches from the critical points. One has to consider in general the complete list of critical points generated by the periodicity of the lattice and those at any general point due to the complexity of the vibration spectrum and the model used in the calculations. In effect, the important conclusion that has emerged from the critical point analysis of the phonon spectra of diamond, silicon, and germanium by Loudon and Johnson (77) is that it is possible to explain satisfactorily the observed spectra with the Γ, L, and X critical points alone.

Considering now the critical points L, X, M, and W, and also those along the Σ, Δ, and Λ directions, we see that these are along the symmetry directions and hence the equations of motion for this case can be easily written by considering a linear chain of atoms. Further, the critical points L, X, and M are situated at the extremities of the dispersion curves along [111], [100], and [110] directions and, therefore, involve a phase difference of π at least along one of the three axes. In particular an examination of the lattice vibration eigenvectors shows clearly that for the critical points L for NaCl and R for CsCl, the six branches of the phonon spectrum are such that in three of them, one set of planes of atoms oscillate, while the others are at rest and in the remaining three, the other set of planes of atoms oscillate with the first set of planes of atoms at rest. The directions of oscillations for the NaCl structure are along [111], [11$\bar{2}$], and [1$\bar{1}$0]; and those for the caesium chloride structure are arbitrary. On account of the cubic symmetry of the lattice and its consequent effect on the elements of the dynamical matrix, the phonon branches at the critical points at L and X of NaCl structures and M and X of the caesium chloride structures are fourfold or threefold degenerate. An additional twofold degeneracy is further introduced for the transverse phonons, and consequently the phonon branches from Γ, L, X or Γ, R, M, X of NaCl and CsCl structures give a total of forty-eight (24p) modes, involving the vibrations of the various planes of atoms, identical with the supercell modes envisaged in Raman's theory. Thus we see that the Raman theory postulated in 1943 is an extremely practicable and simple approach in explaining the second order or two phonon scattering processes and has now received full justification from the critical point analysis of Birman, Loudon, and Johnson.

To explain some of the minor details of the observed spectrum, one has to take into account other critical points situated along the symmetry directions W, Σ, Δ, and Λ; symmetry planes S_I and S_{II}; and lines Z and Q. These critical points correspond to higher order supercell modes in the Raman picture.

The dynamics of the alkali halide structure have been rigorously worked out by many, notably by Cowley, Karo, Hardy, and Krishnamurthy (78) using different models for the forces. The selection rules for the appearance of the octaves and combinations in Raman effect have been worked out by Birman and Loudon. On the basis of the critical point analysis the frequency shifts of the observed peaks in Raman spectra of many cubic crystals have been accounted for in a satisfactory way. The intensity distribution and the polarization characteristics, however, are yet to be satisfactorily accounted for.

B. Impurity Induced Raman Scattering

Further progress during this period is concerned with crystals which have defects. The presence of an impurity destroys the translational periodicity of the lattice and hence the $k = 0$ selection rule. It is possible, therefore, to induce a first order Raman spectrum, in the form of a continuum in crystals where we do not have a first order Raman spectrum in the absence of defects; and it is possible to replace the first order line spectrum by a continuous spectrum reflecting the singularities in the frequency spectra and the resonant localized modes, if they are allowed by group theoretical selection rules.

The Raman spectrum of KCl crystals containing Li^+ ions as impurities has been recorded by Stekhanov and Eliashberg (79). At 77°K, there is a single narrow line at 208 cm^{-1} which is broadened and shifted to 198 cm^{-1} at room temperature. The frequency shift of the Raman line is well within the allowed band of frequencies of the pure KCl lattice [$\omega_{LO}(KCl)$ = 214 cm^{-1}] and, therefore, it corresponds to a resonant mode and not an overtone. Stekhanov and Eliashberg have studied also the Raman spectra of KCl containing Li^{+}, Br^{-}, and I^{-} impurities (80) and they have attributed the lines to resonant modes. The theory of the impurity induced Raman scattering by the F$_{1g}$ modes in KCl containing U centers has been worked out by Xuan Xinh, Maradudin, and Horsfall (81). Theoretical predictions on the defect induced Raman spectra of Si containing Ge and ^{12}C as defects have been given by Xuan Xinh (unpublished). A theoretical study of the Raman spectra of CaF$_{2}$ crystals containing H^{-} impurities at fluorine sites has been made by Ashkin (82). Attempts to record the spectra due to localized modes were not successful.

Raman scattering by F-centers in additively colored and γ irradiated NaCl and KCl has been observed by Worlock and Porto (83) and the recorded spectra are found to be due to intrinsic phonon branches only. On the other hand, infrared absorption studies of the localized modes in alkali halides are extensive and have been completely reviewed by Maradudin (84). Besides the U-center infrared maxima Mirlin and Reshina (85) and Barth and Fritz (86) have observed side bands due to the presence of pairs of defects in the first and second neighbor coordination sphere. These have been explained using the models by Jaswal (87) and Krishnamurthy and Haridasan (88).

C. Laser Excitation

In recent years, there has been an unusual revival of interest in the Raman effect. This is mainly due to the development of the laser which has since become an invaluable tool for the study of Raman spectra. Argon ion and helium-neon lasers are more often used for Raman effect studies than the other types of lasers. The main advantages of the laser source are the following:

1. The radiation from a laser source is generally monochromatic and therefore the Raman spectra excited by it are simple and more easily analyzed. In the case of conventional sources such as the mercury arc, there are complications arising from multiple excitation.
2. The very high specific intensity of illumination permits spectra to be recorded easily.

3. The very small sectional area of the laser radiation permits the use of small quantities of the substances. Thus laser Raman spectroscopy competes favorably with infrared spectroscopy.

4. The linear polarization and the perfect geometry between the direction of illumination and observation that one has by the use of the laser enables one to make accurate measurements of the depolarization ratio of the Raman lines and also of the cross section for Raman scattering. This latter terminology has been used in connection with Raman effect studies only after the advent of laser sources.

5. The divergence of a laser beam being negligible, the source could be kept far away from the sample to be studied, thereby eliminating the heating effect, and other disturbing factors that occur with conventional sources.

6. The width of a laser line being of the order of 0.005 cm^{-1} or less, precise information could be obtained on the width and fine structure of the Raman lines.

7. The availability of intense monochromatic radiations in the red and near infrared regions of the spectrum has enabled the study of the Raman effect in colored substances. The Raman spectra of substances which are opaque in the visible region of the spectrum, but transparent in the near infrared region could be investigated now using appropriate laser sources.

Using the laser, Raman effect studies have been made by Porto and his group at the Bell Telephone Laboratories, by Stoicheff and his associates in Canada, and by Russell at the Radar Research Establishment in England. Their results on single crystals of silicon, gallium phosphide, magnesium fluoride, ferric and manganese fluorides, alumina, etc., have proved to be of fundamental importance (89). Lippincott and his co-workers have applied this technique for the study of colored crystal powders (90). Chantry, Gebbie, and Hilsum (91) in England employed the GaAs semiconductor laser (giving 8400 Å) for recording the Raman spectra of substances which have absorption in the red. The recent papers on this subject have been reviewed by Brandmuller (92).

With the advent of the laser as a source, Raman spectroscopy has again become one of the valuable tools in the hands of analytical chemists. The availability of laser Raman spectrometers commercially has made Raman spectroscopy as useful if not more useful than infrared spectroscopy for chemists.

D. Electronic Raman Effect

Normally the Raman effect is associated with the excitation or de-excitation of rotational and vibrational quanta. But it is not essential that the nature of the transitions excited in ordinary Raman effect should be only vibrational or rotational. A similar effect should be observed for transitions between electronic states with energies E_1 and E_2 by the absorption of a photon of energy $h\nu_0$ and the emission of one with the energy $h\nu_1$ where $h(\nu_0 - \nu_1) = E_2 - E_1$. However in the Raman effect, there being two photon interactions, the transitions are between states of the same parity and for this reason the Raman effect is particularly suited for measuring low lying energy levels with the same parity as the ground state. Such levels exist in paramagnetic ions, particularly those of the rare earths, which are of considerable current interest as laser materials. States which display magnetic order also have low lying co-operative excitations or spin waves which can be studied by this method (Elliott and Loudon, 93).

Prior to 1964, the only known convincing report of an electronic Raman effect in the visible or ultraviolet region is that of Rasetti (94) who observed on a partially resolved pure rotational Raman spectrum of NO both a Stokes and an anti-Stokes line at the frequency of the doublet splitting in the $^2\Pi$ electronic ground state of NO. Later in 1939 Sibaiya and Venkataramiah (95) tentatively reported an electronic Raman effect in samarium nitrate solutions but later concluded that the observed lines arose from a selective absorption by the samarium ions from the continuous background of the mercury arc (Sibaiya 96). Recently Das Gupta (97) has reported an electronic Raman effect in the X-ray region, obtained by scattering X-rays from samples containing lithium, beryllium, boron, and carbon.

A search for electronic Raman transitions in the Pr^{3+} ion in $PrCl_3$, by Hougen and Singh (98) led to the detection of 10 lines, which arise from transitions from the ground Stark level of the $^3H_4$ state of the free P_r^{3+} ion to three other Stark levels of the $^3H_4$, the five Stark levels of the $^3H_5$ state, and two Stark levels of the $^3F_2$ state. The frequencies and the polarizations of these lines are in agreement with the known energy levels of the Pr^{3+} ion. Chau (99) found the electronic Raman effect in Ce ions in a calcium tungstate crystal with 4358 Å Hg radiation as exciter. Using a He–Ne gas laser Koningstein (100) reported electronic Raman lines of the Yb, Eu, and Nd ions in Y-garnets. Electronic Raman scattering by neutral acceptors like Zn and Mg in GaP was reported by Henry, Hopfield, and

Luther (*101*). More details of the electronic Raman effect are given in a later chapter of this book.

E. Stimulated Raman Effect

Until now we have mainly been discussing normal Raman scattering, which occurs when the intensity of the incident light corresponds to that of the conventional sources or lasers. But, when giant pulses of short duration and high peak power, which can be obtained from lasers of the ruby type, are incident on a scattering medium, nonlinear phenomena are observed. One such phenomenon is stimulated Raman scattering. In this process, the incident light wave of frequency v_0 induces a gain in the scattering medium at another frequency $v_0 - v_R$ where v_R is the frequency of some Raman active vibration. If the incident intensity is above a threshold value, the gain can exceed the losses and the scattered beam with the frequency $v_0 - v_R$ gets amplified. In fact, the brightness of a stimulated Raman line is greater than the brightness of the spontaneous emission by a factor of e^{10} to e^{20} and hence it is easily seen and photographed. This stimulated emission unlike the normal Raman effect is coherent. The observation of the stimulated Raman effect was first made by Woodbury et al. (*102*) in nitrobenzene, only one Raman line at 1344 cm^{-1} being observed in the process. This effect has since also been observed in other cases (*103*).

Often when the intensity of the incident radiation is sufficiently high, higher order Stokes lines with a progressive fall in intensity appear with frequency shifts equal to exactly twice, thrice, four times, etc. of the fundamental frequency. Under suitable experimental conditions corresponding Raman lines are also observed on the anti-Stokes side also. These Stokes and anti-Stokes lines are highly directional. In the case of spontaneous Raman scattering the fundamentals and octaves are not equally spaced. According to the theories of Garmire et al. (*104*) and Hellwarth (*105*) diffuse first order Stokes radiation is initially produced and this interacts with the incident radiation to give rise to the higher order lines. Since usually a single Raman line or at best a very limited number is observed in the stimulated emission process, the stimulated Raman effect does not appear to be of much use to the molecular spectroscopists interested in problems connected with molecular structure and chemical processes. Further details may be found in the chapter by Lallemand in this book.

F. Inverse Raman Effect

According to the quantum theory of the Raman effect, the incoherent scattering of radiation can manifest itself both in emission and in absorption. The normal Raman effect and also the recently observed stimulated Raman scattering are concerned with the emission process. It was A. Kastler (106) who in 1949, discussing a possible application of Raman effect in astrophysics, suggested the name "inverse Raman spectra" for the normal Raman spectra observed in absorption when the excitation is carried out by a source of continuous radiation with a well defined absorption band. But the name "inverse Raman effect" is more appropriately used for the absorption spectra that arise from the stimulated scattering process observed experimentally for the first time by Jones and Stoicheff (107). They irradiated a sample of benzene simultaneously with a monochromatic laser light of intensity below the threshold for stimulated Raman scattering and with an intense continuum of suitable frequency range. This continuum was in fact furnished by a broadened stimulated anti-Stokes Raman line of toluene. The width of this continuum was adjusted so as to cover the position of an anti-Stokes Raman line of benzene. Under such conditions they found a sharp absorption line in the spectrum of this continuum after it traverses benzene and the frequency displacement of this absorption line from the laser light frequency corresponded to a known Raman shift of benzene. Similar induced absorption at optical frequencies has been reported for other liquids also. The importance of the inverse Raman effect can be traced to the fact that no threshold is found and the complete Raman spectrum can in principle be observed. With improvement in the present pulsed technique and the availability of a suitable broad continuum, it should be possible to utilize the inverse Raman effect for the study of gases, liquids, solids, and even free radicals.

G. Resonance Raman Effect

Raman spectra observed when the frequency of the exciting radiation coincides or is in the region of the electronic or vibronic absorption of the molecule show features which cannot be treated by Placzek's polarizability theory and such resonance Raman spectra have been studied in detail by many workers during recent years (108). But the earliest observation on the intensity of the Raman lines as a function of the frequency of the exciting radiation (v) which indicated a deviation from the $(v - v_{kn})^4$ variation predicted by Placzek's theory is that of Ornstein and Went (*109*). They investigated the intensity of the Raman lines in quartz and calcite as a function of the frequency of the incident radiation and found that the 1088 and 288 cm^{-1} Raman lines of calcite showed a much greater increase in intensity in the ultraviolet than that given by the $(v - v_{kn})^4$ law. The larger increase of intensity was explained by correlation with an absorption frequency in the ultraviolet.

In Placzek's derivation of the intensity of a vibrational Raman band, the radiation field is treated classically and the scattering system as a quantized assembly of oscillators. The radiation from the induced dipoles is then related to the elements of the scattering tensor for a transition $k \rightarrow n$ given by

$$\alpha_{\rho\sigma,kn} = \frac{1}{h} \sum_r \left(\frac{(M_\rho)_{rn}(M_\sigma)_{kr}}{v_{rk} - v_0} + \frac{(M_\rho)_{kr}(M_\sigma)_{rn}}{v_{rn} + v_0} \right) \tag{3}$$

where ρ, σ are suffices defining the tensor components in the molecular coordinate system, and M's are the components of the transition moments. The summation is over all the intermediate levels r and v_0 is the frequency of the incident radiation. In the case of gases and liquids an averaging over all possible orientations of the molecules leads to the following expression for the scattered intensity of the Raman shift, v_{kn}:

$$I_{kn} = \frac{2^7 \pi^5}{3^2 c^4} I_0 (v_0 + v_{kn})^4 \sum_{\rho\sigma} |\alpha_{\rho\sigma,kn}|^2 \tag{4}$$

where I_0 is the incident intensity. The above expression for the intensity of the Raman line is not amenable to practical application in view of the fact that the α's involve a summation over all the excited electronic (vibronic) states. Placzek made the simplification of expanding $\alpha_{\rho\sigma}$ as a Taylor series in vibrational normal coordinates, and this is not valid as the exciting frequency approaches the electronic absorption frequency. Shorygin (*110*) developed a semiclassic theory for the resonance Raman effect, under the simplifying conditions that the molecules are in a non-degenerate electronic state, and that they are all oriented identically in space. With these assumptions he found that if only a single excited electronic level r is effective, the intensity of the Raman line of displacement v_{kn} depends on the frequency of the exciting radiation v_0 according to the relation

$$I_{kn} = c(v_0 \pm v_{kn})^4 \left[\frac{v_{rk}^2 + v_0^2}{(v_{rk}^2 - v_0^2)^2} \right]^2 \tag{5}$$

where c is a term independent of v_0. Shorygin studied a group of para-substituted nitrobenzene derivatives, and the intensity of the Raman band due to the symmetric stretching frequency of the NO_2 group increased as the frequency of the exciting radiation increased, and the observed changes were in agreement with the predictions of the above formula. The theory of the resonance Raman effect has been discussed in greater detail in the papers by Behringer (*111*), Volkenstein and Eliashevich (*112*), Albrecht (*113*), Kondilenko et al. (*114*), Loudon (*115*), and Trifonov and Peuker (*116*). While the quantum mechanical treatments have given a better insight to the link between the excited electronic states and vibronic spectroscopic observations and the Raman intensities in resonance or near resonance scattering, the use of these theories for the interpretation of individual experimental results is beset with difficulties, and several simplifying assumptions have to be made concerning the excited electronic states and the vibronic transitions. In spite of these, the predicted form of the frequency dependence of scattered intensity and the depolarization factors for certain vibrational modes have been successfully employed for studying the electronic structure of some molecules, solvent and substituent effects, and for the interpretation of the Raman spectra of colored substances etc. [Behringer and Brandmuller (*117*), Rea (*118*), Maier and Dorr (*119*)]. In fact, the resonance Raman effect is a sensitive method of studying the structural changes in molecules and excited electronic states and can usefully supplement absorption and fluorescence studies.

H. Hyper-Raman Effect

When a very large electric field strength, associated with the radiation produced by a giant pulse laser such as a ruby laser, was used for excitation, besides the stimulated Raman effect, a new spectroscopic phenomenon termed the "Hyper-Raman Effect" was observed by Terhune et al. (*120*). The moment induced in a molecule by an applied electric field E is not given by the simple Eq. (1), but by the more general nonlinear equation

$$M = \alpha E + \tfrac{1}{2}\beta E^2 + \tfrac{1}{6}\gamma E^3 + \dots \tag{6}$$

The first term in E on the right-hand side accounts for the first order Raman effect. The term in E^2 becomes significant for very large fields and accounts for the appearance of the hyper-Raman effect, the intensity of which is determined by the properties of the third order hyper-polarizability tensor β. This has a frequency dependence of the form $2v_0 \pm v_i$ and hence the Raman lines are expected to appear on either side of the octave of the laser radiation. Since the selection rules for the hyper-Raman effect (*121*) are quite different from those for the normal first order Raman effect, fundamentals which are inactive in infrared and Raman may be hyper-Raman active. This affords a new method of study of molecular vibrational states previously regarded as spectroscopically inaccessible. A few theoretical papers dealing with the subject have appeared recently (*122*). As the phenomenon is extremely weak, so far only the hyper-Raman spectra of of water, fused quartz, carbon tetrachloride and methyl cyanide have been recorded (*120*).

I. New Interactions

With the use of suitable laser sources, new types of crystalline excitations have been reported recently (*123*). They are as follows:

1. Raman scattering from magnons or collective excitations in magnetic systems like MnF_2, FeF_2, NiF_2, CoF_2, $RbNiF_3$ and their mixed systems at low temperatures (*124*).
2. Spin flip Raman scattering from neutral donors and acceptors in CdS.
3. Raman scattering from plasma, i.e., from single particle electron and hole excitations in semiconductors such as GaAs and GaP.
4. The Raman scattering by optical modes of metals like Zn, Mg, and Bi.
5. Electric field induced Raman scattering in diamond, cubic perovskite crystals and InSb.
6. Raman scattering from polaritons present in polar crystals, which arise from the interaction of the transverse optical phonons and photons whose energies and momentum vectors are nearly equal (*125*).

In conclusion, the development of lasers and their application for Raman spectroscopy, has opened a vista into basic physics and with the present trend one can expect during the next decade vast progress in our knowledge of the phonon spectra of mixed crystals, ferroelectrics and semiconductors, and the electronic structure of molecules and crystals.

Acknowledgment

I wish to express my gratitude to Prof. P. S. Narayanan for critically reading the manuscript and for valuable suggestions.

BIBLIOGRAPHY OF GENERAL ARTICLES ON THE RAMAN EFFECT

1. K. W. F. Kohlrausch, "Der-Smekal Raman Effekt," in *Struktur der Materie in Einzeldar-Stellungen XII)*, Julius Springer, 1931.

2. P. Daure, *Introduction A L'etude de L'Effet Raman*, Editions de la Revue O'optique Theorique et Instrumentalle, 1933.

3. G. Placzek, "Rayleigh-Streuung und Raman Effekt," in *Handbuch der Radiologie*, Vol. VI, Akademische Verlagsgesellschaft, 1934.

4. H. A. Stuart, *Molekul Struktur*, Julius Springer, 1934.

5. J. Weiler, *Raman Effekt*, Landolt Bornstein Physikalisch Chemische Tabellen, 1935.

6. G. B. B. M. Sutherland, *Infrared and Raman Spectra*, Metheun's Monograph Series, 1935.

7. M. Magat, "Numerical Data on the Raman Effect," Annual Tables of Constants and Numerical Data, Vol. XI, 1936.

8. H. Sponer, *Molekulspektren und Ihre Anwendung Auf Chemische Problems (II)*, Julius Springer, Berlin, 1936.

9. H. A. Stuart, "Lichtzerstreuung im Gebiete Sichtbaren Spectrums," *Hand Und Jahrbuch Der Chemischen Physik, Band 8*, Julius Springer, 1936.

10. A. Kastler, "L'effect Raman et la Chimie," *Rev. Generale Sciences*, 1936.

11. K. W. F. Kohlrausch, *Der Smekal-Raman-Effekt*, Erganzungs Band, 1931–37 Julius Springer, 1938.

12. J. H. Hibben, *The Raman Effect and Its Chemical Applications*, Reinhold, New, York, 1939.

13. S. Bhagavantam, *Scattering of Light and the Raman Effect*, Andhra University, Waltair, 1940.

14. G. Glockler, "The Raman Effect," *Rev. Mod. Phys.*, 15, 1943.

15. G. Herzberg, *Infrared and Raman Spectra of Polyatomic Molecules*, Van Nostrand Inc., 1945.

16. J. P. Mathieu, *Spectres de Vibration et Symetrie des Molecules et des Cristaux*, Hermann, E. T. Cie, ed., Paris, 1945.

17. Ta-You Wu, *Vibrational Spectra and Structure of Polyatomic Molecules*, J. W. Edwards, Michigan, 1946.

18. R. C. Johnson, *An Introduction to Molecular Spectra*, Methuen and Co. Ltd., London, 1949.

19. M. V. Volkenstein, M.A. Eliashevich, and B. I. Stephanov, *Molecular vibrations*, Technical Publications, Leningrad, 1949.

20. G. Herzberg, *Spectra of Diatomic Molecules* Van, Nostrand, Inc., 1950.

21. P. P. Shorygin, *The Line Intensities of the Combined Scattering of Light (Raman Effect) and Problems of Organic Chemistry*, National Research Council of Canada, Technical Translation TT 228, 1950.

22. Walter Otting, *Der Raman-Effekt Und Seine Analytische Anwendung*, Julius Springer, 1952.

23. M. Born and K. Huang, *Dynamical Theory of Crystal Lattices*, Oxford University Press, 1954.

24. E. B. Wilson, J. C. Decius, and P. C. Cross, *Molecular Vibrations*, McGraw-Hill Inc., 1955.

25. S. I. Mizushima, "Raman Effect," *Handbuch Der Physik, Vol. XXVI*, Light and Matter, 1958.

26. B. P. Stoicheff, "High Resolution Raman Spectroscopy," *Advances in Spectroscopy*, *Vol. I*, H. W. Thompson, ed. Interscience, New York, 1959.

27. A. B. F. Duncan, "Theory of Infrared and Raman Spectra," *Chemical Applications of Spectroscopy*, *Vol. IX*, J. Weissberger, ed. Interscience, 1959.

28. R. Norman Jones and Camille Sandorfy, "The Application of Infrared and Raman Spectrometry to the Elucidation of Molecular Structure," *Chemical Applications of Spectroscopy*, *Vol. IX*, A. Weissberger, ed. Interscience, 1959.

29. H. Stammereich, "Long Wave Excitation of Raman Spectra," *Pure Appl. Chem.*, **4**, 97–103, 1962.

30. B. P. Stoicheff, "Raman Effect," *Methods, Exptl. Phys.*, 111–55, 1962.

31. D. A. Long, "Progress in Infrared and Raman Spectroscopy," *Ann. Rept. Progr. Chem.*, *Chem. Soc. London*, 60, 120–48, 1963.

32. H. A. Szymanski, ed., *Raman Spectroscopy—Theory and Practice*, Plenum Press, New York, 1967.

33. N. Bloembergen, "The Stimulated Raman Effect," *J. Phys.* (1967).

34. A. J. Downs, D. A. Long and L. A. K. Staveley, eds. *Essays on Structural Chemistry*. MacMillan, London, 1971.

REFERENCES

1. K. R. Ramanathan, *Proc. Indian Assoc. Cult. Sci.*, **8**, 18, (1923).

2. K. S. Krishnan, *Phil. Mag.*, **50**, 697 (1925).

3. C. V. Raman, *J. Opt. Soc. Am.*, **15**, 185 (1927).

4. C. V. Raman and K. S. Krishnan, *Indian J. Phys.*, **2**, 387, (1928).

5. C. V. Raman and K. S. Krishnan, *Nature*, **121**, 501, 619, (1928).

6. C. V. Raman and K. S. Krishnan, *Indian J. Phys.*, **2**, 399, (1928).

7. C. V. Raman and K. S. Krishnan, *Proc. Roy. Soc.*, **122A**, 23, (1928).

8. P. Pringsheim, *Die Naturwiss*, **16**, 567, (1928).

9. R. W. Wood, *Nature*, **122**, 349, (1928).

10. G. Landsberg and L. Mandelstam, *Z. Physik*, **50**, 769, (1928). *Die Naturwiss*, **16**, 557, 772, (1928).

11. A. Smekal, *Die Naturwiss*, **11**, 875, (1923).

12. H. A. Kramers and W. Heisenberg, *Z. Physik.*, **31**, 681, (1925).

13. P. A. M. Dirac, *Proc. Roy. Soc.* (*London*) **114**, 710, (1927).

14. K. S. Krishnan, *Nature*, **122**, 650, (1928).

15. F. G. Brickwedde and M. F. Peters, *Phys. Rev.*, **33**, 116, (1929).

16. G. Landsberg and M. Leontowitsch, *Z. Physik.*, **53**, 439, (1929).
G. Landsberg and L. Mandelstam, Ibid, **60**, 364, (1930).

17. T. Fujioka, *Inst. Phys. Chem. Res.*, *Tokyo, Sci Papers*, **204**, 205 (1929).

18. G. Placzek, *Handbuch der Radiologie*, Vol. VI, (1934).

19. E. Fermi, *Z. Physik.*, **71**, 250, (1931).

20. H. L. Welsh, M. F. Crawford, T. R. Thomas, and G. R. Love, *Can. J. Phys.*, **30**, 577, (1952).

21. B. P. Stoicheff, Ibid., **31**, 755, (1953).

22. F. Rasetti, *Phys. Rev.*, **34**, 367, (1929). *Z. Physik.*, **61**, 396, (1930).

23. R. S. Krishnan, *Proc. Indian Acad. Sci.*, **A18**, 298, (1943).

24. R. S. Krishnan, Ibid., **A19**, 216, 298, (1944).

25. R. W. Wood, *Phil. Mag.*, **7**, 858, (1929).

26. P. Krishnamurti, *Indian J. Phys.*, **5**, 87, (1930).

27. C. S. Venkateswaran, *Proc. Indian Acad. Sci.*, **1**, 120, (1934).
28. N. S. Ham and A. Walsh, *J. Chem. Phys.*, **36**, 1096, (1962).
29. E. J. Woodbury and W. Ng, *Proc. IRE.*, **50**, 2367, (1962).
    G. Eckhardt, R. W. Hellwarth, F. J. McClung, S. E. Schwarz, D. Weiner, and E. J. Woodbury, *Phys. Rev. Letters*, **9**, 455 (1962).
30. R. W. Wood, *Phil. Mag.*, **6**, 729, (1928).
31. F. Rasetti, *Phys. Rev.*, **34**, 367, (1929).
32. B. P. Stoicheff, *Can. J. Phys.*, **32**, 330 (1954).
33. H. L. Welsh, C. Cumming and E. J. Stansbury, *J. Opt. Soc. Amer.*, **41**, 712, (1951).
34. R. Bar, *Nature*, **124**, 692, (1929).
    A. C. Menzies, Ibid., 124, 511, (1929).
    R. Ananthakrishnan, Ibid., **138**, 803, (1936).
35. R. Ananthakrishnan, *Current Sci. (India)*, **5**, 131, (1936).
36. A. Langseth, *Z. Physik*, **72**, 350, (1931).
37. C. K. Wu and G. B. B. M. Sutherland, *J. Chem. Phys.*, **6**, 114 (1938).
38. A. C. Menzies, *Proc. Roy. Soc. (London)*, **172**, 89, (1939).
39. G. Herzberg, *Molecular Spectra and Molecular Structure*, "II-Infrared and Raman spectra of polyatomic molecules," (van Nostrand Co., New York, 1962), p. 241 and 245.
40. D. M. Dennison, *Rev. Mod. Phys.*, **3**, 280, (1931). *Phys. Rev.*, **41**, 304 (1932).
    G. B. B. M. Sutherland and D. M. Dennison, *Proc. Roy. Soc. (London)*, **148**, 250 (1935).
41. C. Manneback, *Ann. Soc. Sci. Brussels*, **55**, 5 & 129 (1935).
42. A. C. Menzies, *Rept. Prog. Phys.*, **16**, 83 (1953).
43. R. Loudon, *Adv. in Phys.*, **13**, 423, (1964).
44. M. Born and Th. von Karman, *Phys. Z.*, **13**, 297 (1912).
    M. Born, *Dynamik der Kristallgitter*, Tenbuer, 1915. *Atomtheorie des festen Zustandes*, Tenbuer, 1923.
45. B. D. Saksena, *Proc. Indian Acad. Sci.*, **A11**, 229 (1941).
46. S. Bhagavantam and T. Venkatarayudu, Ibid., **9A**, 224 (1949). *Theory of Groups and its Applications to Physical Problems*, Andhra University, Waltair (1962).
47. R. S. Halford, *J. Chem. Phys.*, **14**, 8, (1946).
48. D. F. Hornig, Ibid., **16**, 1063, (1948).
49. J. P. Mathieu, *Spectres de Vibration et Symmetric des Molecules et des Cristaux*, Hermann et Cie, 1945.
50. T. M. K. Nedungadi, *Proc. Indian Acad. Sci.*, **A14**, 242 (1941).
51. L. Couture, *Ann. Phys. (Paris)*, **2**, 5 (1947).
    L. Couture and J. P. Mathieu, Ibid., **3**, 521 (1948).
52. J. P. Mathieu, Couture Mathieu and H. Poulet, *J. Phys. Radium*, **16**, 781 (1955).
    H. Poulet and J. P. Mathieu, Ibid., **17**, 472 (1956).
53. M. Blackman, *Proc. Roy. Soc. (London)*, **A148**, 365, 384 (1935). **149**, 117, (1935). **159**, 416 (1937). *Phil. Trans. Roy. Soc.*, **A236**, 103 (1936).
54. C. V. Raman, *Proc. Indian Acad. Sci.*, **A18**, 237 (1943). Ibid., **A54**, 253 (1961).
55. G. N. Ramachandran, Ibid., **A18**, 266 (1943).
56. F. Rasetti, *Nature*, **127**, 626 (1931).
57. E. Fermi and F. Rasetti, *Z. Physik.*, **171**, 689 (1931).

58. R. S. Krishnan, *Proc. Roy. Soc.* (*London*) **A187,** 188 (1946). *Proc. Indian Acad. Sci.,* **A26,** 419, 432 (1947).
    R. S. Krishnan and P. S. Narayanan, Ibid., **A28,** 296 (1948). *Nature,* **163,** 570 (1949). *J. Indian Inst. Sci.,* **A34,** 85 (1957). P. S. Narayanan, *Proc. Indian Acad. Sci.,* **A34,** 1, (1951). Ibid., **A42,** 303 (1955).
59. M. Born and M. Bradburn, *Proc. Roy. Soc.* (*London*) **A188,** 161 (1948).
60. H. M. J. Smith, *Phil. Trans. Roy. Soc.* (*London*) **A241,** 105 (1948).
61. A. C. Menzies and J. Skinner, *J. Phys. Radium,* **9,** 993 (1948).
62. E. F. Gross and A. I. Stekhanov, *Nature,* **160,** 508 (1947).
    E. F. Gross, P. P. Pavinskii and A. I. Stekhanov, *Dokl. Akad. Nauk.,* *SSSR,* **68,** 27 (1949).
    A. I. Stekhanov and M. L. Petrova, *J. Exptl. Theo. Phys,* (*JETP*)., *USSR,* **19,** 1108 (1949).
    A. I. Stekhanov, Ibid., **20,** 830 (1950).
    A. I. Stekhanov, A. Z. Gabrichidze, and M. B. Elishaberg, *Sov. Phys.-Solid State,* **3,** 964 (1961).
    A. I. Stekhanov and M. B. Elishaberg, Ibid., **2,** 2096 (1961), *Opt. Spectrosc.,* **10,** 348 (1961).
63. C. J. Brester, Thesis, Utrecht (1923), *Z. Physik,* **24,** 324 (1924).
64. E. Wigner, *Gottingen Nachrichten,* 133 (1930).
65. L. Tisza, *Z. Physik.,* **82,** 48 (1933).
66. E. B. Wilson, *Phys. Rev.,* **45,** 706 (1934). *J. Chem. Phys.,* **2,** 432 (1934).
67. J. E. Rosenthal and G. M. Murphy, *Rev. Mod. Phys.,* **8,** 317 (1936).
68. E. B. Wilson, *J. Chem. Phys.,* **7,** 1047 (1939). **9,** 96 (1941).
69. T. M. K. Nedungadi, *Proc. Indian Acad. Sci.,* **11A,** 86 (1940).
70. R. S. Krishnan, Ibid., **24A,** 45, (1946). **27A,** 321, (1948).
71. P. K. Narayanaswami, Ibid., **26A,** 511 (1947). Ibid., **26A,** 521 (1947). Ibid., **28A,** 40 (1948).
72. C. Shanthakumari, *Proc. Indian Acad. Sci.,* **31A,** 348 (1950). Ibid., **32A,** 177 (1950).
73. R. Srinivasan, Ibid., **37A,** 405 (1953).
74. L. Van Hove, *Phys. Rev.,* **89,** 1189 (1953).
75. J. L. Birman, Ibid., **131,** 1489 (1963).
76. R. Loudon, *Proc. Roy. Soc.* (*London*) **A275,** 218 (1963).
77. R. Loudon and F. A. Johnson, Ibid., **A281,** 274 (1964).
78. R. A. Cowley, *Proc. Phys. Soc.* (*London*) **A84,** 281 (1964). *J. Phys.* (*Paris*), **26,** 659 (1965).
    G. Dolling and R. A. Cowley, *Proc. Phys. Soc.* (*London*) **A85,** 463 (1966).
    A. M. Karo, J. R. Hardy, and I. Morrison, *J. Phys.* (*Paris*), **26,** 668 (1965).
    S. Ganesan, E. Burstein, A. M. Karo, and J. R. Hardy, Ibid., **26,** 639 (1965).
    S. Ganesan and E. Burstein, Ibid., **26,** 645 (1965).
    N. Krishnamurthy, *Indian J. Pure and Appl. Phys.,* **4,** 63 (1966).
    N. Krishnamurthy and T. M. Haridasan, Ibid., **4,** 337 (1966).
79. A. I. Stekhanov and M. B. Eliashberg, *Sov. Phys. Solid State,* *SSSR,* **5,** 2185 (1964).
80. A. I. Stekhanov and M. B. Eliashberg, Ibid., **6,** 2718 (1965).
81. Nguyen xuan xinh, A. A. Maradudin, and R. A. Coldwell Horsfall, *J. Phys.* (*Paris*) **26,** 717 (1965).
82. M. Ashkin, Ibid., **26,** 709, (1965).
83. J. M. Worlock and S. P. S. Porto, *Phys. Rev. Letters,* **15,** 697 (1965).

84. A. A. Maradudin, *Solid State Physics*, Seitz and Turnbull, Academic, 1966, Vol. 18 and 19.

85. D. N. Mirlin and I. I. Reshina, *Sov. Phys. Solid State*, **8,** 116, (1966).

86. W. Barth and B. Fritz, *Phys. Status Solidi*, **19,** 515 (1961).

87. S. S. Jaswal, *Phys. Rev.*, **140,** A687 (1966). *Phys. Rev., Letters*, **17,** 585 (1966).

88. N. Krishnamurthy and T. M. Haridasan. Unpublished work.

89. S. P. S. Porto, P. A. Fleury, and T. C. Damen, *Phys. Rev.*, **154,** 522 (1967).
S. P. S. Porto, J. A. Giordmaine, and T. C. Damen, Ibid., **147,** 608 (1966).
S. P. S. Porto and R. S. Krishnan, *J. Chem. Phys.*, **47,** 1009 (1967).
J. P. Russell, *J. Phys. (Paris)*, **26,** 620 (1965).

90. E. R. Lippincott and M. Margoshes, *Proc. X Coll. Spectr. Int.*, Washington, 1963, S339.

91. G. W. Chantry, H. A. Gebbie, and C. Hilsum, *Nature*, **203,** 1052 (1964).

92. J. Brandmuller, *Die Naturwiss.*, **54,** 3 (1967).

93. R. J. Elliott and R. Loudon, *Phys. Letters*, **3,** 189 (1963).

94. F. Rasetti, *Z. Phys.*, **66,** 646 (1930).

95. L. Sibaiya and H. S. Venkataramiah, *Phys. Rev.*, **56,** 381 (1939).

96. L. Sibaiya, *Phys. Rev.*, **60,** 471, (1941).

97. K. Das Gupta, *Phys. Rev. Letters*, **3,** 38 (1959). *Phys. Rev.*, **128,** 2181 (1962).

98. J. T. Hougen and S. Singh, *Phys. Rev. Letters*, **10,** 406 (1963). *Proc. Roy. Soc. (London)* **277A,** 193 (1964).

99. J. Y. H. Chau, *J. Chem, Phys.*, **44,** 147, 1708 (1966).

100. J. A. Koningstein, *J. Opt. Soc. Am.*, **56,** 1405 (1966).

101. C. H. Henry, J. J. Hopfield and L. C. Luther, *Phys. Rev. Letters*, **17,** 1178 (1966).

102. G. Eckhardt, R. W. Hellwarth, F. J. McClung, S. E. Schwarz, D. Weiner, and E. J. Woodbury, Ibid., **9,** 455 (1962).

103. B. P. Stoicheff, *Phys. Letters*, **7,** 186 (1963).
R. Chiao and B. P. Stoicheff, *Phys. Rev. Letters*, **12,** 290 (1964).
E. R. Lippincott, C. E. Meyers, and P. J. Hendra, *Spectros. Chim. Acta.*, **22,** 1493 (1966).

104. E. Garmire, F. Pandarese, and C. H. Townes, *Phys. Rev. Letters*, **11,** 160 (1963).
R. Loudon, *Proc. Phys. Soc. (London)* **82,** 393 (1963).
K. Nishik and F. Takano, *J. Phys. Soc. Japan*, **22,** 1446 (1967).

105. R. W. Hellwarth, *Current Sci. (India)* **33,** 120 (1964).

106. A. Kastler, *J. Chim. Phys.*, **46,** 72 (1949).

107. W. J. Jones and B. P. Stoicheff, *Phys. Rev. Letters*, **13,** 657 (1964).

108. J. Behringer, Dessertation, Ludwig-Maximilians-Universitat Zu Munchen (1957).
W. Hoffman and H. Moser, *Z. Electrochem.*, **64,** 310 (1960).
J. Brandmuller, *Z. Analy. Chem.*, **170,** 29 (1959).
P. P. Schorygin, L. Kuzina, and L. Ositjanskaja, *Mikrochim Acta.*, **2,** 630 (1955).
W. Schrotter, *Z. Elektrochem.*, **64,** 853 (1960).
M. Ya. Tsenter and Ya. S. Bobovich, *Opt. Spectrosc.* **16,** 134, 228, (1964).
I. I. Kondilenko and V. L. Strizhevskii, *Opt. Spectrosc.*, **11,** 137 (1961).
A. Selvarajan and K. Krishnan, Unpublished work.

109. L. S. Ornstein and J. J. Went, *Physica*, **2,** 391 (1935).

110. P. P. Shorygin, *Doklady Akad. Nauk.*, *SSSR*, **87,** 201 (1952). *Izvest. Akad. Nauk.*, *SSSR*, **17,** 581 (1953). *J. Chim. Phys. Physico. Chim. biol.*, **50,** D31 (1953).

111. J. Behringer, *Z. Elektrochemie*, **62,** 906 (1958).

112. M. V. Volkenstein and M. A. Eliashevich, *Izvest. Akad. Nauk., S.S.R. Ser. Fiz.*, **12,** 548 (1948).

113. A. C. Albrecht, *J. Chem. Phys.*, **34,** 1476 (1961).

114. I. I. Kondilenko, P. A. Korotov, and V. L. Strizhevskii, *Opt. Spectros.*, **9,** 13 (1960).

115. R. Loudon, *J. Phys. (Paris)*, **26,** 677 (1965).

116. E. D. Trifonov and K. Peuker, *Ibid.*, **26,** 738 (1965).

117. J. Behringer and J. Z. Brandmuller, *Elektrochem.*, **60,** 643 (1956).

118. D. G. Rea, *J. Mol. Spectry.*, **4,** 499 (1960).

119. W. Maier and F. Dorr, *Appl. Spectry.*, **14,** 1 (1960).

120. R. W. Terhune, P. D. Maker, and C. M. Savage, *Phys. Rev. Letters.* **14,** 681 (1965).

121. S. J. Cyvin, J. E. Ranch, and J. C. Decius, *J, Chem. Phys.* **43,** 4083 (1965).

122. B. Fanconi, L. A. Mafie, W. Small, and W. L. Peticolas, *J. Chem. Phys.* **51,** 3993 (1969).

B. Fanconi and W. L. Peticolas, *J. Chem. Phys.* **50,** 2244 (1969).

D. A. Long and L. Stanton, *Proc. Roy. Soc. (London)* **A318,** 441 (1970).

123. Proceedings of the International Conference on Light Scattering Spectra of Solids. G. B. Wright, ed., Springer-Verlag, New York, 1969.

124. P. A. Fleury, S. P. S. Porto, and R. Loudon, *Phys. Rev. Letters,* **18,** 658 (1967).

S. P. S. Porto, P. A. Fleury, and T. C. Damen, *Phys. Rev.* **154,** 522 (1967).

P. A. Fleury and R. Loudon, *Phys. Rev.*, **166,** 514 (1968).

125. C. H. Henry and J. J. Hopfield, *Phys. Rev. Letters,* **15,** 964 (1965).

S. P. S. Porto, B. Tell, and T. C. Damen, *Phys. Rev. Letters,* **16,** 450 (1966).

CHAPTER 2

Polarizability Theory of the Raman Effect

G. W. CHANTRY

NATIONAL PHYSICAL LABORATORY
TEDDINGTON, MIDDLESEX, UNITED KINGDOM

I. CLASSICAL THEORY OF RAMAN AND RAYLEIGH SCATTERING

The Raman effect is the scattering of electromagnetic radiation by matter with a change of frequency. The most commonly discussed example is that of monochromatic light of frequency v_o scattered by a molecule. The molecule can, of course, only exist in one of the stationary states which are solutions of the total wave equation for the molecule, but under the influence of the electromagnetic wave, the molecule can undergo a transition from state m, say, to state n, and the wave be scattered with lower (or higher) frequency given by

$$v_o - v = [E_n - E_m]/h \tag{1}$$

The process bears more than a passing resemblance to the Compton scattering of X-ray photons by electrons. Also, since molecular transitions are commonly under study, the Raman effect is closely related in practice to infrared and visible spectroscopy in which the photon is actually absorbed, and, therefore,

$$v_o = [E_n - E_m]/h \tag{2}$$

49

A simple classical treatment of the Raman effect and the associated Rayleigh effect (i.e., scattering without change of frequency) is in terms of the dipole moments induced in a polarizable molecule by the electric field of the radiation; thus,

$$\mu = \alpha E_o \cos 2\pi v_o t \tag{3}$$

where α is the molecular polarizability (a second order tensor), E_o the amplitude of the electric field oscillations, and v_o the frequency of the incident radiation. The polarizability will vary with the configuration of the molecule, i.e., be a function of the vibrational or other motion of the nuclei, so that for a given normal mode of frequency, v_m,

$$\alpha = \alpha_o + \alpha_1 \cos[2\pi v_m t + \beta] \tag{4}$$

where β is an arbitrary phase.
Substituting in Eq. (3),

$$\mu = \alpha_o E_o \cos 2\pi v_o t + \alpha_1 E_o \cos 2\pi v_o t \times \cos[2\pi v_m t + \beta] \tag{5}$$

By classical electromagnetic theory (1), an oscillating dipole radiates power at a rate given by

$$I = \frac{16\pi^4 v^4}{3c^3} \cdot (\mu)^2 \tag{6}$$

Substituting in this equation the previous expression for μ one finds

$$I = \frac{16\pi^4 v^4}{3c^3}\left[\begin{array}{l} \alpha_o{}^2 E_o{}^2 \cos^2 2\pi v_o t + \alpha_1{}^2 E_o{}^2 \cos^2 2\pi(v_o + v_m)t + \beta] \\ + \alpha_1{}^2 E_o{}^2 \cos^2[2\pi(v_o - v_m)t - \beta] + \text{cross terms} \end{array}\right] \tag{7}$$

The cross terms can usually be neglected, since in most experiments the power they propagate integrates to zero over a sufficient time interval; however, with square law detectors such as photomultipliers, it is possible in principle to detect the sum and difference frequencies arising from these cross terms, but so far severe electronic difficulties have prevented the exploitation of this attractive form of spectroscopy.

Although Eq. (7) is derived solely within the classical framework, and one expects an adequate treatment of Raman scattering to be possible only within the field of quantum electrodynamics, nevertheless, several valuable indications can be drawn from it. The first term corresponds to scattering without change of frequency and in phase with the incident light, i.e., coherent Rayleigh scattering: its intensity depends only on the molecular polarizability and so this phenomenon will be expected to arise with all substances. The second and third terms correspond to scattering with change of frequency, i.e. Raman scattering; the high frequency term, by analogy with fluorescence is called the anti-Stokes line, and the low frequency term, the Stokes line. The phase difference β will be different for each scattering molecule so that the observed radiation which is the sum of that from all the scatterers will be incoherent. As this is the case, Raman scattering will be an insensitive function of physical state (crystalline or liquid) and will vary only slowly with angle. Rayleigh scattering on the other hand, should be very weak from crystalline samples due to destructive interference of the wavelets from the regularly spaced scatterers and the scattered intensity will be strongly peaked in the forward direction (2). Another and most significant aspect of Rayleigh and Raman scattering to emerge from the classical treatment is the phenomenon of depolarization of the scattered radiation. The molecular polarizability, as mentioned earlier, is a second order tensor so that even with plane polarized radiation, dipole moments will be induced at right angles to the electric vector. The equation in tensor form is

$$\boldsymbol{\mu} = \alpha \mathbf{E} \tag{8}$$

which can be expanded as

$$\mu_x = \alpha_{xx}E_x + \alpha_{xy}E_y + \alpha_{xz}E_z$$
$$\mu_y = \alpha_{yx}E_x + \alpha_{yy}E_y + \alpha_{yz}E_z$$
$$\mu_z = \alpha_{zx}E_x + \alpha_{zy}E_y + \alpha_{zz}E_z \tag{9}$$

If a crystalline sample is being studied, then clearly rather complex scattering patterns will be observed with polarization varying with angle in the general case. This is quite similar (though much more complex) to the polarization phenomena observed in the infrared spectra of non-cubic crystals. However, unique to the scattering effect, polarization phenomena are observed even when the scatterers are randomly oriented or rotating freely as in a gas. This is because unlike the vector case, the average of the squares of polarizability components over all angles are not equal. To see this most readily it is helpful to remember that the subscripts in Eq. (9) refer to the laboratory frame of reference; if this is changed, e.g., by altering the angle of observation, then all the quantities have to be transformed to the new frame of reference. As is well known, this is achieved by the matrix operation:

$$\mu' = A\mu \quad \text{and} \quad E' = A\mathbf{E} \tag{10}$$

where μ' and E' are the dipole moment and electric field strength in the new system and A is an orthonormal 3×3 matrix. In fact, its entries are merely the direction cosines of the new axes with respect to the old. Substituting in Eq. (8) using Eq. (10) one derives

$$\mu' = A\alpha A^{-1}E' = \alpha'E' \tag{11}$$

$$\alpha' = A\alpha A^{-1}$$

It is a general theorem of linear algebra that a matrix A always exists (i.e., a frame of reference can always be found) such that α' becomes diagonal, that is, entries only occur in the $x'x'$, $y'y'$, and $z'z'$ positions. This theorem is related to the expression giving the transformation of the equation of an ellipsoid in terms of its natural axes to an arbitrary set related to the natural axes by rotations. As a result, the mathematical treatment of ellipsoids and second order tensors such as the polarizability tensor and the momental tensor is the same, and such tensors are often referred to as ellipsoids. It will be seen, therefore, that the general tensor with six independent entries (six because within present physical theory $\alpha_{xy} = \alpha_{yx}$ etc.) can be thought of as containing three physical quantities; namely, the half axes of the ellipsoid and three observational quantities giving the angles between the laboratory frame of reference and the innate molecular axes. By considering the orthonormal properties of the elements of A it is readily shown (3) that two quantities are independent of A; these are

$$\bar{\alpha} = \tfrac{1}{3}[\alpha_{xx} + \alpha_{yy} + \alpha_{zz}] \tag{12}$$

$$\gamma^2 = \tfrac{1}{2}[(\alpha_{xx} - \alpha_{yy})^2 + (\alpha_{yy} - \alpha_{zz})^2 + (\alpha_{zz} - \alpha_{xx})^2 + 6(\alpha_{xy}^2 + \alpha_{yz}^2 + \alpha_{zx}^2)]$$

These two quantities are, therefore, rotational invariants, and hence physically observable for a macroscopic sample consisting of randomly oriented scatterers; they are referred to as the mean value or isotropic part $(\bar{\alpha})$ and the anisotropy (γ^2). The anisotropy is a measure of the departure of the corresponding ellipsoid from a sphere, for referred to the natural axes $\alpha_{xy} = \alpha_{yz} = \alpha_{zx} = $ zero and for a sphere $\alpha_{xx} = \alpha_{yy} = \alpha_{zz}$ and, therefore, $\gamma^2 = $ zero. The mean values of the squares of the tensor elements (averaged over all orientations) can be expressed in terms of the two rotational invariants; the results are (3)

$$\overline{\alpha_{xx}^2} = \overline{\alpha_{yy}^2} = \overline{\alpha_{zz}^2} = \tfrac{1}{45}[45\bar{\alpha}^2 + 4\gamma^2] \tag{13}$$

$$\overline{\alpha_{xy}^2} = \overline{\alpha_{yz}^2} = \overline{\alpha_{zx}^2} = \tfrac{1}{15}\gamma^2$$

One can now compute the results of observation of Rayleigh scattering (or identically of Raman scattering where one considers the invariants of the tensor α_1) for various practical cases. Rayleigh observations are normally made at right angles to the exciting beam because of the difficulties of sorting out scattered from unscattered light, and although the frequency shift of the Raman radiation in principle permits observation even head-on, the experimental difficulties with imperfect monochromators are such that it is still commonest to observe at right angles. Two practical cases are important:

1. Irradiation with unpolarized radiation—say that of a mercury arc—along the z direction and observation along x.
2. Irradiation with polarized radiation—say that from a laser—along z and observation along x.

In case (1) the intensity polarized along the y direction (proportional to μ_y^2) is seen to be

$$I_y \sim \mu_y^2 \sim \overline{\alpha_{yy}^2}E_y^2 + \overline{\alpha_{xy}^2}E_x^2$$

or since $E_x = E_y$ and using Eq. (13)

$$I_y \sim \bar{\alpha}^2 + \tfrac{7}{45}\gamma^2$$

$$I_z \sim \tfrac{6}{45}\gamma^2$$

Thus, the ratio of radiation polarized in the y direction to that polarized in the z direction is seen to be

$$\rho_n = \frac{6\gamma^2}{45\bar{\alpha}^2 + 7\gamma^2} \qquad (14)$$

This is a most important result for one sees that information about the anisotropy of the polarizability is available even when nonoriented samples are studied. The corresponding expression for case (2) is

$$\rho_p = \frac{3\gamma^2}{45\bar{\alpha}^2 + 4\gamma^2} \qquad (14a)$$

To pursue this important characteristic of Rayleigh and Raman scattering further, it is necessary to consider molecular symmetry. As is well known, an isolated molecule possesses symmetry elements which form a group in the mathematical sense. These groups are isomorphous with the point groups since there is always one point in the molecule which is sent into itself by all the symmetry operations. For an authoritative discussion of the application of group theory to molecules, the standard work by Wilson, Decius, and Cross (4) should be consulted, and the matter will be taken up again later in this chapter; it will suffice here to remark that the principal values of the polarizability· tensor may be related by symmetry operations. Thus, if the molecule contains a threefold or higher axis of symmetry, then two of the principal values are necessarily equal and then having only two unknowns, say α_{xx} and $\alpha_{yy} = \alpha_{zz}$ these can be determined from the measured values of $\bar{\alpha}$ and γ. In the still simpler case, when there are two or more noncoincident rotational axes of threefold or higher symmetry, then the molecule belongs to a cubic point group and all three principal values are equal, and γ is identically zero. This method of determining molecular polarizabilities, by observing the intensity and depolarization of Rayleigh scattering is assuming new importance with the development of laser sources and, as will be shown in the next section, it has always been of great value in deriving molecular properties from observed Raman spectra.

We have seen, therefore, that the simple classical treatment of Rayleigh and Raman scattering leads to a fair insight into the phenomena, showing how Stokes and anti-Stokes lines arise, how the shifts are related to molecular frequencies and how polarization phenomena arise, and how these are related to the molecular symmetry. However, within the field of classical physics, no explanation is forthcoming as to why anti-Stokes lines are weaker than their Stokes companions, or why certain selection rules hold, or what factors govern the intensities of Raman lines. Clearly to proceed further, quantum physics will be necessary, and this can be applied in two stages. We can think of an electromagnetic field interacting with the molecule and then either deal with a classical field and a fully quantized molecule; or go the whole hog, and consider a quantized field interacting with a quantized molecule.

II. QUANTUM THEORY OF THE RAMAN EFFECT

The results of the application of quantum mechanics to molecular motion are of course well known (5). To a first order, overall rotational motion, vibrational motion and electronic motion are separable, and any given stationary state (i.e. a state corresponding to a solution of the time independent wave equation) can be assigned labels specifying the electronic, vibrational, and rotational state of the molecule; the corresponding energy is the sum of the three components. As an example, important states of the HCN molecule are $X^1\Sigma$ ($11^10\ J = 10$) and ΣX^1 ($04^00\ J = 10$), perturbations between which are responsible for the strong emission at $337\ \mu$ of the HCN maser (6,7). The symbols have the following meaning: $X^1\Sigma$ means the ground singlet state with zero electronic orbital angular momentum; $11^1 0$ and $04°0$ refer to the vibrational excitation of the three normal modes $Q_1(Q_{2a}Q_{2b})$, and Q_3, with the superscript denoting the amount of vibrational angular momentum induced by the simultaneous excitation of the two degenerate vibrations; J is the rotational quantum number. It will be seen, therefore, that for any molecule there is a large number of possible energy states each characterizable by suitable labels. In thermal equilibrium the molecules of a gaseous sample will be distributed among these possible levels according to the usual function, i.e.,

$$N_E = N_o \, e^{-E/kT} \tag{15}$$

where N_E is the number in the state with energy E. Thus, under the influence of the electromagnetic field, the number of molecules available for Stokes scattering will be larger than that for anti-Stokes scattering because of this Boltzmann factor, since only excited molecules can give anti-Stokes scattering. The intensity behavior of Stokes and anti-Stokes lines is thus successfully accounted for in rather the same way that Planck's quantization of oscillators turned the incorrect Rayleigh–Jeans formula into the correct black-body law.

Another result that can be recovered within this framework is the selection rule for the pure-rotational Raman effect. The energy of a quantum mechanical rotor is determined by the three principal values of the momental ellipsoid I_A, I_B, and I_C. For all cases the total angular momentum J (as always in quantum mechanics) and its projection M on an axis fixed in space are constants of the motion and for each value of J there are $(2J+1)$ sublevels each of which has $(2J+1)$ degenerate components due to the quantum number M. If the three principal values are all different, then the molecule is said to be an asymmetric rotor and expressions for the energy levels cannot be written down in closed form, and what is another facet of the same fact, no "good" quantum number can be defined to label the sublevels of a given J. However, if the molecule possesses a threefold or higher axis of symmetry then two of the moments of inertia become necessarily equal (vide the earlier discussion of the polarizability tensor) and the molecule is said to be a symmetric top; oblate if $I_A > I_B = I_C$ and prolate if $I_A < I_B = I_C$. For symmetric tops the $(2J+1)$ sublevels can be labeled in terms of the quantum number $K(K = -J \ldots 0 \ldots +J)$ which is the projection of J on the symmetry axis and the energy levels (in cm^{-1}) can be written down in the simple form

$$\begin{aligned} E(J, K) = {} & B_v J(J+1) + (A_v - B_v)K^2 - D_J J^2(J+1)^2 \\ & - D_{JK} J(J+1)K^2 - D_K K^4 \end{aligned} \tag{16}$$

where B, A, etc. are constants for a given vibrational state, but do vary slightly with vibrational quantum number (failure of the first order approximation). In this equation

$$A = \frac{h}{8\pi^2 c I_A} \qquad (16a)$$

and D_J, D_{JK}, D_K are very small terms also reflecting the nonperfect separability of rotational and vibrational motion. From Eq. (16) two special cases can be picked out: firstly, linear rotors for which I_A is zero (or very small if electronic motion is considered) and secondly, spherical rotors for which $I_A = I_B = I_C$ and, therefore, $A = B = C$. Linear rotors have A very large so that $E(J, K)$ is of the order of many thousands of cm^{-1} unless K is zero. Consequently at ordinary temperatures only the levels with $K = 0$ are populated and for purposes of ordinary spectroscopy the energy levels take on the simple form

$$E(J) = B_v J(J+1) - D_J J^2 (J+1)^2 \qquad (17)$$

This equation also describes the energy levels of a spherical top for which $(A - B)$ is zero. However, the statistical weights differ since each level of a linear rotor is $(2J+1)$ degenerate whereas every level of a spherical rotor is $(2J+1)^2$ degenerate.

In order to theoretically derive the expected spectrum it is necessary to know the selection rules, i.e. to know which transitions between levels are possible. The selection rules for rotational spectra in both the infrared and Raman can be derived without reference to quantum field theory by recourse to arguments of various degrees of subtlety based on the correspondence principle, i.e.,that under suitable conditions quantum mechanics must pass smoothly into classical mechanics. An alternative approach which uses the concepts of quantum fields without the mathematical complexities is to invoke the law of conservation of angular momentum noting that photons are derived from a classical vector field, i.e., have unit spin (8). Applying these approaches to the rotational spectra of a linear molecule one notes that since K is zero, J is fixed in the molecule, and it immediately follows that in the infrared pure rotation and likewise for all parallel vibration rotation bands

$$\Delta J = \pm 1 \qquad (18)$$

The pure rotation spectrum is thus a series of lines nearly equally spaced given by the relation

$$v = 2B_v (J+1) - 4D_J (J+1)^3 \qquad (19)$$

while the spacing is approximately $2B$. One observes also that for parallel bands, the Q branch ($\Delta J = 0$) will not occur. To derive the Raman selection rules it is readily seen that a principal axis of the polarizability tensor coincides with J and that for a rotation through 180° the tensor will reach an equivalent orientation and thus the tensor is rotating twice as fast as the molecule and it follows that

$$\Delta J = \pm 2 \tag{20}$$

for pure rotation. In photon terms, a photon of spin $+1$ is scattered with a spin of -1 and thus $\Delta J = \pm 2$; it follows also that the photon could be scattered with the same spin sense; in other words $\Delta J = 0$ is also allowed. This is in contrast with the infrared but the difference is that one does not lose a photon in this process as one does in infrared absorption. The pure rotation spectrum observed by Raman scattering has again a series of nearly equally spaced lines but this time given by the relation (9)

$$\Delta v = (4B_v - 6D_J)(J + \tfrac{3}{2}) - 8D_J(J + \tfrac{3}{2})^3 \tag{21}$$

and the spacing this time is approximately twice as great, with the first line occurring at nearly $6B$ instead of the $2B$ in the infrared case. This happy occurrence has of course considerable practical consequences since it is much more difficult to make spectrometers capable of resolving lines of the order 1 cm^{-1} apart in the visible region (where Raman spectra occur) than in the far infrared where pure rotational absorption occurs, and it is very useful to have the extra factor of two in the line spacing. In vibration rotation bands, the sub-bands corresponding to $\Delta J = \pm 2$ are called the 0 and S branches respectively to fit in with the PQR nomenclature. For nonlinear rotors, J is not necessarily fixed in the molecule and an R branch ($\Delta J = +1$) can also occur in the pure rotational Raman spectrum. The lines have half the spacing of the S branch lines, and in all cases the first lines $J = 0 \rightarrow J = 1$ is missing since these two levels have opposite parities and in Raman scattering only levels of the same parity may be involved (10).

A further result of significance can be derived regarding the depolarization ratio of the lines in a pure rotational Raman spectrum, by recourse to the simple classical theory described earlier. For a linear molecule two of the principal values of α are equal (say α_p), and the unique principal value lies along the molecular axis. In the laboratory reference frame the fluctuating polarizability of the rotating molecule is given by

$$\alpha(t) = \begin{bmatrix} \cos \omega t & -\sin \omega t & 0 \\ \sin \omega t & \cos \omega t & 0 \\ 0 & 0 & 1 \end{bmatrix} \begin{bmatrix} \alpha_l & 0 & 0 \\ 0 & \alpha_p & 0 \\ 0 & 0 & \alpha_p \end{bmatrix} \begin{bmatrix} \cos \omega t & +\sin \omega t & 0 \\ -\sin \omega t & \cos \omega t & 0 \\ 0 & 0 & 1 \end{bmatrix} \tag{22}$$

which on multiplication followed by differentiation with respect to time gives

$$\frac{\partial \alpha(t)}{\partial t} = \omega \begin{bmatrix} -(\alpha_l - \alpha_p) \sin 2\omega t, & (\alpha_l - \alpha_p) \cos 2\omega t, & 0 \\ (\alpha_l - \alpha_p) \cos 2\omega t, & (\alpha_l - \alpha_p) \sin 2\omega t, & 0 \\ 0 & , & 0 & , & 0 \end{bmatrix} \tag{23}$$

The rotational invariants of this derived tensor are

$$\bar{\alpha}' = \text{zero}$$

$$\gamma' = \sqrt{3}\omega(\alpha_l - \alpha_p)$$

and it follows that pure rotation lines will be completely depolarized with $\rho_n = 6/7$. Somewhat more complicated arguments show that this is a general result for all molecules. Of course, both invariants are zero if $\alpha_l = \alpha_p$ that is, if we are dealing with a spherical rotor (accidental or necessary), and no spectrum will be observed. This could also be deduced from the correspondence principle which shows that the selection rule for a spherical rotor is $\Delta J = 0$, i.e., no rotational Raman effect will occur. This selection rule likewise applies to all vibration rotation bands of a spherical rotor which correspond to totally symmetric modes. As a consequence such bands have only a Q branch and are observed as very sharp "lines" in the Raman spectrum.

In order to make further progress in understanding the Raman effect, it is necessary to consider quantization of the electromagnetic field. This is a very difficult branch of mathematical physics, bristling with problems of infinite quantities and its investigation in the present context is principally attributable to Dirac and his followers (11). However, before quoting their results it will be helpful to discuss the classical treatment of the problem. We consider an electromagnetic wave polarized in the x direction and travelling along z and through an absorbing medium.

The two relevant relations are the propagation equation,

$$E(z) = E(o) \cos 2\pi \bar{v} z n \tag{24}$$

(where $\bar{v}$ is the frequency of the wave in cm^{-1} and n is the refractive index) and the attenuation equation—Lambert's law

$$I(z) = I(o) e^{-\beta z} \tag{25}$$

where β is the absorption coefficient. It is common to use the complex form of Eq. (24) to simplify the algebra, and when this is done and the two equations are combined, one has

$$E(z) = E(o) \exp\left(-i2\pi\bar{v}z\left[n - \frac{i\beta}{4\pi\bar{v}}\right]\right) \qquad (26)$$

This equation is to be compared with the generalized expression for propagation of an electromagnetic wave, i.e.,

$$E(z) = E(o) \, e^{-i2\pi\bar{v}zn^*} \qquad (27)$$

where n^* the complex refractive index is defined by

$$n^* = n(1 - i\kappa) \qquad (28)$$

Thus κ the so called extinction coefficient becomes

$$\kappa = \frac{\beta}{4\pi n\bar{v}} \qquad (29)$$

in which β, as above, is the absorption coefficient. Analogously one can define a complex dielectric constant ε^* given by

$$\varepsilon^* = \varepsilon' - i\varepsilon'' \qquad (30)$$

and derive expressions for ε' and ε'' by noting that

$$\varepsilon^* = (n^*)^2 = n^2(1 - \kappa^2) - i \cdot 2n^2\kappa \qquad (31)$$

Of course, so far all this theory is merely mathematical convenience, taking advantage of the form of the expressions, namely exponential with imaginary argument for propagation and exponential with real argument for the attenuation. Nevertheless, there exists a necessary and profound connection between these arguments, and the mathematical expressions take on great significance. This connection arises from the principle of causality which can be stated that no effect can occur before its cause comes into existence: the principle of causality is believed to have universal reference and when it is applied to any physical problem, the additional constraint on the solutions introduces necessary connections between various physical properties. An illustration sometimes used to show this is to imagine a short pulse applied to an electronic circuit with input and output terminals. The input pulse can of course be resolved into its Fourier components, which will be an infinite set of cosine waves all in phase with each other and stretching from $t = -\infty$ to $t = +\infty$, and, of course, these waves completely destructively interfere at all times except during the pulse time from $t = 0$ to the end of the pulse. Now imagine that the electronic circuit introduces a sharp absorption over a range of frequency $v_0 \pm \Delta v$; then the waves within this interval will not appear at the output terminals, and so the complete destructive interference cannot be perfect, and ripples will be observed at the output before the pulse is applied to the input. This violates the principle of causality, and yet the mathematical argument is sound: the way round the paradox is to note that since we have applied an arbitrary (in the mathematical sense) boundary condition we will effect the physical argument. It is clearly always possible to make sharp filters, and the only variable left to change is the phase of the waves. This turns out to be correct, and the presence of the sharp absorption at v_0 affects the phase of waves of frequency remote from v_0, and the perfect cancellation before t_0 is recovered. This is a general result and can be applied to any physical system and to molecules or atoms in particular. The presence of absorption bands in a molecular absorption spectrum necessarily leads to dispersion of the refractive index of the sample, the particular form being the well known anomalous dispersion in the region of the absorption bands. The refractive index is intimately connected with the polarizability, so this too undergoes rapid variations in the neighborhood of absorption bands.

To show this in more detail a simple example will be worked through. Consider a particle of mass M and charge e held to an equilibrium position by an elastic restoring force of force constant K; then if the displacement is x, caused by an electric field E, we have

$$\text{Restoring force} = -Kx = -eE \quad \text{so that} \quad x = eE/K$$

The additional or induced moment ex is, thus, $e^2 E/K$ and since

$$\mu = ex = \alpha E \tag{32}$$

it follows that the polarizability α is equal to e^2/K. Now consider what happens when E is varying cosinusoidally with time, e.g., when an electromagnetic wave of wavelength much longer than x is passing through the system. The motion of the particle will be described by the differential equation

$$m\frac{d^2x}{dt^2} + mg\frac{dx}{dt} + m\omega_0^2 x = eE \tag{33}$$

The second term involving the damping constant g is put in to include frictional effects, and leads to absorption of energy from the wave, and the third term has been changed from $+Kx$ in anticipation of the damped simple harmonic solution of frequency ω_0.

Putting $E = E_o e^{i\omega t}$ Eq. (33) can be easily solved to give

$$ex = \mu = \frac{e^2}{m} \cdot \frac{E}{\omega_o^2 - \omega^2 + i\omega g}, \qquad \alpha = \frac{e^2}{m} \cdot \frac{1}{\omega_o^2 - \omega^2 + i\omega g} \qquad (34)$$

The polarizability is thus a complex quantity, and rationalizing this, one has

$$\alpha = \frac{e^2}{m} \left[\frac{\omega_o^2 - \omega^2}{(\omega_o^2 - \omega^2)^2 + \omega^2 g^2} - i \cdot \frac{\omega g}{(\omega_o^2 - \omega^2)^2 + \omega^2 g^2} \right] \qquad (35)$$

and remembering that the dielectric constant is simply related to α by the following equation (12):

$$\varepsilon = 1 + 4\pi N \alpha \qquad (36)$$

where N is the number of oscillators, it follows that

$$\varepsilon' = 1 + \frac{4\pi N e^2}{m} \cdot \frac{\omega_o^2 - \omega^2}{(\omega_o^2 - \omega^2)^2 + \omega^2 g^2} \qquad (37)$$

$$\varepsilon'' = \frac{4\pi N e^2}{m} \cdot \frac{\omega g}{(\omega_o^2 - \omega^2)^2 + \omega^2 g^2}$$

The form of these expressions is shown in Fig. 1. The general result derived above is thus confirmed by this particular example, viz., that dispersion invariably accompanies absorption and that the two components of the dielectric constant are never independent of each other. Another point worth noting is the presence of the so-called "resonance denominators," for if g is not large the denominators become very small, when

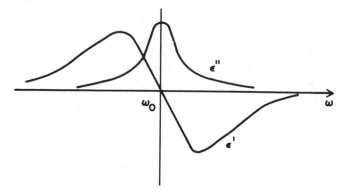

Fig. 1. Variation of the real and imaginary components of ε^* near the resonant frequency.

$\omega = \omega_0$. Consequently the two components of ε^* vary very rapidly when ω is close to ω_0 and this has very important consequencies, not least of which is the phenomenon of resonant Raman scattering, which will be mentioned later.

The equations derived above, although for an idealized classical model, are found in fact to describe the behavior of real systems rather satis-factorily. Thus, the reststrahlen absorption of alkali halide crystals which leads these materials to be highly absorbing and highly reflecting in the far infrared obeys equations of this form; the optical properties of metals are likewise well treated by equations of this form with $\omega_0 = 0$ leading to expressions showing the high conductance and reflectance of metals at low frequencies. Of course, the conduction electrons in metals cannot be assumed to be held to an equilibrium position by a restoring force, but the proper quantum mechanical treatment does lead to equations of the above type. Rather similarly, the absorption bands at high frequencies of molecules due to electronic excitation can also be described by similar equations. In this case however, an additional factor called the f number (*13*) has to be introduced: these f numbers, or oscillator strengths, are always less than unity, and are calculable within the proper quantum mechanical framework which also shows that the f numbers for all transitions starting at a given electronic level obey a sum rule adding up to unity. This reflects again the pervasive correspondence principle which would indicate that when all the possible transitions of a given electron are considered the net effect must pass smoothly into the classical case. It is seen therefore, that the polarizability of a molecule in the visible region is the sum of dispersive terms due to the ultraviolet and visible electronic absorption bands and due also to the infrared vibrational and rotational bands. We are thus now at the core of the Raman problem, viz., how does the polarizability of a molecule vary with vibration, for it is this variation of α which we have previously called α_1. All the treatment so far developed, while giving insight into the interconnections of the various quantities, is of no help in the elucidation of the vibrational Raman effect for the polarizability has not been developed as a function of the internuclear distances. In the quantum mechanical treatment of molecules, however, the electronic wave functions are dependent on the nuclear coordinates, and the intensities of given transitions are dependent to a certain extent on the degree of vibrational excitation. We thus have a mechanism for the variation of polarizability with molecular vibration. The change of electronic transition moment with vibrational excitation can sometimes be spectacular; in certain cases a band forbidden by the selection rules for the vibrationless molecule becomes active when a vibrational mode of suitable symmetry is excited. A famous example occurs in the near ultra-violet absorption spectrum of benzene (14). This molecule belongs to the point group D_{6h}, and allowed transitions from the A_{1g} ground state can only occur to excited states whose symmetry is such that the integral

$$\int \psi_{\text{ground}} \cdot \mu_\rho \cdot \psi_{\text{excited}} \, d\tau \quad (\rho = x, y, z) \tag{38}$$

is not necessarily zero. It is readily seen by the application of the symmetry elements of the molecule to this integral that it vanishes unless ψ_{excited} belongs to an irreducible representation of the molecular point group that also contains μ_x, μ_y, or μ_z. For D_{6h} these latter belong to the irreducible representations $A_{2u}(\mu_z)$ and $E_{1u}(\mu_x, \mu_y)$, and therefore only transitions to states having A_{2u} or E_{1u} symmetry will be allowed. In the absence of electronic-vibration interaction (known for short as vibronic interaction) this selection rule is absolute, but where this interaction occurs then the overall symmetry

$$\Gamma_{\text{overall}} = \Gamma_{\text{electronic}} \cdot \Gamma_{\text{vibrational}} \tag{39}$$

is the appropriate symmetry to be considered in the equation. For benzene, a B_{2u} excited state near 2600 Å is made active by an E_{2g} vibrational mode of frequency 925 cm^{-1}, since (15)

$$\Gamma_{\text{overall}} = B_{2u} \times E_{2g} = E_{1u} \tag{40}$$

The band is, therefore, observed as a series of lines being transitions to the states of B_{2u} with the E_{2g} vibration excited with an odd number of quanta. The intensity of this band is then said to arise solely from its "forbidden character." In the language of perturbation theory, the observed wave function for each of the states of the molecule can be thought of as a linear combination of the ideal wave functions, derived by solving the wave equation for a vibrationless system; the vibration acting as a small perturbation. The observed intensity is then due to "borrowing" by mixing from the strong allowed E_{1u} transitions in the vacuum ultraviolet. Of course, the same arguments apply just as well (though less observably obvious) to allowed bands, all of which may be expected to have a certain amount of "forbidden character" in their makeup. It can now be shown that Raman intensity derives via the dispersion relations just from this vibronically induced "forbidden character" of allowed electronic transitions.

The first treatment of the problem within the concepts of dispersion theory was by Van Vleck (16). The dispersion relations associated with the names of Kramers and Heisenberg (17) are the quantum mechanical analogues of the classical relations between absorption and dispersion. Various ways of writing these down have been used but one is

$$\alpha = \sum_e \frac{4\pi m}{e^2 h} \omega_e |M_{eg}|^2 \times \frac{e^2/m}{\omega_e^2 - \omega^2} \tag{41}$$

which relates the molecular polarizability α to the transition moments from the ground state (g) to excited levels (e). The similarity of this equation to the classical one [vide Eq. (35)] should be noted as should the presence of the multiplicative term

$$f_e = \frac{4\pi m}{e^2 h} \cdot \omega_e |M_{eg}|^2 \tag{42}$$

which is the f number or oscillator strength. For the Raman case we note that (M_{eg}) is a vibronic transition moment as discussed above. Van Vleck and others succeeded in showing that for a molecule in a vibronic state m perturbed by an electromagnetic wave so that it passes into a vibronic state n while scattering light of frequency $v_o + v_{mn}$ ($v_{mn} = v_m - v_n$), the total intensity of scattered light after averaging over all orientations of the molecule is given by the following (18):

$$I_{mn} = \frac{2^7 \pi^5}{3^2 c^4} I_o (v_o + v_{mn})^4 \sum_{\rho\sigma} |(\alpha_{\rho\sigma})_{mn}|^2 \tag{43}$$

where ρ, σ are independently x, y, or z and

$$(\alpha_{\rho\sigma})_{mn} = \frac{1}{h} \sum_r \left[\frac{(M_\rho)_{rn}(M_\sigma)_{mr}}{v_{rm} - v_o} + \frac{(M_\rho)_{mr}(M_\sigma)_{rn}}{v_{rn} + v_o} \right] \tag{44}$$

where r is a vibronic state of the molecule. In this form, the equation is not very helpful, for while each of the transition moments is experimentally or theoretically determinable either from absorption spectroscopy or from the relation

$$(M_\rho)_{mr} = \int \psi_r^* \mu_\rho \psi_m \, d\tau \tag{45}$$

clearly we cannot immediately carry out the summation. Some progress however was possible by the introduction of the Born–Oppenheimer approximation, which states that electrons move so fast compared to nuclei that the electron cloud can immediately and instantly follow the movements of the nuclei. We can thus give two labels to each vibronic state, one to describe the electrons and one to describe the nuclei, and to simplify the nomenclature we will assume that scattering from molecules in their electronic ground state is under consideration: then we have the molecule passing from the state gi to the state gj where i and j are vibrational states of the electronic ground stage g. The next step is to apply first order perturbation theory to get the mixed wave functions from the basis set of vibrationless wave functions, and to use these to get the transition moments. These are,

$$M_{g \to e}(Q) = M_{g \to e}(0) + \sum_s \lambda_{es}(Q) M_{g \to s}(0) \tag{46}$$

$$\lambda_{es}(Q) = \sum_a \frac{h^a_{es} Q_a}{\Delta E^o_{es}} \tag{46a}$$

In this last equation h^a_{es} can be thought of as a perturbation energy per unit displacement of the ath normal mode due to mixing of the vibrationless electronic wave functions of states e and s under the vibrational perturbation. Using these relations, the expression for the matrix element of the polarizability becomes (19) the following:

$$(\alpha_{\rho\sigma})_{gi \to gj} = A + B + C \tag{47}$$

where

$$A = \frac{1}{h} \sum_{en} \left[\frac{1}{v_{en \to gi} - v_o} + \frac{1}{v_{en \to gi} + v_o} \right] [M_\rho)^o_{g \to e} (M_\sigma)^o_{g \to e}]$$
$$\times \int \psi_{gi} \psi_{en} \, d\tau \int \psi_{en} \psi_{gj} d\tau$$

$$B = \frac{1}{h} \sum_{en} \left(\frac{1}{v_{en \to gi} - v_o} \right) \sum_{sa} \frac{h^a_{es}}{\Delta E^o_{es}} [(M_\rho)^o_{ge} (M_\sigma)^o_{gs} \int \psi_{gj} \psi_{en} \, d\tau \int \psi_{en} Q_a \psi_{gi} \, d\tau$$
$$+ (M_\sigma)^o_{ge} (M_\rho)^o_{gs} \int \psi_{gi} \psi_{en} \, d\tau \int \psi^1_{en} Q_a \psi_{gj} \, d\tau]$$

$$C = \frac{1}{h} \sum_{en} \left(\frac{1}{v_{en \to gj} + v_o} \right) \sum_{sa} \frac{h^a_{es}}{\Delta E^o_{es}} [(M_\rho)^o_{ge} (M_\sigma)^o_{gs} \int \psi_{gi} \psi_{en} \, d\tau \int \psi_{en} Q_a \psi_{gj} \, d\tau$$
$$+ (M_\sigma)^o_{ge} (M_\rho)^o_{gs} \int \psi_{gj} \psi_{en} \, d\tau \int \psi_{en} Q_a \psi_{gi} \, d\tau]$$

These expressions are rather complicated, but several important results may be extracted from them. First, one notes the presence of the resonance denominators for terms A and B which will make these terms large when v_o is near the absorption frequency $v_{gi \to en}$. This leads to the well known phenomenon of "Resonance Raman Scattering." Second, one notes that the terms B and C involve *pairs* of excited states, whereas A does not, so one has a physical origin for the difference between Raman scattering and fluorescence. Near resonance, the phenomena of fluorescence and

Raman scattering look akin, but this resemblance is only superficial; the absence of any quenching phenomena in the Raman effect, and the presence of strict selection rules (as contrasted with the Franck–Condon principle) for the latter, confirms this. The derivation of the actual selection rules for the Raman effect is quite straightforward. In the nonresonant case (i.e., $v_o \ll v_{ge}$) the approximate (very good) sum rule developed by Van Vleck (16) leads to

$$\sum_v \int \psi_{gi} \psi_{en} \int \psi_{en} \psi_{gj} = \delta_{ij} = \text{Kronecker delta}$$

$$\sum_v \int \psi_{gi} \psi_{en} \int \psi_{en} Q_a \psi_{gj} = \sum_v \int \psi_{gj} \psi_{en} \int \psi_{en} Q_a \psi_{gi} = \int \psi_{gi} Q_a \psi_{gj} \qquad (48)$$

This latter integral is of course well known in the theory of the harmonic oscillator where the Hermite polynomials (the solutions for ψ_{gi} and ψ_{gj}) have the properties (20) that

$$\int \psi_{gi} Q_a \psi_{gj} = \text{zero} \qquad \text{unless} \qquad n_a^{\ j} = n_a^{\ i} \pm 1$$

where n is the vibrational quantum number. If $n_a^{\ j} = n_a^{\ i} \pm 1$ then the solutions are

$$\int \psi_{gi} Q_a \psi_{gj}\, dt = \sqrt{\left(\frac{(n_a^{\ i} + 1)h}{8\pi^2 \mu v} \right)} \qquad \text{for} \qquad n_a^{\ j} = n_a^{\ i} + 1$$

$$= \sqrt{\left(\frac{n_a^{\ i} h}{8\pi^2 \mu v} \right)} \qquad \text{for} \qquad n_a^{\ j} = n_a^{\ i} - 1$$

$$(49)$$

with μ the reduced mass of the oscillator and v the transition frequency. We thus see that the term A is responsible for Rayleigh scattering and the terms B and C for Raman scattering of fundamentals. To derive a theory adequate to deal with Raman scattering of overtones and combinations it would be necessary to take the perturbation theory to second order. To see which particular normal modes will be scattered, it is necessary to consider the symmetry properties of the two terms A and B. In fact, this is best done by introducing results of Eqs. (48) and (49) and re-arranging the algebra, when a considerable simplification results; one then has (19)

$$(\alpha_{\rho\sigma})_{gi \to gj} = D + E \qquad (50)$$

where

$$D = \frac{1}{h} \sum_e \left(\frac{2v_e}{v_e^{\ 2} - v_o^{\ 2}} \right) (M_\rho)_{ge}^{\circ} (M_\sigma)_{ge}^{\circ} \delta_{ij}$$

$$E = \frac{-2}{h^2} \sum_{\substack{es \\ s>e}} \sum_a \frac{(v_e v_s + v_o{}^2) h_{es}^a}{(v_e{}^2 - v_o{}^2)(v_s{}^2 - v_o{}^2)} \; [(M_\rho)_{ge}^o (M_\sigma)_{gs}^o + (M_\rho)_{gs}^o (M_\sigma)_{ge}^o]$$

$$\times \sqrt{\left(\frac{(n_a{}^i + 1)h}{8\pi^2 \mu v}\right)}$$

for Stokes Raman scattering.

As before D gives Rayleigh scattering and E Raman scattering. For E not to vanish it follows that h_{es}^a [vide Eq. (46a)] must be nonzero, and that transitions from the ground state to both e and s must be allowed by symmetry. If the symmetry species of e and s are Γ_e and Γ_s, each of these must correspond to one of the irreducible representations of the molecular point group that contains Γ_x, Γ_y, or Γ_z. From the equations of perturbation theory (Eq. 46) it is readily seen by inspection that since

$$\Gamma_e = \Gamma_Q \Gamma_s$$

for mixing to be possible, then

$$\Gamma_e \cdot \Gamma_e = \text{totally symmetric representation} = \Gamma_e \Gamma_Q \Gamma_s \qquad (51)$$

To satisfy this equation Γ_Q must be the same as any possible combination of Γ_e and Γ_s namely Γ_{x^2}, Γ_{y^2}, Γ_{z^2}, Γ_{xy}, Γ_{xz}, Γ_{yz}, and one arrives at the selection rule:

"A mode of vibration can be active in Raman scattering if the irreducible representation to which it can be assigned contains x^2, y^2, z^2, xy, xz, or yz."

The expected depolarization properties of the observed lines can be immediately deduced by similar group theoretical analysis of Eq. (50). Since we are dealing with the two rotational invariants of $(\alpha_{\rho\sigma})_{gi \to gj}$, we can consider the case where the molecule is oriented naturally with respect to irradiation and observation to derive the conditions that the mean value should be nonzero. We thus require the symmetry properties of the combination $x^2 + y^2 + z^2$, and by considering any of the possible symmetry elements of the molecule it can be shown quite straightforwardly that this combination is always sent into itself by all the symmetry operations of the group. This is still more readily seen in the ellipsoid type of picture, where we are clearly considering the symmetry properties of a sphere. Thus the combination $x^2 + y^2 + z^2$ always belongs exclusively to the totally symmetric representation, and therefore, only vibrations which belong to this representation can have a depolarization ratio less than six-sevenths. This remarkable property of Raman spectra has of course been of the highest importance in chemical applications, for it means that the stereochemistry of a molecule could often be deduced when only liquid samples were available. Infrared spectra, in general, suffer from the drawback that one needs single crystal samples of most substances before meaningful inferences can be drawn from polarization phenomena. Nevertheless, it cannot be too strongly emphasized how the two techniques are completely complementary since they have different selection rules, that for infrared (identically to the electronic case) being that the vibration in question must belong to an irreducible representation which contains x, y, or z. In particular it should be noted that if the molecule contains a center of symmetry, then under this operation

$$(x, y, z) \rightarrow (-x, -y, -z)$$

whereas

$$(x^2, y^2, z^2, xy, yz, zx) \rightarrow (x^2, y^2, z^2, xy, yz, zx)$$

so that we arrive at the law of mutual exclusion:

"For a centrosymmetric molecule no transition appearing in the infrared spectrum can appear in the Raman spectrum and vice-versa."

To illustrate the power of the combined techniques two very well known examples will be briefly discussed. First, nitrous oxide, N_2O: in the far infrared, a simple line spectrum is observed (21) characteristic of a linear molecule (vide Eq. (17)] and the molecule is thus linear. However, two possible structures can be considered, NNO and NON: the case NO—N with one bond longer than the other is excluded for a ground state molecule within present day valence theory. Of the two cases, the second NON would have a center of symmetry and no coincidences would be expected in the two spectra. The observed spectra, however, both contain strong bands at 1286 and 2223 cm^{-1} which must be fundamentals, therefore, the correct structure is NNO. Second, we consider the pentatomic molecule CCl_4 (22). For this there are quite a few possible structures, i.e., tetrahedral (T_d), square planar (D_{4h}), pyramidal (C_{4v}), and distorted pyramidal (C_{2v}), which are possible on valency grounds. However the occurrence of just four fundamentals in the Raman spectrum (the doublet at 762 and 790 cm^{-1} being satisfactorily explained as arising from Fermi resonance) with only one of them polarized, combined with the observation that the infrared spectrum consists of only two bands both coincident with Raman lines, proves unambiguously that the molecule is tetrahedral.

III. PLACZEK'S THEORY OF RAMAN INTENSITIES

Historically, Raman spectroscopy has been of the first order importance. By using it, spectroscopists have been able to find out the stereochemistry of new molecules, to determine the frequencies of the normal modes of vibration, and to go on from this to estimate the force constants involved and from these to gain some insight into the magnitudes of the forces holding molecules together. However, all this has been achieved with very little reference to the intrinsic intensities of the Raman lines themselves. It has always seemed likely that this additional information could tell us something more about the nature of the bonding in the molecule, and several attempts have been made to pursue this point. Of course there are practical difficulties since the Raman effect is an emission phenomenon and therefore very unlike the corresponding infrared case which involves only the determination of the constant in Lambert's Law [vide Eq. (25)]. Some workers, using careful geometries and high grade photometry, have estimated the absolute intensity of Raman scattering, but in general most workers have been content to use the relative intensities within a given spectrum, or somewhat more dangerously to determine a set of intensities relative to say, that of the v_1 line of CCl_4 by observing the spectra of mixtures. This method is more questionable because the intensity of scattering depends on the field experienced by the scattering molecule, and this will be some function of the refractive index of the mixture modified by specific (and unknown) intermolecular effects. However, when a set of intensities has been observed the question of interpretation arises. From Eq. (50), the observed intensity could be interpreted if the entire ultraviolet absorption spectrum together with mixed polarization data were available. This may well be a practicable feature in the future, but to date most studies of intensities have adopted another approach first clearly spelled out by Placzek (23).

Placzek showed that, provided certain conditions were satisfied, a quantum mechanical analogue of the simple classical theory could be applied. The conditions are that the ground state of the molecule should be a $^1\Sigma$ (singlet sigma) electronic state, that the Born Oppenheimer approximation be valid, and that the exciting frequency v_o be very much less than any electronic frequency of the molecule. It will be seen that these conditions are satisfied for the large majority of molecules. If this is the case, then the common method of finding the quantum mechanical analogue of any classical quantity can be used, i.e.,

$$[\alpha_{\rho\sigma}]_{nm} = \int \psi_n{}^* \alpha_{\rho\sigma} \psi_m \, d\tau \qquad (52)$$

Following the classical treatment we now expand $\alpha_{\rho\sigma}$ in a Taylor's series and hence

$$[\alpha_{\rho\sigma}]_{nm} = \int \psi_n^* \alpha_o \psi_m \, d\tau + \sum_a \frac{\partial\alpha}{\partial Q_a} \int \psi_n^* Q_a \psi_m \, d\tau \tag{53}$$

which simplifies still further when the nature of the normal coordinates (Q) is considered, for in both classical and quantum mechanics the vibrational problem is completely factored when the normal coordinates are used as a basis set; i.e.,

$$[\alpha_{\rho\sigma}]_{nm} = \alpha_o \int \psi_n \psi_m \, d\tau + \frac{\partial\alpha}{\partial Q_{nm}} \int \psi_n^* Q_{nm} \psi_m \, d\tau \tag{54}$$

In passing, it is worthwhile noting this equivalence of classical and quantum mechanical normal coordinates, for basically this is the reason why a vibrational frequency observed in the infrared or Raman corresponds to a real vibrational frequency of the molecule, whereas, in pure rotation this is not the case. Equation (54) can be analyzed as before and clearly the first term is responsible for Rayleigh scattering and the second for Raman scattering of fundamentals. Combining the second term with Eqs. (49) and (43) the equation giving the observed intensity of a vibration band in Raman scattering is

$$I_{mn} = \frac{2^4\pi^3}{3^2 c^4} I_o(v_o + v_{mn})^4 \sum_{\rho\sigma} \left(\frac{\partial\alpha_{\rho\sigma}}{\partial Q_a}\right)^2 \cdot \frac{(n_a' + 1)h}{\mu v} \tag{54a}$$

To get the overall effect we must first clearly sum over all values of n_a, taking account of the Boltzmann factors for each level; i.e.,

$$N_o \sum_n (n+1) \, e^{-nhv/kT}$$

where N_o is the fraction of the molecules in the ground state; this sum is readily shown to be (24)

$$N_o \cdot \frac{1}{(1 - e^{-hv/kT})^2}$$

If the total number of molecules in the exciting beam is N, then simple summation over the Boltzmann weighted levels gives

$$N = \frac{N_o}{(1 - e^{-hv/kT})}$$

The resulting expression for the total observed power radiated by the N molecules in the Stokes line of frequency $(v_o - v)$ is, thus,

$$I_{mn} = \frac{2^4\pi^3}{3^2 c^4} \cdot \frac{hI_o N(v_o - v)^4}{\mu v(1 - e^{-hv/kT})} \sum_{\rho\sigma} \left(\frac{\partial\alpha_{\rho\sigma}}{\partial Q_a}\right)^2$$

Carrying out the summation over ρ and σ via Eq. (13) one arrives at

$$I_{mn} = \frac{2^4 \pi^3}{45 \cdot 3^2 \cdot c^4} \cdot \frac{h I_o N (v_o - v)^4}{\mu v (1 - e^{-hv/kT})} [45(\bar{\alpha}_a')^2 + 7(\gamma_a')^2] \qquad (54b)$$

which is the equation used to determine the derived polarizability quantities from observed intensities. Two modifications are worth mentioning: first, mass weighted normal coordinates are frequently used in the solution of the vibrational problem, and if these are in fact in use, the reduced mass μ disappears from the denominator; second, the degree of depolarization can be introduced via Eq. (14) to give the alternative form

$$I_{mn} = \frac{2^4 \pi^3}{3^2 c^4} \cdot \frac{h I_o N (v_o - v)^4}{v (1 - e^{-hv/kT})} \cdot (\bar{\alpha}_a')^2 \left(\frac{6}{6 - 7\rho} \right) \qquad (54c)$$

In all the above treatment it must be remembered that unlike the a-priori quantum field approach, we are dealing with parameters $(\partial \alpha_{\rho\sigma} / \partial Q_a)$ which are to be determined experimentally. As a consequence, the dependence of Raman scattering on the excited states of the molecule is obscured, but as will become clear in the course of the presentation, information about the bonding in the molecule can still be recovered. Within this framework we can determine the rotational invariants of $\alpha' = \partial \alpha / \partial Q_a$ for each observed Raman line, but no progress in interpreting these will be possible without some theory that predicts the functional dependence of the molecular polarizability on the normal coordinates. Such a theory will probably be framed, rather analogous to the force constant problem, in terms of the dependence of the molecular polarizability on the internal coordinates—changes of bond length, interbond angle, etc. The two sets of coordinates (internal, R, and normal, Q) are related by the transformation,

$$R = LQ \qquad (55)$$

and the matrix L is obtained in the solution of the vibrational problem

$$GFL = L\Lambda \qquad (56)$$

In the equation Λ is a diagonal matrix whose entries are the squares of the vibration frequencies and thus L is the matrix which diagonalizes the matrix product of G, the inverse kinetic energy matrix, and F, the force constant matrix. We will thus need the relationship between the derivatives of the molecular polarizability with respect to normal coordinates (related to the observed intensities), and the derivatives with respect to internal coordinates (to be provided by the theory) and this relationship is easily seen to be

$$\frac{\partial \alpha_{\rho\sigma}}{\partial Q_i} = \sum_j \frac{\partial \alpha_{\rho\sigma}}{\partial R_j} \cdot \frac{\partial R_j}{\partial Q_i} \tag{57}$$

that is

$$\frac{\partial \alpha_{\rho\sigma}}{\partial Q_i} = \sum_j \frac{\partial \alpha_{\rho\sigma}}{\partial R_j} \cdot l_{ji}$$

in which l_{ji} is an element of L. Before going on to consider the theoretical derivation of $\partial \alpha_{\rho\sigma}/\partial R_j$ it is worthwhile to consider Eq. (57) in some depth. The quantities $\partial \alpha_{\rho\sigma}/\partial R_j$ being electronic in origin will be expected, like force constants, to be invariant under isotopic substitution, so one would imagine that additional information could be gained concerning these by determining the intensities (and hence the $\partial \alpha_{\rho\sigma}/\partial Q_i$) of scattering by isotopically substituted molecules. However, in the analogous problem of determining force constants by observing the vibration frequencies of a set of isotopically substituted molecules, certain product rules apply which, being necessary relations, reduce the amount of independent information to be gained (25). If the G and F matrices are expressed in terms of the symmetry coordinates (i.e. those linear combinations of the internal coordinates which provide a basis for a completely reduced representation of the molecular point group) then for each symmetry type it follows that (25)

$$|\mathcal{G}| \times |\mathcal{F}| = \Pi \lambda_i \tag{58}$$

where $\lambda_i = 4\pi^2 v_i^2$, the Π indicates the product over i and the vertical lines indicate the determinant of the corresponding matrix. For the isotopic molecule a similar relation holds, namely

$$|\mathcal{G}^*| \times |\mathcal{F}| = \Pi \lambda_i^* \tag{59}$$

so that necessarily

$$\frac{|\mathcal{G}|}{|\mathcal{G}^*|} = \frac{\Pi \lambda_i}{\Pi \lambda_i^*} \tag{60}$$

The LHS of this equation is a quantity determined only by the masses of the atoms and the geometry of the molecule, and is hence independent of the force constants. In a similar way it can be shown that necessary relations exist between the intensities observed with isotopically substituted molecules. Rewriting Eq. (57) in terms of symmetry coordinates S one has

$$\frac{\partial \alpha_{\rho\sigma}}{\partial Q_i} = \sum_j \frac{\partial \alpha_{\rho\sigma}}{\partial S_j} \cdot \frac{\partial S_j}{\partial Q_i} \tag{61}$$

for which $\partial S_j / \partial Q_i$ is an entry in the matrix $\mathscr{L}$ given by

$$S = \mathscr{L}Q \tag{62}$$

and so is only nonzero for Q_i and S_j belonging to the same irreducible representation. Another way of saying this is that $\mathscr{L}$ is factored into blocks running down the principal diagonal. The quantities $\partial \alpha_{\rho\sigma} / \partial Q_i$ can be assembled into a row vector $\alpha_{\rho\sigma}^Q$ with $3N - 6$ entries and the $\partial \alpha_{\rho\sigma} / \partial S_j$ can be likewise assembled into a row vector $\alpha_{\rho\sigma}^s$ with also $3N - 6$ entries, if all redundancies have been removed. In terms of these, Eq. (61) becomes

$$\alpha_{\rho\sigma}^Q = \alpha_{\rho\sigma}^s \cdot \mathscr{L} \tag{63}$$

Transposing this and multiplying the two equations together one has

$$\alpha_{\rho\sigma}^Q \cdot \tilde{\alpha}_{\rho\sigma}^Q = \alpha_{\rho\sigma}^s \mathscr{L} \tilde{\mathscr{L}} \tilde{\alpha}_{\rho\sigma}^s \tag{64}$$

where the tilde ($\sim$) denotes transposition.

From the theory of molecular vibrations (26) it is known that

$$\mathscr{L} \tilde{\mathscr{L}} = \mathscr{G} \tag{65}$$

and since the LHS of Eq. (64) is proportional to the sum of the observed intensities, it follows that analogously we have a necessary relation between the intensities of isotopically substituted molecules. There is a relation of this form for each symmetry type, but within the type, the actual form of the relation is somewhat complicated since each block of $\mathscr{G}$ is not diagonal. A simple relation for each block can be derived by noting that again from the theory of molecular vibrations (26), for each block

$$\tilde{\mathscr{L}} \mathscr{F} \mathscr{L} = \Lambda \tag{66}$$

where Λ is a diagonal matrix of the λ_i. Inverting both sides of this relation,

$$\mathscr{L}^{-1} \mathscr{F}^{-1} \tilde{\mathscr{L}}^{-1} = \Lambda^{-1} \tag{67}$$

So that if we assemble the product $\alpha_{\rho\sigma}^Q \Lambda^{-1} \tilde{\alpha}_{\rho\sigma}^Q$, this becomes

$$\alpha_{\rho\sigma}^Q \Lambda^{-1} \tilde{\alpha}_{\rho\sigma}^Q = \alpha_{\rho\sigma}^s \mathscr{L} \mathscr{L}^{-1} \mathscr{F}^{-1} \tilde{\mathscr{L}}^{-1} \tilde{\mathscr{L}} \tag{68}$$

$$\alpha_{\rho\sigma}^Q \Lambda^{-1} \tilde{\alpha}_{\rho\sigma}^Q = \alpha_{\rho\sigma}^s \mathscr{F}^{-1} \tilde{\alpha}_{\rho\sigma}^s$$

The right hand side of this equation is a true isotopic invariant, and the left hand side is merely the sum of each intensity (corrected of course, for wavelength dependent factors) divided by the square of the frequency of the corresponding normal mode (since Λ is diagonal). This relationship, first described by Crawford (27) in 1952, is very valuable, since although it shows that not all the intensity information from isotopic studies is independent, it can be used to show that the information obtained is consistent. The consistency can be that all the data is on the same scale or perhaps more intriguingly that the correct assignment of the observed spectra has been made. We now go on to consider the theoretical interpretation of the $\partial\alpha_{\rho\sigma}/\partial R_j$: the most successful treatment so far developed is that due to Wolkenstein (28).

IV. WOLKENSTEIN BOND POLARIZABILITY THEORY

Wolkenstein's treatment essentially is to regard the overall molecular polarizability as the tensor sum of terms for the various kinds of electron in the molecule. Thus there will be terms for the nonbonding core electrons which will be spherical tensors, terms for the lone pair electrons which will be cylindrically symmetric tensors and terms for the bonding electrons which will be cylindrically symmetrical for single and triple bonds but not so for double bonds. The further assumptions are then made that if a given bond is stretched then the components of that bond's polarizability tensor alter but not those of any other bond, and secondly, for a motion involving bond bending the components do not alter in magnitude, but that the overall tensor does alter because of the angular terms involved in a tensor sum. To illustrate these points we will work through a simple example, that of the tetrahedral methane molecule CH_4. Since the final formulas will only involve rotational invariants we can consider the molecule in any orientation relative to an arbitrary set of Cartesian axes, and naturally, therefore, choose the most convenient, which is shown in Fig. 2. CH_1H_2 defines the xz plane and CH_3H_4 the yz plane. The problem now is to transform the various polarizabilities from their own natural system in which they are diagonal to the chosen xyz system and, as before, this is done by premultiplication by the suitable rotation matrix followed by post-multiplication by its inverse. Thus, consider the bond polarizability CH_1: this becomes

$$\alpha_{CH_1}^{xyz} = \begin{bmatrix} \cos\dfrac{\theta_{12}}{2} & 0 & -\sin\dfrac{\theta_{12}}{2} \\ 0 & 1 & 0 \\ +\sin\dfrac{\theta_{12}}{2} & 0 & \cos\dfrac{\theta_{12}}{2} \end{bmatrix} \begin{bmatrix} \alpha_p & 0 & 0 \\ 0 & \alpha_p & 0 \\ 0 & 0 & \alpha_l \end{bmatrix} \begin{bmatrix} \cos\dfrac{\theta_{12}}{2} & 0 & \sin\dfrac{\theta_{12}}{2} \\ 0 & 1 & 0 \\ -\sin\dfrac{\theta_{12}}{2} & 0 & \cos\dfrac{\theta_{12}}{2} \end{bmatrix}$$

$$(69)$$

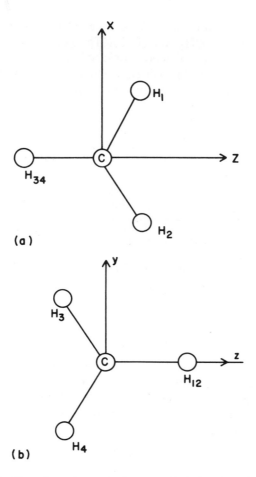

Fig. 2. Cartesian axis system for a tetrahedral XY_4 molecule.

where α_p and α_l are the longitudinal and the perpendicular bond polarizability components, hence,

$$
\alpha_{\mathrm{CH}_1}^{xyz} =
\begin{bmatrix}
\alpha_p \cos^2 \dfrac{\theta_{12}}{2} + \alpha_l \sin^2 \dfrac{\theta_{12}}{2} & 0 & \dfrac{1}{2}(\alpha_p - \alpha_l) \sin \theta_{12} \\[2ex]
0 & \alpha_\rho & 0 \\[2ex]
\dfrac{1}{2}(\alpha_p - \alpha_l) \sin \theta_{12} & 0 & \alpha_p \sin^2 \dfrac{\theta_{12}}{2} + \alpha_l \cos^2 \dfrac{\theta_{12}}{2}
\end{bmatrix}
$$

$$(70)$$

Similar expressions can be derived for the remaining three bond polarizabilities namely CH_2, CH_3, and CH_4. The core polarizability for the
carbon atom is spherical and hence constant in all axis systems, and in the
present case there are no lone pair effects to be considered. Using the two
Wolkenstein postulates the following is immediately evident:

$$\frac{\partial \alpha_{\text{molecule}}}{\partial R_1} = \frac{\partial \alpha_{CH_1}}{\partial R_1}$$

$$= \begin{bmatrix} \alpha_p' \cos^2 \dfrac{\theta_{12}}{2} + \alpha_l' \sin^2 \dfrac{\theta_{12}}{2} & 0 & \tfrac{1}{2}(\alpha_p' - \alpha_l') \sin \theta_{12} \\ 0 & \alpha_p' & 0 \\ \tfrac{1}{2}(\alpha_p' - \alpha_l') \sin \theta_{12} & 0 & \alpha_p' \sin^2 \dfrac{\theta_{12}}{2} + \alpha_l' \cos^2 \dfrac{\theta_{12}}{2} \end{bmatrix}$$

and, adding the contributions from CH_1 and CH_2,

$$\frac{\partial \alpha_{\text{molecule}}}{\partial \theta_{12}} = \begin{bmatrix} (\alpha_l - \alpha_p) \sin \theta_{12} & 0 & 0 \\ 0 & 0 & 0 \\ 0 & 0 - (\alpha_l - \alpha_p) \sin \theta_{12} \end{bmatrix} \tag{71}$$

in which $\alpha_p' = \partial \alpha p / \partial R$, etc. The Raman intensities for methane are thus
determined by just four quantities α_l, α_p, α_l', and α_p'. Now this pentatomic molecule will have nine $(3N-6)$ normal modes of vibration and
since the representation of the molecular point group (T_d) formed by
the normal coordinates reduces to (29)

$$\Gamma_Q = \Gamma_{A_1} + \Gamma_E + 2\Gamma_{F_2} \tag{72}$$

there will be four observable Raman "lines." Thus all four parameters
can be deduced from absolute Raman intensity measurements. The actual
formulas to be used are derived from Eq. (57) via the relation connecting
the symmetry and internal coordinates, viz.,

$$S = UR \tag{73}$$

and putting in the value for the tetrahedral angle $(\cos \theta = -\tfrac{1}{3})$, the
results are (30)

$$\left. \begin{array}{l} \bar{\alpha}_1' = 2M_H^{-\frac{1}{2}} \bar{\alpha}_{CH}' \\ \gamma_1' = \text{zero} \end{array} \right\}$$

$$\bar{\alpha}_2' = \text{zero}$$

$$\gamma_2' = \sqrt{(8)} M_H^{-\frac{1}{2}} \frac{\gamma_{CH}}{r_o} \left.\vphantom{\begin{matrix}a\\b\\c\end{matrix}}\right\}$$

$$\bar{\alpha}_3' = \bar{\alpha}_4' = \text{zero} \tag{74}$$

$$\gamma_i' = \frac{2}{\sqrt{3}} \left[l_{3i} \gamma_C' + l_{4i} \frac{\gamma_{CH}}{r_o} \right]; \quad i = 3, 4$$

in which

$$\bar{\alpha}_{CH}' = \tfrac{1}{3}[\alpha_l' + 2\alpha_p'], \quad \gamma_{CH} = [\alpha_l - \alpha_p], \quad \text{and} \quad \gamma_{CH}' = [\alpha_l' - \alpha_p']$$

For the case of methane, there is a great deal of information from isotope studies, Coriolis coupling constants, centrifugal distortion constants, etc. which is relevant to the calculation of the force constants. Consequently the l_{ij} are known with fair precision; then, since the four nonzero relations of Eq. (74) involve only three parameters an internal check of the Wolkenstein hypotheses is available using relative intensity data only. For methane, the observed (31) values are $\gamma_2'/\bar{\alpha}_1' = 0.338$, $\gamma_3'/\bar{\alpha}_1' = 1.229$ and from these $\gamma_4'/\bar{\alpha}_1'$ is calculated to be 0.055. The ν_4 band should, thus, be of very small intensity compared with the other three bands. This agrees with observation (31). Similarly good agreement is found for CCl_4 (30) but Woodward and his coworkers (32) have found that the agreement gets very much worse as one goes to heavier XY_4 tetrahedral molecules such as $SnCl_4$. Of course for molecules such as this, approximate force fields have to be used of necessity, and the one favored by Woodward et al. was the Urey Bradley force field in the mathematical formulation of Shimanouchi (33). The reason for the lack of agreement for the heavier molecules is thus somewhat obscured since the defect could be in the Wolkenstein theory or in the force field employed. Molecules of other symmetries have been investigated by Long (34) and his associates from the same standpoint of an internal check based on relative intensities, but with these a new computational difficulty arises. Equation (61) tacitly ignores vibration rotation interaction, and while this is a good assumption for most cases, the exception is when a vibrational mode belongs to an irreducible representation that also contains one of the primitive rotations R_x, R_y, or R_z. When this is the case, the vibration will necessarily induce rotational motion of the type called "libration" and the intensity formulae for a mode which is pure bond stretching (e.g., ν_3 of H_2O) will involve terms in the nonderived bond polarizabilities. Long (35) has given the methods for deriving the intensity formulae under this circumstance.

Absolute Raman intensity measurements are much more difficult to obtain than the relative ones, but once obtained, when combined with the known molecular polarizability, they yield all four bond components. As has been remarked above, the relative methane intensities agree well with Wolkenstein's theory so it seems worthwhile to solve Eq. (74) using the absolute data of Yoshino and Bernstein (31, 36); the results are

$$\alpha_l = 0.858 \text{ Å}^3 \qquad\qquad \alpha_p = 0.546 \text{ Å}^3$$

$$\alpha_l' = 2.441 \text{ Å}^2 \qquad\qquad \alpha_p' = 0.34 \text{ Å}^2$$

The only comparable estimates in the literature are due to Denbigh (37), who by somewhat intricate arguments not involving Raman measurements at all has published values for the bond polarizability components for CH_4 and his values, viz., $\alpha_l = 0.79$ Å, $\alpha_p = 0.58$ Å are in quite good agreement. This is heartening, but still further evidence in favor of Wolkenstein has been collected. Woodward and his coworkers (38) have noted that the v_2 vibration for molecules of the type $X(CH_3)_4$ should be of vanishing intensity according to Wolkenstein, apart from the parts of the normal coordinate Q_2 due to C—H stretching and X—C stretching. These molecules are of such high symmetry (T_d), that there is a real chance of getting a meaningful force field and hence meaningful estimates of this mixing, and, therefore, a good experimental test of Wolkenstein is available. Their results strongly support the validity of the Wolkenstein theory. These methods can of course be applied to other molecules, the only proviso being that a good force field be available. Thus, consider acetonitrile CH_3—C≡N for which there are four vibrations belonging to the A_1 representation of C_{3v}. The four symmetry coordinates are

$$S_1 = \frac{1}{\sqrt{3}}[\Delta r_1 + \Delta r_2 + \Delta r_3] \qquad\qquad r = \text{C—H}$$

$$S_2 = \Delta R \qquad\qquad R = \text{C≡N}$$

$$\text{(75)}$$

$$S_3 = \frac{1}{\sqrt{6}}[\Delta\alpha_1 + \Delta\alpha_2 + \Delta\alpha_3 - \Delta\beta_1 - \Delta\beta_2 - \Delta\beta_3] \qquad \alpha = \text{H—C—H}$$

$$\beta = \text{H—C—C}$$

$$S_4 = \Delta L \qquad\qquad L = \text{C—C}$$

Inverting Eq. (63) and taking the rotational invariants one has

$$\bar{\alpha}_{Qi}' \cdot \mathscr{L}_{A_1}^{-1} = \bar{\alpha}_{si}' \qquad\qquad \text{(76)}$$

so that $\partial\bar{\alpha}/\partial S_3$ can be obtained from the measured intensities ($\bar{\alpha}'_{Qi}$). This quantity is indeed found to be very small (zero if Wolkenstein strictly applies), so that again strong support for Wolkenstein is observed. The finite—though small—value found may be a consequence of the approximations used in obtaining the force constants and hence $\mathscr{L}_{A_1}^{-1}$.

Another and very novel way of testing the Wolkenstein hypotheses is via the vibrational amplitudes. The result of molecular vibration is that the instantaneous internuclear separations observed with a large number of molecules are randomly distributed about the average position. This becomes manifest in electron diffraction experiments where a "damping" of the diffraction pattern is observed as a consequence of the absence of a unique set of internuclear separations. From the magnitude of the "damping," the "spread" of internuclear separations can be deduced, i.e., the mean square amplitudes of vibration can be worked out. These quantities can also be calculated quite simply if the force field of the molecule is known. To show this, and incidentally to justify a great deal of what has gone before, we calculate the mean square amplitudes of vibration of a classical oscillator to which the arbitrary condition, that its energy be quantized, is applied. The potential energy of a molecule regarded as a set of simple harmonic oscillators is given by

$$2V = Q\Lambda\tilde{Q} \tag{77}$$

so that for each mode

$$2V_i = 4\pi^2 v_i^2 \cdot Q_i^2 \tag{78}$$

Applying now the quantum condition

$$T_i + V_i = (n_i + \tfrac{1}{2})hv_i \tag{79}$$

where n_i is the vibrational quantum number, it follows that if

$$Q_i = Q_o \cos 2\pi v_i t$$

then

$$Q_o^2 = \frac{(n_i + \tfrac{1}{2})h}{2\pi^2 v_i} \tag{80}$$

Hence the mean square amplitude of vibration is

$$\overline{Q_i^2} = \frac{(n_i + \tfrac{1}{2})h}{4\pi^2 v_i} \tag{81}$$

This is a most important result for comparison of it with Eq. (49) in terms of mass adjusted normal coordinates, proves the assertion made earlier, that the amplitudes of the classical and the quantum mechanical oscillators are identical (except for the usual zero point contribution). This identity is the sole justification for the use of the purely classical methods of vibrational analysis as typified by Eqs. (56), (65), (66), etc. in the analysis of molecular motion. The observed amplitudes in an electron diffraction experiment arise from molecules in all possible vibrational states, with of course the usual Boltzmann weighting, so that we need to sum Eq. (81) over all values of n_i to get the corresponding theoretical quantity; this summation leads to the result

$$\overline{Q_i^2} = \frac{h}{8\pi^2 v_i} \coth\left(\frac{h v_i}{2kT}\right) \tag{82}$$

The amplitude of each normal coordinate is thus calculable solely in terms of its corresponding frequency. If the L matrix is known, the amplitudes of all the internal coordinates can be computed since

$$\overline{R_i^2} = \sum_j 1_{ij}^2 \overline{Q_j^2}, \tag{83}$$

this equation having no cross terms of the type $Q_j Q_k$ because of the time averaging. The RHS of Eq. (83) is derived from spectroscopic studies, and the LHS from electron diffraction studies, so that in principle the electron diffraction measurements could be used to tell how accurately the l_{ij} had been determined, and hence to throw light on the question of whether small observed departures of the predictions of the Wolkenstein theory have their origin in defects in this theory or in the approximations involved in the force-field. Unfortunately the amplitudes are not sensitive to the l_{ij}, whereas the intensities are, so the check cannot be done in this way. However, the question can be asked, for any particular molecule, "is there a real force field which will correctly reproduce the observed frequencies, and in terms of which the Wolkenstein hypotheses are strictly true?" It turns out that for all molecules so far investigated, there always is such a field and fields of this type have been christened W-fields. The manner of deriving these W-fields is quite interesting. For XY_4 as an example, the A_1 and E force constants are uniquely defined by the corresponding frequencies but in the F_2 class there are three force constants and only two frequencies to determine them. This degree of freedom is reflected in the 2×2 $\mathscr{L}_{F_2}$ block, which has four entries, among which there are three necessary relations given by Eq. (65). One more relationship among these is derivable (assuming Wolkenstein to be correct) from Eq. (74) by eliminating γ'_{XY} and γ_{XY} from the relations for γ_2', γ_3' and γ_4'. In fact this fourth relation is as follows:

$$\frac{\sqrt{3}}{2} l_{33}\gamma_4' - \frac{\sqrt{3}}{2} l_{34}\gamma_3' = \frac{\gamma_2' M_Y}{2\sqrt{2}} |\mathscr{L}_{F_2}| = \gamma_2' \sqrt{(\mu_Y + 4\mu_X)} \tag{84}$$

where $\mu_Y = M_Y^{-1}$ and $\mu_X = M_X^{-1}$. Equation (65) gives quadratic relationships among the l_{ij} so there will always be as it turns out, four distinct fields which satisfy the boundary conditions. The next question to be asked is "do these W-fields give amplitudes in agreement with experiment?" The answer to this is "yes." For molecules such as $SnCl_4$, the amplitudes observed are nearly twice as large as those calculated using the orthodox UBS force field, which also leads to an unsatisfactory test of the Wolkenstein theory, whereas those from the W-field agree almost exactly with experiment. The W-fields are rather novel in that one derives the normal coordinates straight away without going through the procedure of solving the vibrational problem in terms of a set of force constants. Should these potential constants be required, they can be readily obtained from the $\mathscr{L}$ matrix by rearranging Eq. (66) thus:

$$\mathscr{F} = \tilde{\mathscr{L}}^{-1}\Lambda\mathscr{L}^{-1} \tag{85}$$

In fact an examination of the W-field force constants for $SnCl_4$, obtained from the above relation, is rather interesting, since the constants fit well to the qualitative picture frequently used to relate interaction force constants to the orbital hybridization present in the bonds.

The evidence in favor of the simple Wolkenstein theory is thus impressive, and we are led to think of a bond polarizability as a real physical quantity, and not just a mathematical artifice conjured up by our preference for an internal coordinate system involving bonds and interbond angles. This is still more strongly hinted at, by the observation that bond polarizabilities for similar bonds in similar molecules are very much the same. The contrast with the relative failure of the bond-moment picture to interpret infrared intensities is marked. The reason for this is fairly clear if we consider a diatomic molecule and plot molecular polarizability as a function of internuclear distance as shown in Fig. 3.

At $r =$ zero the polarizability has to be that of the combined atom and at $r = \infty$ it has to be the sum of the polarizabilities of the two separated atoms. These boundary conditions together with the form of the quantum mechanical relations for α are sufficient to make α a monotonic function of r, and more than that to make α essentially a linear function of r in the neighborhood of the equilibrium distance r_e. In the bond moment case, since μ_∞ can be ∞ or zero, there is no such restriction and μ need not be a monotonic function of r. The consequences of these two quite different forms of behavior are of considerable practical significance. Following Placzek (23), [vide Eq. (54)] a linear variation of α with r will lead only to Raman scattering of fundamentals since overtones will involve terms of

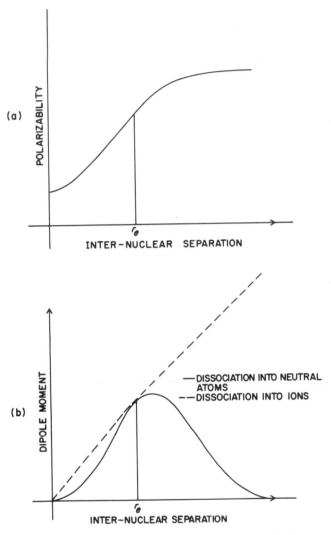

Fig. 3. Variation of (a) polarizability and (b) dipole moment of a diatomic molecule as a function of internuclear separation.

the form $d^n\alpha/dr^n$. This is in fact observed—overtones and combinations, Fermi resonance apart, being very rare in the Raman effect. In the infrared spectrum on the other hand combination and overtone bands are common and frequently match fundamentals in intensity. Since μ is so sensitive a function of r, a slight shift of the equilibrium position, as might occur, e.g., due to steric forces from other atoms in a polyatomic molecule, can alter completely the value of $d\mu/dr$. Consequently, bond moments are not found to be transferable from one molecule to another. The Raman case is quite different; the insensitivity of $\partial\alpha/\partial r$ to r being reflected in the excellent transferability noted above. This being the case, it becomes worthwhile to compare the values of the bond polarizabilities between different bonds, to see if any information is forthcoming about the nature of these bonds. It would seem likely that the derived bond polarizabilities will be more helpful in this context than the nonderived quantities since these latter cannot easily be disentangled from the core and lone pair polarizabilities, whereas, if Wolkenstein is correct, the derived quantities reflect only the properties of the bonding electrons. It has been known for some time now that this picture is at least qualitatively correct, for $\bar{\alpha}'_{bond}$ correlates well with the degree of ionic character of the bond, being very small for pure ionic bonds and very much larger for covalent bonds (39). Yoshino and Bernstein (36) have shown that $\bar{\alpha}'_{CH}$ is constant for the series C_2H_6, C_2H_4, C_2H_2, and C_6H_6, which may well be an illustration of the effect mentioned above, since the bond lengths vary considerably in this series, but most remarkably they have also shown that $\bar{\alpha}'_{CC}$ is proportional to bond order. This at first sight would seem to suggest that the σ and π contributions to $\bar{\alpha}'_{CC}$ are equal, which is rather surprising, since in terms of the dispersion theory one would expect the π contributions to be larger, as the corresponding excited states are lower in energy for the π transitions than for the σ transitions. This effect is not apparently observed (40) for oxyanions such as SO_4^{-2} where π electrons make a larger contribution to $\bar{\alpha}'_{XO}$. The bonding in complex cyanides such as $Fe(CN)_6^{3-}$ has also been investigated (41) by these methods, and a consistent picture obtained. Nevertheless there does remain the difficulty that meaningful comparisons, at present, can only be made within isoelectronic series, since the effects of large changes of atomic number cannot be estimated. It is possible that a way round this difficulty may be found in the work of Long and Plane who used a delta-function potential model to calculate derived polarizabilities (42). Functions of this type had been used earlier by Lippincott and his colleagues ($43,44$) to calculate a number of molecular parameters, and their success inspired the extension of the method by Long and Plane. Perhaps we may now meaningfully compare NH and PH bonds for example. Future work will clarify the position, but the value of Raman intensity studies to the theoretical chemist is unlikely to be undermined. Even more than force constant investigations, the study of the derived bond polarizabilities goes right to the heart of the bonding problem, telling us directly about the bonding electrons themselves.

The broad picture painted above has shown how Raman intensities can be interpreted, and how their study can contribute to chemistry: in particular the Wolkenstein treatment has stood up well to investigation. However, the Wolkenstein hypotheses are distinctly drastic, and several workers have compared them by analogy with the simple valence force field which is obtained by setting all off diagonal elements of the matrix F [vide Eq. (56)] equal to zero, or in other words, ignoring all interbond interactions. That this approach is unsatisfactory for the molecular vibration problem is well known, as is illustrated by the case of ethylene (45) C_2H_4 for which no real simple valence force field can be found, and therefore it is to be expected that the Wolkenstein intensity approach can only be thought of as a first approximation albeit a good one. Of course, for most molecules, it is difficult to know whether the departures from expected behavior are due to the inadequacies of the Wolkenstein theory or due to inadequacies of the force field used; nevertheless some authors have already felt sufficiently sure of their ground to postulate the necessity for use of a modified Wolkenstein theory. The modification principally favored is to abandon the suggestion that the mean polarizability be independent of interbond angle; the additional terms are of course very much smaller than the principal terms.

The practical details of Raman intensity measurements have been glossed over in this chapter, since instrumentation is discussed elsewhere, but it is worthwhile to discuss one or two rather important points here. First, it has been tacitly assumed throughout the derivations of the intensity formulae, that the direction of illumination of the sample and the direction of observation are well defined with respect to one another. In practice this would not be expected to be the case, at least with arc lamp sources, since both the source and the detector will subtend finite solid angles at the sample. To get the observed signal at the detector for each polarization will involve a vector integration over solid angle, an awkward procedure, to get the so-called instrument function. This function will change of course, with any change to the apparatus, e.g., the refractive indexes of the samples varying, and clearly the position is not very satisfactory. There are two ways round this impasse. First to study only lines having the same degree of depolarization, such as non-totally symmetric modes, or else the totally symmetric modes of spherically symmetrical molecules for which the isotropy enables one to ignore the solid angle effects, and second, the sample can be surrounded with a suitably oriented polarizer. The first approach is clearly of limited application, but the serious loss of intensity involved in the second method is a weighty factor to be considered especially when gaseous samples are being investigated for, of course, these scatter very weakly compared to liquid samples. It was partly for this reason that Woodward and Waters (*38*) chose the spherically symmetrical $X(CH_3)_4$ molecules for their test of the Wolkenstein theory. However, for the large majority of samples, the losses just have to be endured and it is essential for the sample to be surrounded by a polaroid film so oriented that the electric vector of the exciting light is perpendicular to the axis of the tube. The topic of light losses leads on naturally to a consideration of the absolute power radiated from the sample in a typical Raman experiment.

V. ABSOLUTE POWER RADIATED

The absolute power radiated in all directions by the sample is given by Eq. (54b). It is worthwhile pointing out that this equation can be derived classically from Eq. (6), merely by applying the quantum conditions (Eqs. 49, 80) on the vibrational amplitudes. This is to be expected as a consequence of the Feynman theorem, which points out that quantum mechanics does not introduce any new forces into physics but merely lays down a new set of "rules" for the system to obey. Applying this we have

$$\mu = \frac{\partial \alpha}{\partial Q} \cdot Q \cdot E \tag{87}$$

and from classical electromagnetic theory

$$cE^2 = I_o \tag{88}$$

where I_o is the power per sq cm of the exciting radiation, thus

$$I = \frac{16\pi^4 \nu^4}{3c^4} \cdot \left(\frac{\partial \alpha}{\partial Q}\right)^2 Q^2 I_o \tag{89}$$

Putting in the quantum value for Q^2, carrying out the averaging over rotational configurations, doing likewise for the Boltzmann population of levels, and multiplying by 4π to get the power radiated in all directions, we obtain Eq. (54b). We can now imagine a real experiment in which we have a Raman tube 10 cm long and 1 cm in cross sectional area irradiated longitudinally with argon ion laser radiation of wavelength ≈ 5000 Å, mean power 1 W, and beam area $\ll 1\ cm^2$. The Raman tube contains carbon tetrachloride, and we are observing the v_1 mode with frequency shift $\Delta\bar{v} = 459\ cm^{-1}$. Taking $\bar{\alpha}'_{C-Cl} = 2.00\ Å^2$, computing $\bar{\alpha}_1'$ from Eq. (74) and substituting this in Eq. (54c) the total power emitted is found to be 10^{-7} W in all directions. If the spectrometer is observing the tube in the "head on" configuration then with reasonable experimental arrangements 10^{-10} W will arrive at the detector. A good photomultiplier can detect 10^{-16} W in an integrating time of 1 sec, so, in this photon noise limited case, one would expect a record of the spectrum to be obtained with a signal-to-noise ratio of ≈ 1000 to 1. The earlier type of excitation with mercury arc lamps suffered from the drawback that high power densities could not be achieved, but this was compensated to a certain extent by the use of diffuse reflecting cavities, so that signal-to-noise ratios of the same order were achievable. It will thus be seen that with good design of Raman equipment, records will be achieved with a signal-to-noise ratio in excess of 100 to 1. With laser excitation it is much easier to cope with the geometrical difficulties mentioned earlier, because the laser beam is well defined and highly polarized. As a result, intensity measurements should be quite straightforward, and of course since we are dealing with an emission phenomenon the whole system is linear. In this respect Raman intensity measurements are much easier to obtain than the corresponding infrared intensities where as is well known (46) the determination of integrated absorption presents severe problems.

To conclude this chapter we will discuss, at somewhat greater length, two topics briefly mentioned earlier in the chapter, namely resonance effects and the proper treatment of Rayleigh scattering.

VI. RESONANCE RAMAN EFFECT

It is now a well established fact that when the exciting frequency approaches that of an absorption band, a considerable enhancement of the intensities of some of the "lines" in the Raman spectrum is encountered. Under these conditions the simple Placzek theory is inapplicable. Experimentally, if one is attempting to determine bond polarizability components, a routine check to determine the intensities from say the mercury green line (5461 Å), the blue line (4358 Å), and the violet line (4047 Å) is usually applied to ensure that strict fourth power dependence is in fact observed, and that no resonance phenomena are present. The theory of the resonance Raman effect is quite interesting and has been discussed by Shorygin (47) and in particular by Behringer (48) and also by Rea (49). The mathematical theory has been further developed by Albrecht (19) who has (as usual in dispersion theory) introduced a damping term into the resonance denominator and obtained

$$[\alpha_{\rho\sigma}]_{gi \to gj} = \frac{1}{h} \sum_{en} \frac{(M_\rho)_{en \to gj}(M_\sigma)_{gi \to en}}{v_{en \to gi} - v_0 + i\gamma_e'} \tag{90}$$

by ignoring the now very small second term.

The sharp division between terms giving Rayleigh scattering and terms giving Raman scattering is no longer valid but nevertheless in practice it is expected that the mixing will be small. Equation (50) takes on the form (19)

$$[\alpha_{\rho\sigma}]_{gi \to gj} = F + G \tag{91}$$

where

$$F = \frac{1}{h} \sum_n \frac{(M_\rho)_{ge}^0 (M_\sigma)_{ge}^0 \int \psi_{gi}\psi_{en}\, d\tau \int \psi_{en}\psi_{gj}\, d\tau}{v_{en \to gi} - v_0 + i\gamma_e'}$$

$$G = \frac{-1}{h^2} \sum_n \sum_s \sum_a h_{es}^a [(M_\rho)_{ge}^0 (M_\sigma)_{gs}^0 \int \psi_{gj}\psi_{en}\, d\tau \int \psi_{en}Q_a\psi_{gi}\, d\tau$$

$$+ (M_\sigma)_{ge}^0 (M_\rho)_{gs}^0 \int \psi_{gi}\psi_{en}\, d\tau \int \psi_{en}Q_a\psi_{gj}\, d\tau] \times \frac{1}{(v_{eg} - v_0 + i\gamma_e')(v_s - v_e)}$$

It will be seen that the term $(v_s - v_e)$ in the denominator tends to select the lowest lying state s and the term $(v_{eg} - v_0 + i\gamma_e')$ tends to select the particular level v_{en} close to v_0. Thus those vibrations which mix the level near to v_0 with the lowest lying (and strongly allowed) level above (or below) it will become enhanced in Raman scattering. This is a most important result for immediately it emphasises the role that Raman studies can play in interpreting vibronic effects in molecular spectra. In particular of course since assignments are usually available for the Raman vibrations, the polarization characteristics of vibronic spectroscopy can be elucidated.

VII. PRESENT STATE OF RAMAN THEORY

The Raman effect is but one of the numerous phenomena that are covered under the general heading of "Scattering Theory." This topic has always been close to the main front of physical advance as is evidenced by the present interest in the scattering of subatomic particles in collisions at high energy. There was a similar intense interest in the inelastic scattering of photons in the first three decades of this century and this led to the development of satisfactory theories of the normal Raman effect and of resonance fluorescence. After this had been achieved, physicists lost interest in these topics and theoretical advance languished, but the two phenomena did become very useful tools for the structural chemist. However, as will be clear from the exposition of Raman theory given earlier in this chapter, the two topics are treated in very different ways and there is at present no very satisfactory way of linking them up.

The need for such a unified approach has become more urgent in recent years, with the development of laser sources and the discovery of new phenomena such as stimulated Raman emission and electronic Raman scattering. The warning signs were evident ten years ago when resonant Raman scattering was first encountered. The principal characteristic of a resonant Raman spectrum is the enormous enhancement of the intensity of certain of the Raman lines as the exciting frequency approaches that of an absorption band of the scattering sample. Clearly one can imagine the exciting frequency moving into coincidence with a narrow absorption line and then the question has to be faced, "Does one get two separate phenomena namely resonant Raman scattering and resonant fluorescence or do the two phenomena merge smoothly into one another?" In other words, "Is resonant fluorescence merely the limit of resonant Raman scattering?" The question is in principle answerable within the quantum mechanical dispersion relations, but as was mentioned earlier these are quite intractable and the two sets of approximations used to make them manageable apply either on the one hand for absolute coincidence (resonant fluorescence) or on the other for very poor coincidence (Raman effect). The intervening cases are not treated within either framework. Attempts to develop a unified theory will, therefore, have to be semi-empirical and perhaps a possible approach will lie in the direction of line shape theory. Every spectral absorption line has a natural width even in the absence of such well known broadening mechanisms as collision and Doppler broadening. The natural width arises from the uncertainty principle and is a direct corollary of the finite lifetime of the upper state. It follows, therefore, that the natural line shape function is always finite at all frequencies, though of course it is very strongly peaked at the resonant frequency. Within this approach, resonant fluorescence and Raman scattering are akin, both involving the absorption and re-emission of a photon and the differences can be understood in terms of the lifetimes of the bound-states, the lifetime of the nonresonant absorption bound-states being, by the uncertainty principle, very short indeed.

Let us consider now the intensity distribution in the pure rotation Raman band observed with a gaseous sample of a linear molecule. If the exciting radiation is at a much lower frequency than the $0 \to 0$ absorption band of the first intense electronic transition, then the absorption coefficient of each rotational line of that band at the frequency of the exciting line will be more or less the same. Molecules in the ground state having a rotational quantum number J can "absorb" the existing radiation and re-emit it with change of J

$$\Delta J = 0, \pm 2 \tag{92}$$

Since all J levels are populated with their respective Boltzmann weighting, the result will be the familiar Raman band with Stokes and anti-Stokes branches whose intensity profiles are determined just by the Boltzmann factors. When the exciting radiation coincides with a rotational absorption line of the electronic absorption band then scattering by strongly absorbing molecules will be much greater than those which are not, and one line in each band will be enormously enhanced and we will be observing a characteristic resonance fluorescence spectrum. Similar arguments apply to the rotation–vibration bands, but here we do encounter a difficulty in that resonance fluorescence is not characterized by any selection rules for the vibrational quantum number whereas the normal Raman effect is. This difficulty is not serious, however, for the selection rule arises from the use of first order perturbation theory, and this becomes progressively less and less justifiable as resonance is approached. Experiments are needed to investigate this matter more closely, but it would seem likely that overtone and combination bands will become relatively stronger and stronger as resonance is approached. The recent development of "tuneable" lasers should permit decisive experiments of this kind to be performed. The polarizability theory of Placzek is much less suitable for discussing cases involving close approach to absorption lines but nevertheless it is interesting to observe that the smoothly monotonic function as shown in Fig. 3a would be expected to change drastically for frequencies close to resonance, and again an enhancement of overtones and combinations might be expected.

Electronic Raman spectra are not commonly observed, the only convincing example from the early days of Raman spectroscopy being Rasetti's (50) observation of the doublet splitting in the $^2\Pi$ electronic ground state of NO. A different kind of theory is of course necessary to discuss this type of scattering and an approach to this has been discussed by Hougen and Singh (51) who observed electronic Raman transitions in the Pr^{3+} ion in crystals of $PrCl_3$. Their theoretical approach leads to the result that the intensities of Raman transitions between electronic states are proportional to the intensities of electric quadrupole transitions between the same states, but again their approach is not expected to be useful for the resonant case. A particularly interesting result from their treatment is that in general the scattering tensor will not be symmetrical, i.e., the xy element need not equal the yx element (see Chapter 8, by Koningstein and Mortensen).

Stimulated Raman emission was first observed in 1962 (52). It is observed when the intense radiation from a "giant" pulse laser is focused in liquids or solids. Very intense (up to 10% of the incident beam power) emission of Stokes–Raman radiation occurs in a rather diffuse fashion around the exciting beam. There is a threshold of incident laser power below which no stimulated Raman emission is observed but when the laser power is above the threshold no further threshold appears to be necessary for the production of anti-Stokes radiation, or for the production of harmonics at frequencies $\omega_L \pm \omega_R$ where ω_L is the laser frequency and ω_R the vibrational frequency. The anti-Stokes emission is confined to a narrow cone about the exciting beam. So far only totally symmetric Raman lines have been observed in stimulated emission and as a consequence, the phenomenon, despite the enormous power available, is of little value to the structural chemist who needs the entire spectrum. To physicists, however, the series of intriguing observations following one another from the work of the experimentalists has presented a challenge to develop theories adequate to account for all the observed phenomena. The first attempt at this was by Hellwarth (53) who developed a phenomenological theory based quite closely on the normal Raman theory. His approach showed that whereas normal Raman scattering is proportional to I_L (the laser intensity), the stimulated emission depended on the product $I_L \times I_R$ where I_R is the intensity of Raman scattering. Thus loosely, the stimulated emission depends on I_L^2 and the origin of the threshold phenomenon is revealed. The next advance came from Townes and his colleagues (54) who developed a treatment closely resembling the simple classical theory of Raman scattering. The classical approach was sketched out in the first part of this chapter, where it was implied that the molecules have to be vibrating in order that they may amplitude modulate the incident light wave and thus generate the Raman "side-bands." In fact it follows quite simply that the light wave will force the molecules to vibrate even if there is no dipole moment change associated with the vibration and even if the light frequency is much greater than the natural vibration frequency. To see this one notes that the energy of a polarizable molecule in a field E is given by (55)

$$V = -\tfrac{1}{2}\alpha E^2 \tag{93}$$

and thus the nuclei are subject to a stretching force

$$F = \frac{dV}{dr} = -\tfrac{1}{2}\frac{\partial\alpha}{\partial r}E^2 \tag{94}$$

This force is oscillating at the light frequency, i.e., we are dealing with the classical problem of the forced vibration of a pendulum at a frequency much higher than its natural frequency. The result, in the context of light and a molecule, is the extremely weak Raman emission at the frequencies $\omega' = \omega_0 \pm \omega_R$ where ω_R is the natural molecular vibration frequency. We now have two light fields present in the material, an intense one at frequency ω_L and a very weak one at ω' and as a consequence the driving force (which depends on E^2) has a component at $\omega_0 - \omega'$ that is the natural resonant frequency. If the power in the laser reaches a sufficiently high level, the molecules will begin to oscillate more and more violently with a consequent transfer of more and more power from the laser to the Raman radiation, and eventually the gain in the Raman modes will exceed the losses and stimulated Raman emission will be observed. Townes and his colleagues also discuss the same phenomenon from the point of view of macroscopic behavior and show that the properties of the system can be described in terms of a nonlinear polarization associated with a susceptibility of the form

$$\chi = \chi_0 + \chi' E^2 \tag{95}$$

where χ' has a highly resonant imaginary component at ω_R. From this point of view the phenomenon is akin to stimulated fluorescence, and the question of the Raman line width arises since the sharper this is the more highly resonant will be the imaginary component of χ'. This may well be the explanation of why only totally symmetric modes have so far been observed, for such modes give in general much sharper Raman bands than do the non-totally symmetric modes. An account of stimulated Raman emission in terms of quantum field theory has been given (56) by Buckingham. Basically his approach is in terms of the conversion of two light photons into a pair of Stokes and anti-Stokes Raman photons. A discussion of this type of scattering in which the molecule starts and finishes in its ground state requires fourth order time dependent perturbation theory and the final results are quoted in terms of molecular hyperpolarizabilities. Buckingham's theory gives a much more satisfactory account of the peculiar properties of the stimulated anti-Stokes radiation, and he is also able to account for the newer phenomena such as the inverse Raman effect first observed by Jones and Stoicheff (57); these effects are discussed in other chapters.

It will be seen therefore that in recent years the subject of Raman spectroscopy as a basic phenomenon in physics has been rejuvenated. New experimental results are coming out all the time, and we can look forward to parallel theoretical developments which will result in still further insight into the properties of molecules.

Acknowledgments

It would be impossible to give a full and proper listing of all the workers who have contributed to the field of Raman theory. I should therefore merely thank those from whom I have personally benefitted. These include Dr. L. A. Woodward of Oxford University, Dr. D. A. Long of Bradford University, Professor R. A. Plane of Cornell University, and especially Professor A. C. Albrecht whose clear and lucid exposition of the dispersion theory I have so heavily relied upon.

REFERENCES

1. J. C. Slater and N. H. Frank, *Introduction to Theoretical Physics*, McGraw-Hill, New York, 1933, p. 293.
2. H. Z. Cummins and R. W. Gammon, *J. Chem. Phys.*, **44**, 2785 (1966).
3. E. B. Wilson, Jr., J. C. Decius, and P. C. Cross, *Molecular Vibrations: The Theory of Infra-red and Raman Vibrational Spectra*, McGraw-Hill, New York, 1955, p. 47.
4. E. B. Wilson, Jr., J. C. Decius, and P. C. Cross, *Molecular Vibrations: The Theory of Infra-red and Raman Vibrational Spectra*, McGraw-Hill, New York, 1955, pp. 77–140.
5. L. Pauling and E. B. Wilson, Jr., *Introduction to Quantum Mechanics*, McGraw-Hill, New York, 1935.
6. H. A. Gebbie, N. W. B. Stone, and F. D. Findlay, *Nature*, **202**, 685 (1964).
7. D. R. Lide and A. G. Maki, *Appl. Phys. Letters*, **11**, 62 (1967).
8. A. Messiah, *Quantum Mechanics*, Vol. II, North Holland Publishing Company, Amsterdam, 1962, p. 1034.
9. G. Herzberg, *Spectra of Diatomic Molecules*, van Nostrand, New York, 1950, 2nd Ed., p. 105.
10. G. Herzberg, *Infra-red and Raman Spectra*, van Nostrand, New York, 1945, p. 34.
11. P. A. M. Dirac, *The Principles of Quantum Mechanics*, Oxford, 4th Ed., 1958.

12. J. C. Slater, *Quantum Theory of Matter*, McGraw-Hill, New York, 1951, p. 379.
13. Ibid, page 391.
14. J. N. Murrell and J. A. Pople, *Proc. Phys. Soc. (London)*, **69A**, 245 (1956).
15. Reference 3, p. 331.
16. J. H. Van Vleck, *Proc. Natl. Acad. Sci. U.S.*, **15**, 754 (1929).
17. H. A. Kramers and W. Heisenberg, *Z. Physik*, **31**, 681, 1925.
18. J. Behringer and J. Brandmuller, *Z. Elektrochem*, **60**, 643 (1956).
19. A. C. Albrecht, *J. Chem. Phys.*, **34**, 1476 (1961).
20. E. B. Wilson, Jr., J. C. Decius, and P. C. Cross, *Molecular Vibrations: The Theory of Infra-red and Raman Spectra*, McGraw-Hill, New York, 1955, p. 290.
21. G. W. Chantry and H. A. Gebbie, unpublished observations.
21a. R. C. Milward, *Infra Red Physics*, **9**, 59 (1969).
22. Reference 10, p. 310.
23. G. Placzek, *Handbuch der Radiologie*, E. Marx, ed., Akademische Verlagsgesellschaft Leipzig, 1934, Vol. VI, part 2, p. 205.
24. L. A. Woodward and D. A. Long, *Trans Faraday Soc.*, **45**, 1131 (1949).
    G. W. Chantry, *J. Chem. Phys.*, **32**, 222, 1960.
25. Reference 3, p.183.
26. Ibid, p. 309.
27. B. L. Crawford, *J. Chem. Phys.*, **20**, 977 (1952).
28. M. Wolkenstein, *C.R. Acad. Sci. URSS.*, **32**, 185 (1941).
29. Reference 10, p. 140.
30. G. W. Chantry and R. A. Plane, *J. Chem. Phys.*, **33**, 634 (1960).
31. T. Yoshino and H. J. Bernstein, *Molecular Spectroscopy*, **2**, 241 (1958).
32. D. A. Long, T. V. Spencer, D. N. Waters and L. A. Woodward, *Proc. Roy. Soc. (London)*, **A240**, 499 (1957).
33. T. Shimanouchi, *J. Chem. Phys.* **17**, 245 (1949).
34. D. A. Long and G. Miller, *Trans Faraday Soc.*, **54**, 330 (1958).
35. D. A. Long, *Proc. Roy. Soc. (London)*, **A217**, 203 (1953).
36. T. Yoshino and H. J. Bernstein, *Molecular Spectroscopy*, **2**, 213 (1958).
37. K. G. Denbigh, *Trans Faraday Soc.*, **36**, 936 (1940).
38. D. N. Waters and L. A. Woodward, *Proc. Roy. Soc. (London)*, **A246**, 119 (1958).
39. L. A. Woodward and D. A. Long, *Trans Faraday Soc.*, **45**, 1131 (1949).
40. G. W. Chantry and R. A. Plane, *J. Chem. Phys.*, **32**, 319 (1960).
41. G. W. Chantry and R. A. Plane, *J. Chem. Phys.*, **35**, 1027 (1961).
42. T. V. Long and R. A. Plane, *J. Chem. Phys.*, **43**, 457, (1965).
43. E. R. Lippincott and M. O. Dayhoff, *Spectrochim. Acta*, **16**, 807 (1960).
44. E. R. Lippincott and J. M. Stutman, *J. Phys. Chem.*, **68**, 2926 (1964).
45. H. W. Thompson and J. W. Linnett, *J. Chem. Soc.*, p. 1376 (1937).
46. E. B. Wilson and A. J. Wells, *J. Chem. Phys.*, **14**, 578 (1946).
47. For discussion of Shorygin theory see J. Behringer and J. Brandmuller, *Z. Elektrochem.*, **60**, 643, 1956.
48. J. Behringer, *Z. Elektrochem.*, **62**, 906 (1958).
49. D. G. Rea, *J. Molec. Spectroscopy*, **4**, 499 (1960).
50. F. Rasetti, *Z. Phys.*, **66**, 646 (1930).
51. J. T. Hougen and S. Singh, *Proc. Roy. Soc. (London)*, **277**, 193 (1964).
52. G. Eckhardt, R. W. Hellwarth, F. J. McClung, S. E. Schwarz, D. Weiner, and E. J. Woodbury, *Phys. Rev. Letters*, **9**, 455 (1962).

53. R. W. Hellwarth, *Phys. Rev.*, **130,** 1850 (1963).
54. E. Garmire, F. Pandarese and C. H. Townes, *Phys. Rev. Letters*, **11,** 160 (1963).
55. J. C. Slater, *Quantum Theory of Matter*, McGraw-Hill, New York, 1951, p. 393.
56. A. D. Buckingham, *J. Chem. Phys.*, **43,** 25 (1965).
57. W. J. Jones and B. P. Stoicheff, *Phys. Rev. Letters*, **13,** 657 (1964).

CHAPTER 3

The Theory of Raman Scattering from Crystals

R. A. COWLEY*

CHALK RIVER NUCLEAR LABORATORIES
CHALK RIVER
ONTARIO, CANADA

*Present Address: Dept. of Natural Philosophy, University of Edinburgh, Scotland.

I. INTRODUCTION

The Raman effect in crystals has been known since the late 1920's (*1,2*) and has been qualitatively understood since that time. However, until recently it was a technique which was practiced in only a few laboratories and which attracted little theoretical interest. This was in a large part because the intensity of the scattered light was very weak and the experiments correspondingly difficult and painstaking.

The improvement in the experimental technique during the last few years is the direct result of the development of laser sources. In the early experiments the low intensity of the scattering led to the use of large sources and to the collection of the light scattered over a large solid angle. With lasers, however, measurements with well collimated light beams of definite polarization are very much easier. Consequently it is now possible to examine the Raman scattering in far more detail and with far greater precision than was practical earlier.

On the theoretical side, Raman scattering has attracted more attention because of the wealth of detailed information about excitations which has become available in recent years. This has enabled the Raman scattering to be more readily interpreted. An example of this is in the two-phonon Raman spectrum where in the early theories neither the mechanism of the Raman scattering nor the phonon spectrum was known. Now at least the phonon spectrum has been measured for many materials thereby eliminating one source of error in the calculation of the two-phonon Raman spectrum.

An excellent review of the field was written by Loudon (*3*) in 1964 immediately prior to the development of laser sources. It is a measure of the development of the field since that time that many of the experiments discussed below have been performed since his review was written. Although the material covered here inevitably overlaps considerably with the material in Loudon's review, some attempt has been made to concentrate on the more recent developments.

By far the majority of Raman scattering experiments on solids have studied the scattering by the normal modes of vibration of crystals. A large part of this review is concerned with this type of scattering.

In the next section we outline the principles of Raman scattering as applied to the scattering by the normal modes of vibration of a harmonic crystal. The information obtained by the one- and two-phonon processes is discussed and is shown to depend in large part on the laws of conservation of energy and momentum. Further selection rules for the scattering may be deduced, however, using the techniques of group theory. These are described and applied to both the one and two-phonon processes in Section III.

In Section IV we return to a more detailed discussion of those lattice vibrations which have wavelengths much greater than interatomic distances. This includes a description of polaritons, and the effect of doping in semiconductors. Section V contains a more detailed account of the two-phonon spectra and a discussion of some of the calculations which have been performed.

Up to this point in the article we have assumed the phonons to be exact eigenstates of the Hamiltonian of the crystal. In Sections VI and VII this limitation is removed by considering the effect of anharmonic coupling between the phonons (Section VI) and the changes resulting from the introduction of defects into the crystal (Section VII). Both of these subjects are worthy of whole articles in themselves and hence the descriptions are very brief. In Section VI we describe the effects of anharmonicity on the one-phonon spectra, the difficulty of distinguishing between the one- and two-phonon spectra of an anharmonic crystal, and the different sound velocities which may be measured with Brillouin scattering. In Section VII we describe the Raman scattering by the localized modes which may be associated with defects, and the way in which defects may induce additional one-phonon scattering.

Raman scattering may be used to study excitations other than phonons in crystals. In Section VIII the scattering by electronic excitations, magnons, excitons, and plasmons are described. Lastly, the material is summarized and the technique compared with other experimental techniques in Section IX.

II. RAMAN SCATTERING AND PHONONS

A. Scattering Theory

Raman scattering is the inelastic scattering of photons by a crystal. Photons of energy, $\hbar\omega_o$, and well defined direction, specified by the momentum $\mathbf{k}_o$, are incident on a crystal and scattered to give photons of energy, $\hbar\omega_s$, and momentum, $\mathbf{k}_s$. The initial state of the crystal, i, has energy E_i and the final state, f, an energy E_f. The probability of the scattering is given by the well known golden rule of second order perturbation theory as

$$w = \frac{2\pi}{\hbar} \rho(\omega_s) \mid H(\mathbf{k}_o, i:\mathbf{k}_s, f) \mid^2 \delta(\hbar\omega_o + E_i - \hbar\omega_s - E_f) \tag{1}$$

where $\rho(\omega_s)$ is the density of states of the photons, which is given by (4)

$$\rho(\omega_s) \, d\omega_s \, d\Omega = \left(\frac{1}{2\pi c}\right)^3 \frac{\omega_s{}^2}{\hbar} \, d\omega_s \, d\Omega \tag{2}$$

where $d\Omega$ is an element of solid angle. The interaction between the photons and the crystal is specified by the Hamiltonian, H.

The interaction between electromagnetic radiation and the crystal is in full generality a very complex problem. In Raman scattering, however, the wavelength of both the incident and scattered light is much greater than the sizes of the atoms. Furthermore the electric fields associated with the light nearly always give rise to the Raman scattering. The interaction Hamiltonian may, therefore, be written in terms of the polarizability, P, of the crystal as

$$H = \sum_{\alpha\beta} P_{\alpha\beta}(\mathbf{k}_o i:\mathbf{k}_s f) E_\alpha(o) E_\beta(s) \tag{3}$$

where $\mathbf{E}(o)$ and $\mathbf{E}(s)$ are the electric fields associated with the incident and scattered light, and α and β denote the Cartesian coordinates. In order to substitute this result into Eq. (1) we need to rewrite the electric field in terms of the photon creation, $b^+(\mathbf{k})$, and destruction, $b(\mathbf{k})$, operators (4)

$$\mathbf{E}(o) = i(2\pi\hbar\omega_o)^{\frac{1}{2}}\mathbf{\varepsilon}(o)[b(\mathbf{k}_o) - b^+(-\mathbf{k}_o)] \tag{4}$$

where we have introduced the polarization vector for the photons $\mathbf{\varepsilon}(o)$. The electric field varies in space with the wavevector of the photon, viz. $\exp(i\mathbf{k}_o \cdot \mathbf{R})$.

The conventional expression for the Raman scattering (5) is expressed in terms of the energy scattered for a particular incident electric field. The energy scattered is $\hbar\omega_s w$ and the number of quanta is given in terms of the incident electric field by $\bar{n} = (E(o) \cdot E(o))/2\pi\hbar\omega_o$. With the aid of these results and Eqs. (2) and (3) the intensity of the Raman scattering from a state i to a state f of the crystal becomes

$$I \, d\Omega \, d\omega_f = \frac{\omega_f{}^4}{2\pi c^3} \sum_{\alpha\beta\gamma\delta} P_{\alpha\beta}(\mathbf{k}_o i : \mathbf{k}_s f) P_{\gamma\delta}^+(\mathbf{k}_o i : \mathbf{k}_s f) E_\alpha(o) E_\gamma(o) \varepsilon_\beta(s) \varepsilon_\delta(s)$$
$$\delta(E_i + \hbar\omega_o - E_f - \hbar\omega_s) \tag{5}$$

The total Raman scattering intensity is then obtained by averaging over the initial and final states of the crystal and weighting them by the appropriate thermodynamic factors to give

$$I \, d\Omega \, d\omega_f = \frac{\omega_f{}^4}{2\pi C^3} \sum_{\alpha\beta\gamma\delta} E_\alpha(o) E_\gamma(o) \varepsilon_\beta(s) \varepsilon_\delta(s) I_{\alpha\beta\gamma\delta} \tag{6}$$

where

$$I_{\alpha\beta\gamma\delta} = \sum_{if} \rho_i P_{\alpha\beta}(\mathbf{k}_o i : \mathbf{k}_s f) P_{\gamma\delta}^+(\mathbf{k}_o i : \mathbf{k}_s f) \delta(E_i + \hbar\omega_o - E_f - \hbar\omega_s) \tag{7}$$

and the thermodynamic probability is $\rho_i = \exp(-\beta E_i)/Z$, and β is the inverse temperature, $1/k_B T$ and Z the partition function. This expression is identical with that obtained by Born and Huang (5).

For some purposes it is useful to rewrite the delta function in Eq. (7) in terms of an integral over time. When a polarizability operator is also introduced Eq. (7) becomes

$$I_{\alpha\beta\gamma\delta} = \frac{1}{2\pi} \int_{-\infty}^{\infty} \langle\langle P_{\alpha\beta}(\mathbf{k}_o \mathbf{k}_s, t) P_{\gamma\delta}^+(\mathbf{k}_o \mathbf{k}_s, o) \rangle\rangle \exp(i\omega t) \, dt \tag{8}$$

where the polarizability operators are written in the Heisenberg representation, and ω is the frequency transfer,

$$\omega = \omega_o - \omega_s \tag{9}$$

The brackets, $\langle\langle \ldots \rangle\rangle$, represent the thermodynamic average.

B. Normal Modes of Vibration of Crystals

The displacements of atoms from their equilibrium positions in crystals are described by their normal modes of vibration. There are several excellent accounts of the theory of these normal modes available (5–7) and we shall only briefly review the results in order to establish the notation for later sections.

The potential energy of the crystal is expanded in a power series of the displacements of the ions from their equilibrium positions:

$$\phi = \phi_0 + \tfrac{1}{2} \sum_{\substack{l_1 k_1 \alpha \\ l_2 k_2 \beta}} \phi_{\alpha\beta}\begin{pmatrix} l_1 l_2 \\ k_1 k_2 \end{pmatrix} U_\alpha\begin{pmatrix} l_1 \\ k_1 \end{pmatrix} U_\beta\begin{pmatrix} l_2 \\ k_2 \end{pmatrix} + \cdots \tag{10}$$

In this expansion $\mathbf{U}(lk)$ is the displacement of the kth type of atom in the lth unit cell, while $\phi_{\alpha\beta}\begin{pmatrix} l_1 l_2 \\ k_1 k_2 \end{pmatrix}$ is the appropriate second derivative of the potential which is minus the force on the atom $(l_1 k_1)$ in the α direction when the atom $(l_2 k_2)$ is displaced a unit amount in the β direction. The linear terms in the expansion are absent because the expansion is about the equilibrium positions of the atoms, $\mathbf{R}(lk)$. Terms with three or more displacements give rise to the anharmonic effects and are neglected in the harmonic approximation. Strictly this expansion is only valid within the adiabatic approximation, but since this is nearly always valid in real situations, Eq. (10) is quite adequate for our purposes.

The equation of motion of the atom $(l_1 k_1)$ is given by

$$M_{k_1} \ddot{U}_\alpha\begin{pmatrix} l_1 \\ k_1 \end{pmatrix} = - \sum_{\beta l_2 k_2} \phi_{\alpha\beta}\begin{pmatrix} l_1 l_2 \\ k_1 k_2 \end{pmatrix} U_\beta\begin{pmatrix} l_2 \\ k_2 \end{pmatrix} \tag{11}$$

where the mass of atoms of type k_1 is M_{k_1}. This equation is simplified by introducing Bloch waves for the displacements so that

$$\mathbf{U}(lk) = \left(\frac{1}{NM_k}\right)^{\tfrac{1}{2}} \sum_{\mathbf{q}} \mathbf{U}(k \mid \mathbf{q}) \exp i(\mathbf{q} \cdot \mathbf{R}(lk) - \omega t) \tag{12}$$

and N is the number of unit cells in the crystal. When Eq. (12) is substituted into Eq. (11) the result is

$$\omega^2 U_\alpha(k \mid \mathbf{q}) = \sum_{\beta k'} D_{\alpha\beta}(kk' \mid \mathbf{q}) U_\beta(k' \mid \mathbf{q}) \tag{13}$$

where the dynamical matrix is

$$D_{\alpha\beta}(kk' \mid \mathbf{q}) = \left(\frac{1}{M_k M_{k'}}\right)^{\tfrac{1}{2}} \sum_l \phi_{\alpha\beta}\begin{pmatrix} ol \\ kk' \end{pmatrix} \exp i\mathbf{q} \cdot \left(\mathbf{R}\begin{pmatrix} l \\ k' \end{pmatrix} - \mathbf{R}\begin{pmatrix} o \\ k \end{pmatrix} \right)$$

The normal modes of vibration are obtained by diagonalizing the dynamical matrix to give the eigenvalues $\omega^2(\mathbf{q}j)$ and eigenvectors $\mathbf{e}(k \mid \mathbf{q}j)$

for the jth normal mode. These eigenvectors are normalized by the condition

$$\sum_k \mathbf{e}(k \mid \mathbf{q}j) \cdot \mathbf{e}^+(k \mid \mathbf{q}j') = \delta_{jj'}$$

For many purposes it is useful to introduce the phonon coordinates $A(\mathbf{q}j)$ which are the sum of phonon creation and destruction operators

$$A(\mathbf{q}j) = a(\mathbf{q}j) + a^+(-\mathbf{q}j)$$

In terms of these operators the displacements of the atoms are given by $(5,6)$:

$$\mathbf{U}(lk) = \sum_{\mathbf{q}j} \left(\frac{\hbar}{2\omega(\mathbf{q}j)NM_k}\right)^{\frac{1}{2}} \mathbf{e}(k \mid \mathbf{q}j) \exp\left[i\mathbf{q}\cdot\mathbf{R}(lk)\right] A(\mathbf{q}j) \qquad (14)$$

The formal development of phonon theory is completed by studying the time development of the operators $a(\mathbf{q}j)$ and $a^+(\mathbf{q}j)$. In the Heisenberg representation $A(\mathbf{q}j, t)$ is given by

$$A(\mathbf{q}j, t) = a(\mathbf{q}j, o) \exp\left(i\omega(\mathbf{q}j)t\right) + a^+(-\mathbf{q}j, o) \exp\left(-i\omega(\mathbf{q}j)t\right) \qquad (15)$$

The thermodynamic expectation value of these operators is obtained with the aid of Bose statistics as:

$$\langle\!\langle a(\mathbf{q}j)a^+(\mathbf{q}j) \rangle\!\rangle = n(\mathbf{q}j) + 1$$

$$\langle\!\langle a^+(\mathbf{q}j)a(\mathbf{q}j) \rangle\!\rangle = n(\mathbf{q}j) \qquad (16)$$

where the population factor is given by:

$$n(\mathbf{q}j) = 1/\{\exp\left[\beta\hbar\omega(\mathbf{q}j)\right] - 1\} \qquad (17)$$

The development as yet is very formal; it does, however, enable the frequencies of the normal modes to be obtained, if the interatomic potential is known. The dynamical matrix is a square matrix of size three times the number of atoms in each unit cell, s. There are therefore, $3s$ different frequencies for each wavevector, $\mathbf{q}$. A complete description of the normal modes is a list of these frequencies and the associated eigenvectors for all wavevectors lying within the first Brillouin zone. When the wavevector is at a point of high symmetry within the Brillouin zone, degeneracies of some of the frequencies are found, as illustrated by the phonon dispersion curves of diamond shown in Fig. 1. In diamond there are two atoms in each unit cell giving rise to six branches, values of j, for each wavevector. Six branches are shown in the [110] direction but in the [100] and [111] directions the transversely polarized branches Δ_5 and

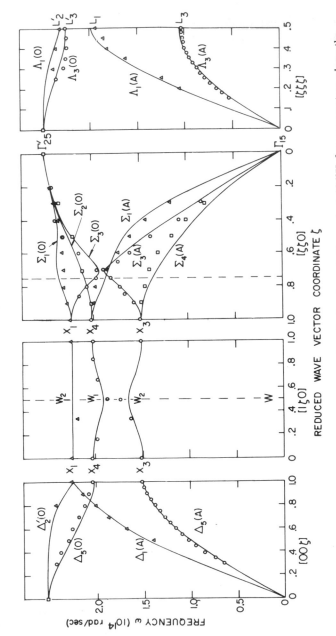

Fig. 1. The dispersion relation for the normal modes of vibration of diamond at 296°K for wavevectors along the principal symmetry directions. The curves represent a shell model fit to the experimental data points. (Reprinted from Ref. (48) p. 806.)

Λ_3, are doubly degenerate. As the wavevector $|\mathbf{q}|$ becomes small three of the branches have frequencies given by $\omega(\mathbf{q}j) = C\,|\,\mathbf{q}\,|$. These are the acoustic modes and at long wavelengths become the normal elastic waves in the crystal.

Before the phonon dispersion curves may be calculated, it is necessary to use a model of the crystal. (Little progress has been made in making a-priori calculations of the phonon dispersion curves of crystals of interest in Raman scattering). Three models (7) are in common use for insulating crystals. The first of these is the Born von-Kàrmàn model in which the interatomic forces are restricted to neighboring atoms. There are then only a few independent constants needed to describe the expansion of the potential energy, Eq. (1), and these are obtained by comparison of the model with some experimental results. This model is mainly useful for metals and covalently bonded crystals. In ionic crystals the long range electrostatic forces are important and the rigid ion model is an extension of the Born von-Kàrmàn model to include these forces.

These models frequently give a poor description of the experimental results, because they neglect the distortions of the electron wavefunctions as the lattice vibrates. These are included in an approximate manner by the shell model (7). The outer electrons of the atoms are represented by a shell which is allowed to displace from the rest of the atom. In this manner the model allows for the polarizability of the atoms and represents a considerable improvement on the other models. The dispersion curves shown in Fig. 1 were calculated with this model. A more comprehensive description of these and other models has been given earlier (7).

C. Classification of Raman Processes

In Section IIA the Raman scattering was deduced in terms of the polarizability of the crystal. In this section we expand the polarizability in terms of the normal mode coordinates, $A(\mathbf{q}j)$, introduced in the preceding section. It is not immediately apparent that this is a valid procedure. In most Raman scattering experiments, however, the incident frequency is much greater than the frequency transfer, $\omega_o \gg \omega$, and also ω_o is not close to any of the frequencies of the electronic excitations of the crystal. Under these approximations the polarizability is symmetric in α and β and may be expanded in a series:

$$P_{\alpha\beta} = P^o_{\alpha\beta} + \sum_{\mathbf{q}j} P_{\alpha\beta}\begin{pmatrix}\mathbf{q}\\j\end{pmatrix} A\begin{pmatrix}\mathbf{q}\\j\end{pmatrix} + \sum_{\substack{\mathbf{q}_1\mathbf{q}_2\\j_1j_2}} P_{\alpha\beta}\begin{pmatrix}\mathbf{q}_1\mathbf{q}_2\\j_1j_2\end{pmatrix} A\begin{pmatrix}\mathbf{q}_1\\j_1\end{pmatrix} A\begin{pmatrix}\mathbf{q}_2\\j_2\end{pmatrix} + \cdots \quad (18)$$

In this expansion the coefficients are assumed to be independent of the frequency transfer, while conservation of momentum shows for the one-phonon term that

$$\mathbf{k}_o - \mathbf{k}_s = \mathbf{Q} = \mathbf{q} \qquad (19)$$

where $\mathbf{Q}$ is the momentum transfer, and for the two-phonon term

$$\mathbf{Q} = \mathbf{q}_1 + \mathbf{q}_2 \qquad (20)$$

The one-phonon Raman scattering cross-section is obtained by using the Heisenberg representation for the phonon operators, Eq. (15), and their expectation values, Eq. (16), and substituting into Eq. (8) to give

$$I^I_{\alpha\beta\gamma\delta} = \sum_j P_{\alpha\beta}\binom{\mathbf{Q}}{j} P^+_{\gamma\delta}\binom{\mathbf{Q}}{j} [n(\mathbf{Q}j)\delta(\omega+\omega(\mathbf{Q}j)) + (n(\mathbf{Q}j)+1)\delta(\omega-\omega(\mathbf{Q}j))]$$
$$(21)$$

This expression shows that the one-phonon Raman scattering occurs at the frequencies of the phonons whose wavevectors are equal to the wavevector transfer in the experiment. The Stokes process is the one in which the light quanta lose energy in the scattering, and the anti-Stokes process the one in which energy is gained by the light.

The wavelength of the incident light in a typical experiment is much longer than interatomic distances. Consequently the available momentum transfers, $\mathbf{Q}$, are much smaller ($<10^{-3}$) than the momentum of many of the phonons. It is therefore a sufficiently accurate approximation to take $|\mathbf{Q}| = 0$ in the scattering unless the frequencies $\omega(\mathbf{Q}j)$ vary rapidly with wavevector for small wavevectors. There are two cases, discussed in Section IV, where the momentum transfer is important. One of these is Brillouin scattering which is the scattering by acoustic modes for which the frequency clearly depends strongly on the wave vector. The other occurs in piezoelectric crystals when the infrared active modes couple with the photons propagating in the crystal to give a Raman spectrum which depends on the momentum transfer.

The two-phonon Raman spectrum may be calculated in the same manner. In this case however, the size of the momentum transfer is not of importance, except in the Brillouin scattering region, and the intensity becomes:

$$I^{II}_{\alpha\beta\gamma\sigma} = \sum_{\mathbf{q}j_1j_2} P_{\alpha\beta}\binom{\mathbf{q}-\mathbf{q}}{j_1j_2} P_{\gamma\beta}\binom{\mathbf{q}-\mathbf{q}}{j_1j_2} (1-\exp(\beta\hbar\omega))^{-1}$$
$$\times [(n(\mathbf{q}j_1)+n(\mathbf{q}j_2)+1)\delta(\omega-\omega(\mathbf{q}j_1)-\omega(\mathbf{q}j_2))$$
$$- \delta(\omega+\omega(\mathbf{q}j_1)+\omega(\mathbf{q}j_2)) + (n(\mathbf{q}j_1)-n(\mathbf{q}j_2))(\delta(\omega-\omega(\mathbf{q}j_2)+\omega(\mathbf{q}j_1))$$
$$- \delta(\omega+\omega(\mathbf{q}j_2)-\omega(\mathbf{q}j_1))] \qquad (22)$$

This intensity consists of a continuous distribution of frequencies in contrast to the sharp lines given by the one-phonon spectrum. The intensity of the anti-Stokes and Stokes distributions are in the ratio $\exp(-\beta\hbar\omega)$, which is also the ratio of these components in the one-phonon spectrum. Under the conditions of this section that $\omega \gg \omega_o$ and ω_o is well removed from the excitation frequencies of the crystal, this is a general result. It may be derived from Eq. (7) directly by interchanging the labeling of the initial and final states.

It is possible to extend the discussion to higher order Raman processes without difficulty. The results become progressively more cumbersome, harder to calculate and difficult to interpret.

D. The Polarizability

1. THE DIRECT METHOD

The expansion in terms of the phonon coordinates, Eq. (18), is a formal device for obtaining the expressions for the intensity of the Raman scattering. In this section we discuss the coefficients in this expansion and the extent to which they may be calculated. The most direct approach is to compute the polarizability from the known electronic properties of the crystal.

The incident frequency of the light, ω_o, is usually much greater than any of the normal modes of vibration of the crystal. The coupling to the lattice is therefore weak and the polarizability arises largely from the electronic distortions. One possible mechanism for Raman scattering is that the incident light couples directly with a phonon of long wavelength which then couples to the Raman active mode. This process would be expected to be important only in piezoelectric crystals, but numerical estimates (3) suggest that since the incident frequency is so large compared with that of the lattice vibrations, the process is even there of negligible importance in practice.

The most important mechanism was developed in detail by Loudon (8) and is illustrated in Fig. 2. In the one-phonon case, Fig. 2a, the incident light excites a virtual electron-hole pair, e_1, which either creates or absorbs a phonon to give the pair, e_1, and then recombines emitting the scattered photon. The magnitude of the polarizability may be calculated by third order perturbation theory as proportional to

$$\sum_{e_1 e_2} \frac{\langle i \mid H_I^\alpha \mid e_1 \rangle \langle e_1 \mid H_{II} \mid e_2 \rangle \langle e_2 \mid H_I^\beta \mid f \rangle}{(\omega_{e1} - \omega_o)(\omega_{e2} - \omega_s)}$$

where $H_I{}^\alpha$ represents the coupling with the incident light polarized in the α direction, $H_I{}^\beta$ the coupling with the scattered light in the β direction, and H_{II} the electron-phonon scattering by which state e_1 is scattered to e_2 with the production of the Raman active phonon.

This result enables us to discuss the validity of the expansion (*18*) of the preceding section. The polarizability is independent of ω, only if

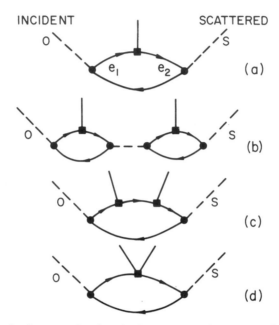

Fig. 2. Schematic diagrams showing the Raman scattering process for one-phonon (a) and two-phonons (b-d); $----$ = photon, $\longrightarrow$ = photon, $\rightarrow\!\!-$ = electron, $-\!\!\leftarrow$ = hole. Similar diagrams may be drawn incorporating the phonon-hole interactions.

$|\omega_{e_1} - \omega_o| \gg \omega$. If $\hbar\omega_o$ is close to one of the energies, $\hbar\omega_{e_1}$, the polarizability is enhanced and the effect is known as the resonant Raman effect; this is briefly discussed in other Chapters. The polarizability is strictly symmetric in α and β, only if ω_o and ω_s may be interchanged without altering the result. This is the case if ω_o and ω_s are both large compared with ω, and also if their differences from ω_{e_1} and ω_{e_2} are large. The polarizability tensor is not symmetric if these conditions are not attained, as for example in resonant Raman scattering. Ovander (*9*) has discussed the additional features which occur when the polarizability is not symmetric.

Numerical estimates of the scattering have been made by Loudon (8) based on this approach. The electron-lattice interaction in diamond was approximated by the deformation potentials, and the electron–photon coupling by use of the perturbation—$cA \cdot p/mc$. The results gave the correct order of magnitude.

More recently the theory has been extended by Ganguly and Birman (10). They included the effect of the Coulomb interaction between the electrons and holes and showed this gave good agreement with the resonant Raman measurements of Leite and Porto on CdS (11).

The terms in the expansion involving pairs of phonons are even more difficult to calculate. Some of the diagrams are shown in Fig. 2(b–d); in diagram (b) the phonons are scattered by two successive one-phonon Raman processes, in which the intermediate photon may have any frequency. This process leads to the scattering by pairs of phonons both of which are Raman active. The spectrum from this term consists of lines at the frequencies of pairs of one-phonon active phonons. The other diagrams of Fig. 2(c) and (d) give rise to contributions from phonons with any wavevectors, q. Diagram (c) represents two separate interactions between the electron system and the phonons while (d) represents the interaction between the electrons and a pair of phonons; very few calculations of these terms have been performed.

2. THE EXPANSION TECHNIQUE

The expansion technique was developed by Born and Bradburn (12). The polarizability was expanded above, Eq. (18), in powers of the phonon coordinates. In the expansion technique the expansion is performed in powers of the displacements of the atoms;

$$P_{\alpha\beta} = P^o_{\alpha\beta} + \sum_{\gamma l k} P_{\alpha\beta,\gamma}\binom{l}{k} U_\gamma\binom{l}{k} + \sum_{\substack{\gamma l_1 k_1 \\ \delta l_2 k_2}} P_{\alpha\beta,\gamma\delta}\binom{l_1 l_2}{k_1 k_2} U_\gamma\binom{l_1}{k_1} U_\delta\binom{l_2}{k_2} + \cdots \tag{23}$$

The coefficients of Eq. (18) can be obtained in terms of these new coefficients as

$$P_{\alpha\beta}\binom{q}{j} = \sum_{\gamma k} \left(\frac{\hbar N}{2\omega(qj)M_k}\right)^{\frac{1}{2}} P_{\alpha\beta,\gamma}\binom{l}{k} e_\gamma(k\,|\,qj) \exp i\left(q\cdot R\binom{o}{k}\right) \tag{24}$$

and

$$P_{\alpha\beta}\binom{q_1 q_2}{j_1 j_2} = \sum_{\substack{k_1 k_2 l \\ \gamma\delta}} \left(\frac{\hbar^2}{4\omega(q_1 j_1)\omega(q_2 j_2)M_{k_1}M_{k_2}}\right)^{\frac{1}{2}} P_{\alpha\beta,\gamma\delta}\binom{o\quad l}{k_1 k_2}$$

$$\times e_\gamma(k_1\,|\,q_1 j_1)e_\delta(k_2\,|\,q_2 j_2) \exp i\left[q_1\cdot R\binom{o}{k_1} + q_2\cdot R\binom{l}{k_2}\right] \tag{25}$$

The advantage of this expansion is that it is easier to make approximations with the real space coefficients than with their transforms. This is not of great assistance with the one-phonon terms, but with the two-phonon terms the restriction to neighboring atoms drastically reduces the number of independent constants involved. Furthermore, the assumption of some explicit form for the polarizability gives a further contraction in the number of parameters. An example of this is the calculation of the two-phonon spectrum of germanium, silicon and diamond (13) where the form assumed was

$$P_{\alpha\beta,\gamma\delta}\begin{pmatrix} o\ l \\ k_1 k_2 \end{pmatrix} = CR_\alpha R_\beta R_\gamma R_\delta$$

where C is a constant and $\mathbf{R}$ is the vector joining the two neighboring atoms. This approximation enables the two-phonon spectra to be obtained with only one unknown parameter.

The difficulty with the theory is that it does not give the contribution from pairs of one-phonon active phonons represented by Fig. 2(b). The parameters of the theory are also difficult to estimate because they cannot be readily related to the results of other measurements. Despite these difficulties however, the approach will undoubtedly be of considerable value because at the very least, it provides a comparatively simple way of calculating the Raman spectra with proper regard for the selection rules.

3. THE SHELL MODEL

The shell model has proved itself to be useful in describing the vibrations of the atoms in crystals (7,14,15,16). It has been extended to calculate the Raman spectra (17) although the results at present are not very encouraging. The shell model includes the electronic distortions on the ions within the dipole approximation. The total dipole moment produced on the crystal at optical frequencies is given by

$$\mathbf{M} = \frac{1}{Nv} \sum_{lk} \mathbf{p}(lk) \tag{26}$$

where $\mathbf{p}(lk)$ is the electronic dipole moment on the (lk)th ion, and v the volume of a unit cell.

In the normal shell model, terms are added to the potential energy, Eq. (10), which depend on the dipole moments and are of the form;

$$\sum_{\substack{\alpha\beta \\ l_1 l_2 \\ k_1 k_2}} \left[\frac{1}{2} S_{\alpha\beta}\begin{pmatrix} l_1 l_2 \\ k_1 k_2 \end{pmatrix} p_\alpha\begin{pmatrix} l_1 \\ k_1 \end{pmatrix} p_\beta\begin{pmatrix} l_2 \\ k_2 \end{pmatrix} + T_{\alpha\beta}\begin{pmatrix} l_1 l_2 \\ k_1 k_2 \end{pmatrix} p_\alpha\begin{pmatrix} l_1 \\ k_1 \end{pmatrix} U_\beta\begin{pmatrix} l_2 \\ k_2 \end{pmatrix} \right] \tag{27}$$

The equations of motion of the dipole moments are obtained from the Hamiltonian of the model. If an electric field $\mathbf{E}$ is applied to the crystal this leads to the equation for the (ok)th dipole moment as

$$E_\alpha = \sum_{\beta l k'} \left[S_{\alpha\beta}\begin{pmatrix} ol \\ kk' \end{pmatrix} p_\beta \begin{pmatrix} l \\ k' \end{pmatrix} + T_{\alpha\beta}\begin{pmatrix} ol \\ kk' \end{pmatrix} U_\beta \begin{pmatrix} l' \\ k' \end{pmatrix} \right] \tag{28}$$

If the electric field is uniform and of a sufficiently high frequency that the ions cannot respond, the polarizability becomes

$$P^o_{\alpha\beta} = \frac{1}{v} \sum_{kk'} D_{\alpha\beta}(kk')$$

where $D_{\alpha\beta}(kk')$ is the inverse matrix of $\sum_l S_{\alpha\beta}\begin{pmatrix} ol \\ kk' \end{pmatrix}$.

The Raman scattering is obtained by introducing cubic and quartic terms in the expansion of the potential energy, Eq. (27). The one-phonon terms result from the terms:

$$\sum_{\substack{l_1 l_2 l_3 \\ k_1 k_2 k_3 \\ \alpha\beta\gamma}} \left[H_{\alpha\beta\gamma}\begin{pmatrix} l_1 l_2 l_3 \\ k_1 k_2 k_3 \end{pmatrix} p_\alpha\begin{pmatrix} l_1 \\ k_1 \end{pmatrix} p_\beta\begin{pmatrix} l_2 \\ k_2 \end{pmatrix} U_\gamma\begin{pmatrix} l_3 \\ k_3 \end{pmatrix} + J_{\alpha\beta\gamma}\begin{pmatrix} l_1 l_2 l_3 \\ k_1 k_2 k_3 \end{pmatrix} p_\alpha\begin{pmatrix} l_1 \\ k_1 \end{pmatrix} \right.$$

$$\left. \times p_\beta\begin{pmatrix} l_2 \\ k_2 \end{pmatrix} p_\alpha\begin{pmatrix} l_3 \\ k_3 \end{pmatrix} \right] \tag{29}$$

When these are substituted into the equation of motion new terms occur which are quadratic in the dipole moments and the displacements. The equation may be solved for the $\mathbf{p}\begin{pmatrix} l \\ k \end{pmatrix}$ by iteration and the result substituted into Eq. (26) to find the polarizability. The result for the one-phonon coefficients is

$$P_{\alpha\beta}\begin{pmatrix} \mathbf{q} \\ j \end{pmatrix} = \frac{1}{v}\left(\frac{\hbar N}{2\omega(\mathbf{q}j)} \right)^{\frac{1}{2}} \sum_{\substack{kk'k_1k_2k_3 \\ \gamma\delta\gamma l_1 l_2}} \left(\frac{1}{Mk_3} \right)^{\frac{1}{2}} D_{\alpha\gamma}(kk_1)D_{\beta\delta}(k'k_2)$$

$$\times \left[H_{\gamma\lambda\delta}\begin{pmatrix} o\ l_2 l_1 \\ k_3 k_2 k_1 \end{pmatrix} e_\lambda(k_3\,|\,\mathbf{q}j) + J_{\gamma\delta\lambda}\begin{pmatrix} o\ l_2 l_1 \\ k_3 k_2 k_1 \end{pmatrix} f_\lambda(k_3\,|\,\mathbf{q}j) \right]$$

$$\times \exp\,i\mathbf{q}\cdot\left[\mathbf{R}\begin{pmatrix} o \\ k_3 \end{pmatrix} + \mathbf{R}\begin{pmatrix} l_2 \\ k_2 \end{pmatrix} - \mathbf{R}\begin{pmatrix} l_1 \\ k_1 \end{pmatrix} \right] \tag{30}$$

where $f_\lambda(k_3\,|\,\mathbf{q}j)$ is the eigenvector for the dipole moments in the normal mode $(\mathbf{q}j)$.

The expressions for the two-phonon contribution to the polarizability may be found by including quartic terms into the potential energy. The results are then of two types. One arises from the second order solution of the cubic terms in the equation of motion and contains a product of the H and J potentials. This term gives the two-phonon term for the phonons which are one-phonon active and is exactly comparable to the contribution shown in Fig. 2(b). The other terms are of very similar form to Eq. (30) for the one-phonon term but even more cumbersome; we refer to the original paper (*17*) for further details.

The advantage of this approach to the Raman scattering is that it is more closely related to the physical situation than the expansion technique. The potentials occurring here can be obtained from the shell model with the aid of very reasonable physical approximations without introducing further parameters. Thus the Raman scattering is calculated without the need for a whole set of new parameters. The difficulty with the approach is that it is quite complex to perform the calculations and also that the model does not include all the effects, e.g. it gives no Raman scattering in the germanium structure. This nonphysical result suggests that further tests of the model would be very useful.

III. SYMMETRY PROPERTIES

A. Group Theory

In the preceding section we described the Raman scattering and made use of translational symmetry to establish the momentum conservation rules of Eq. (19) and (20). The point group symmetry of crystals, however, places further restrictions on the phonons which may contribute to the Raman scattering, and also on the form of the scattering. It is the object of this section to describe the effect of this symmetry.

Although many symmetry properties may be used by an intelligent use of inspection, it is desirable to have a systematic approach to ensure that all the symmetry is included. This approach is provided by the use of group theory and the application of which to solid state physics has been described by, e.g., Heine (*18*) and Tinkham (*19*).

Suppose the symmetry of the crystal is a group, G, composed of symmetry operations, S, of both a translational and rotational character. We wish to describe the effect of symmetry on a property of the crystal which may be expressed in terms of functions, ψ_i. The number of these functions which are independent depends on the particular crystal property. The effect of symmetry element, S, on the functions, ψ_i, is to transform them into one another, as given by

$$\psi_i = \sum_j S_{ij}\psi_j$$

The matrices S_{ij} form a representation of the group, G, and the ψ_i functions are known as basis vectors. It is possible to find linear combinations of the basis functions, such that the matrices S_{ij} become reduced to block diagonal form. These linear combinations then transform under the symmetry operators not into all of the basis functions but only into a limited set of these functions. This new representation is known as the irreducible representation and because the irreducible representation transforms under the symmetry operators in a unique manner it contains information about the symmetry of the property. The classification of a property into the irreducible representations determines the number of different possible components needed to describe that property and the way they transform under the symmetry operators.

The irreducible representations of many of the groups commonly occurring in solid state physics have been enumerated (20). The symmetry properties of a particular quantity are calculated by first choosing a representation and then reducing that representation to find the number of times each irreducible representation enters into the description of the physical quantity. Fortunately, the reduction to the irreducible representations is easily performed by use of the character of the representations. The character $\chi(S)$ of the representation of symmetry element S is the sum of the diagonal elements of the transformation matrix, S_{ij}:

$$\chi(S) = \sum_i S_{ii}$$

Group theory (18,19) then states that for each symmetry element

$$\chi(S) = \sum_\lambda C_\lambda \chi^\lambda(S) \tag{31}$$

where C_λ is the number of times the λ irreducible representation is present in the original representation and $\chi_\lambda(S)$ is the character of symmetry element, S, in the irreducible representation. For each S Eq. (31) gives a set of simultaneous equations for the C_λ and hence enables the representation to be reduced. So far the development has used the whole symmetry group of the crystal. Since this has an exceedingly large number of translational elements it is convenient to take account of these separately from the rotational parts. This is accomplished by the well known use of

Bloch waves and the description of a crystal property in terms of a wave-vector, $\mathbf{q}$ restricted to one Brillouin zone. When this is done the rotational part of the symmetry may be divided into two parts; one part transforms $\mathbf{q}$ into a new vector $\mathbf{q}'$, while the other part leaves $\mathbf{q}$ unchanged. The latter part forms what is known as the little group of the wavevector and produces additional symmetry requirements. In those space groups which are symmorphic (do not have essential screw axes or glides planes) the little group is one of the crystal point groups, whose irreducible representations are well known (20). Using the theory of little groups a crystal property is classified by the wavevector, $\mathbf{q}$, and the irreducible representations of the little group of that wavevector. In the nonsymmorphic space groups difficulty is encountered when $\mathbf{q}$ lies on a Brillouin zone boundary. The little group is not then a crystal point group and the irreducible representations must be computed from first principles. Fortunately this has been done for many common crystal structures (20).

The usefulness of this formalism becomes apparent once we consider its application to the calculation of selection rules. Initially suppose we consider the product of two functions, $\phi_j \psi_i$. We may reduce both these functions to their irreducible representations, and express the product as a sum of products of irreducible representations. This new representation has characters which are the product of the individual characters of the ϕ_j and ψ_i, and may be reduced to the irreducible representations. This product representation is useful in computing matrix elements of the form;

$$M_{ij} = \langle \psi_i | o | \psi_j \rangle$$

M_{ij} is nonzero if and only if the product representation of $\psi_i \psi_j$ contains at least one irreducible representation which is present in the reduction of the operator, o. Group theory gives many more results of use in treating Raman spectra. However, the above results are the most useful ones and we refer to the literature for further details and developments (18,19).

B. Raman Tensor

Raman scattering is specified by the tensor, $I_{\alpha\beta\gamma\delta}$, of Eq. (7) and (8). Within the adiabatic approximation $|\omega_o - \omega_e| \gg \omega$ it is symmetric for interchange of α and β, for interchange of γ and δ and for interchange of $\alpha\beta$ and $\delta\gamma$. Initially suppose we neglect the wavevector of the light. (This is not valid for piezoelectric crystals or for Brillouin scattering). The Raman tensor has the full point group symmetry of the crystal and is

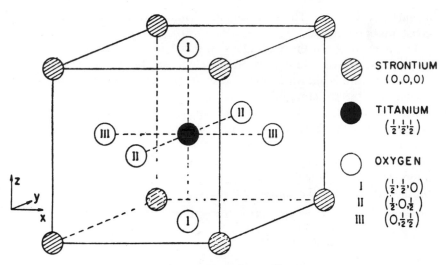

Fig. 3. The perovskite structure of strontium titanate, SrTiO$_3$.

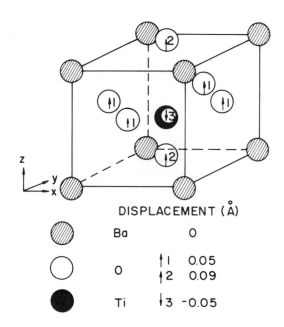

Fig. 4. The structure of BaTiO$_3$ in its tetragonal ferroelectric form as quoted by Jona and Shirane (*116*).

a fourth rank tensor. The symmetry is identical with that of the elastic constants of the crystal.

In order to apply the techniques outlined in the preceding section, three particular cases are considered. These are the cubic perovskites, whose structure is shown in Fig. 3, the semiconductors germanium and silicon, and the structure of $BaTiO_3$ in its tetragonal ferroelectric form, which is shown in Fig. 4. The point group symmetry of the first two cases is $m3m$ and of the third is $4\,mm$. The symmetry of the Raman tensor for permutation of the indices permits a maximum of 21 independent coefficients of the form; I_{xxxx}, I_{xyxy} etc. These 21 coefficients form the basis of a representation of the above point groups which may be reduced to give for the cubic crystals the representations

$$3\Gamma_1 + 3\Gamma_{12} + \Gamma'_{25} + 3\Gamma'_{15}$$

and for the tetragonal structure

$$6\Delta_1 + \Delta_1' + 3\Delta_2 + 3\Delta_2' + 4\Delta_5$$

where we have used the notation of Koster (20). Since the Raman scattering is invariant under the symmetry operations of the crystal the only measureable quantities transform like the identity representation, namely Γ_1 and Δ_1. These results show that there are 3 independent Raman scattering tensors in the cubic crystals and 6 in the tetragonal crystal. In the case of the cubic crystals these are I_{xxxx}, I_{xxyy}, and I_{xyxy} while for the tetragonal crystal they are I_{xxxx}, I_{xxyy}, I_{xxzz}, I_{zzzz}, I_{xyxy}, and I_{xzxz}. A complete measurement of the Raman scattering therefore is a measurement of each of these independent tensors as a function of frequency. In Fig. 5 we show three different experiments which would permit the measurement of these different components for the cubic crystals.

In the case of piezoelectric crystals and Brillouin scattering, it is not adequate to put $\mathbf{Q} = 0$. The appropriate symmetry of the Raman tensor is not the full point group of the crystal but the little group of the wave-vector $\mathbf{Q}$ as emphasized by Theimer (21). This considerably reduces the symmetry of the Raman scattering since if $\mathbf{Q}$ is along the [001] direction in the perovskite structure the little group is $4\,mm$ and the symmetry identical with that for the ferroelectric phase of $BaTiO_3$. A complete description of the Raman scattering consists in these circumstances of a measurement of this larger number of independent components for all directions and magnitudes of the wavevector transfer, $\mathbf{Q}$. In practice it is usually sufficient to restrict attention to $\mathbf{Q}$ parallel to directions of high symmetry in the crystal.

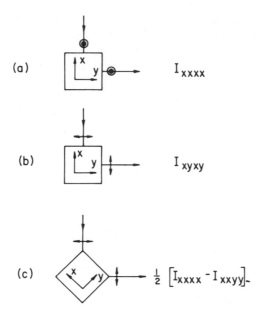

Fig. 5. Schematic diagram showing the way in which it is possible to measure the three different components of the Raman Tensor in cubic crystals. The incident and scattered light are polarized either (a) perpendicular to or (b)(c) parallel to the scattering plane.

C. Normal Modes of Vibration

Group theory is useful in the classification of the normal modes of vibration of crystals. The methods employed have been described by Lax (22), Chen (23), Maradudin and Vosko (24), and by Warren (25), for example. The Fourier transform of the atomic displacements $U_\alpha(k \mid \mathbf{q})$, Eq. (12), is chosen to give a representation of the space group. This representation is reduced by the use of the little group symmetry of the wavevector, $\mathbf{q}$, to give the transformation properties of the normal modes for each wavevector.

Let us apply these techniques to the normal modes in the perovskite lattice (26). There are five atoms in each unit cell, Fig. 3, and hence fifteen components of the vector $U(k \mid \mathbf{q})$. The characters of the different symmetry operators may be obtained quite readily. When $\mathbf{q} = 0$ the symmetry is $m3m$ and the irreducible representations are:

$$4\Gamma_{15} + \Gamma_{25} \tag{32}$$

In practice, as described in Section IV, B, optic modes which are infrared active need careful consideration. The infrared active modes transform like a vector, namely Γ_{15}, so that there are four modes of this type. The Γ_{25} modes represent a triply degenerate set of normal modes.

When $\mathbf{q}$ is along the [001] direction the little group is $4\,mm$ and the irreducible representations are:

$$4\Delta_1 + \Delta_2 + 5\Delta_5 \tag{33}$$

The Δ_1 and Δ_2 modes are of longitudinal polarization and the Δ_5 modes transverse and doubly degenerate.

At the [001] zone boundary the little group is $4\,mmm$ and the irreducible representations are;

$$2M_1 + M_3 + 2M_4' + 3M_5 + 2M_5', \tag{34}$$

where we have corrected a label in Koster's (20) table to agree with the more conventional usage (18,19).

With $\mathbf{q}$ in the [111] direction the little group is $3m$ and the irreducible representations are;

$$4\Lambda_1 + \Lambda_2 + 5\Lambda_3 \tag{35}$$

and at the zone boundary the group is $m3m$ giving rise to the representations

$$\Gamma_2' + \Gamma_{12}' + \Gamma_{25} + \Gamma_{25}' + 2\Gamma_{15} \tag{36}$$

In the [111] direction there are in general 5 longitudinal modes, Λ_1 and Λ_2 and five doubly degenerate transverse branches Λ_3. At the zone boundary there is additional degeneracy giving rise to four triply degenerate modes, one doubly degenerate, Γ_{12}', and one nondegenerate, Γ_2'.

In the distorted $BaTiO_3$ structure the symmetry is reduced so that for $q = 0$, the little group is $4\,mm$. The irreducible representations are:

$$4\Delta_1 + \Delta_2 + 5\Delta_5 \tag{37}$$

and Δ_1 modes are infrared active with the electric vector polarized along the z axis, while Δ_5 corresponds to infrared active modes polarized perpendicular to the z axis.

In the germanium structure the point group symmetry at $q = 0$ is $m3m$ and the irreducible representations are:

$$\Gamma_{25}' + \Gamma_{15} \tag{38}$$

A vector transforms as Γ_{15}.

D. One-Phonon Raman Scattering

In section IIC the Raman scattering by one-phonon processes was
calculated by expanding the polarizability in powers of the phonon
coordinates, Eq. (17). Symmetry may be used to restrict the different terms
in the summations over the phonon branches. If we neglect, for the
moment, processes in which the magnitude of the wavevector transfer Q
is important, it is quite straightforward to use group theory to deduce
these restrictions. The polarizability is, in the adiabatic approximation, a
symmetric second rank tensor and has six independent components.
These form a representation which may be reduced by the usual methods
to give the irreducible representations of the point groups. In the point
group $m3m$ the representations are:

$$\Gamma_1 + \Gamma_{12} + \Gamma'_{25} \tag{39}$$

while in the point group $4\,mm$, they are

$$2\Delta_1 + \Delta_2 + \Delta_2' + \Delta_5 \tag{40}$$

These different irreducible representations corresponds to a different
form of the polarizability, e.g., Γ_1 and Γ_{12} have the form $P_{\alpha\beta} = C_1\delta_{\alpha\beta}$,
while for Γ'_{25}, $P_{\alpha\beta} = C_2(1-\delta_{\alpha\beta})$. The forms of these matrices for the
different representations of all the crystal point groups are given by
Loudon (3).

It follows from the group theory described in Section IIIA that a single
phonon will contribute to the polarizability if and only if it belongs to one
of the irreducible representations present in the reduction of the polarizability. Correspondingly a comparison of Eq. (39) and (32) shows that
there are no first order Raman active phonons in the perovskite structure.
Equations (39) and (38) show that the Γ'_{25} mode is Raman active in the
germanium structure while Eqs. (37) and (40) show that all the $q = 0$
modes are Raman active in the distorted perovskite structure. These
results show the power of the group theory method for producing results
without the aid of a particular model of the crystal.

A number of general results may be derived which are of interest. In a
crystal having a center of symmetry the polarizability is unchanged by the
inversion. Consequently its irreducible representations have the same
characters for both the inversion and the identity elements. The dipole
moment operator for the dielectric constant is odd under inversion and
hence modes are infrared active only if their representations have characters
of opposite sign for the inversion and identity elements. It follows that in
crystals with centers of symmetry, a normal mode may be either infrared

or Raman active but not both. This is the reason why infrared and Raman spectroscopy frequently give complementary information about the normal modes of vibration.

If a mode is both Raman active and infrared active it follows that the Raman second rank tensor contains the same irreducible representation as the dipole moment vector. This is the same requirement that the second rank strain tensor have the same irreducible representation as the dipole moment, in which case the crystal is piezoelectric.

Another result of symmetry occurs when all the atoms of a crystal are situated on centres of symmetry. The character of the atomic displacements for the inversion operator is minus that of the identity operator, showing that there are no Raman active modes. This is in agreement with the result found for the perovskite structure.

As yet we have only discussed the situation when the wavevector transfer is taken to be zero. This is not adequate for Brillouin scattering from the acoustic modes. These modes correspond to a nearly uniform translation of the crystal and hence transform as vectors. In the point group $m3m$ they transform as Γ_{15} and in $4\,mm$ as $\Delta_1 + \Delta_5$. In order to calculate the selection rules for these modes the polarizability and the normal modes must be reduced by the little group of the wavevector, $\mathbf{Q}$. In the perovskite structure with $\mathbf{Q}$ along the [001] direction the polarizability has the same symmetry as in the distorted perovskite structure, Eq. (40). The acoustic modes have symmetries Δ_1 and Δ_5 and so both give rise to Brillouin scattering. Note that if $\mathbf{Q}$ is taken to be zero, the scattering is given incorrectly as zero. The finite size of $\mathbf{Q}$ leads therefore to a breaking of the selection rules.

Although in principle the finite size of $\mathbf{Q}$ leads to a similar breaking of the selection rules for the optic modes, in practice the effects are negligible except for modes which are both Raman and infrared active. We shall discuss these modes in detail in Section IV, B.

E. Two-Phonon Processes

The selection rules for the two-phonon Raman processes may be obtained using very similar techniques to those described for the one-phonon process. The transformation properties of the product $A(\mathbf{q}j)A(-\mathbf{q}j')$ may be calculated by reducing the product of the irreducible representation of mode $(\mathbf{q}j)$ with that of mode $(\mathbf{q}j')$ within the little group of the wavevector, $\mathbf{q}$. The polarizability is then also expressed in terms of these irreducible representations and hence the selection rules obtained as described by Elliott and Loudon (*27*).

Let us consider as an example the perovskite structure. When $\mathbf{q}$ is along [100] the point group is $4\,mm$ and the irreducible representations, Eq. (39), become:

$$\Gamma_1 \rightarrow \Delta_1, \quad \Gamma_{12} \rightarrow \Delta_1 + \Delta_2 \quad \text{and} \quad \Gamma'_{25} \rightarrow \Delta_2' + \Delta_5 \qquad (41)$$

The irreducible representations of the products of phonons, Eq. (33), are:

$$\begin{array}{lll} \Delta_1 \times \Delta_1 \rightarrow \Delta_1 & \Delta_1 \times \Delta_2 \rightarrow \Delta_2 & \Delta_1 \times \Delta_5 \rightarrow \Delta_5 \\ \Delta_2 \times \Delta_2 \rightarrow \Delta_1 & \Delta_2 \times \Delta_5 \rightarrow \Delta_5 & \Delta_5 \times \Delta_5 \rightarrow \Delta_1 + \Delta_1' + \Delta_2 + \Delta_2' \end{array}$$

A comparison of the irreducible representations occurring on the right hand sides of this equation and Eq. (41) shows that all possible combinations are allowed by symmetry to contribute to the scattering.

At the zone boundary, however, not all combinations are permitted. The Γ_1 part of the polarizability has combinations arising from $M_1 \times M_1$, $M_3 \times M_3$, $M_4' \times M_4'$, $M_5 \times M_5$, and $M_5' \times M_5'$. The same pairs contribute to the Γ_{12} part and in addition a contribution arises from $M_1 \times M_3$. The contributions permitted to the Γ'_{25} part of the polarizability are $M_5 \times M_5$, $M_5' \times M_5'$, $M_3 \times M_5$, $M_4' \times M_5'$.

When the phonon wavevector, $\mathbf{q}$, lies along the [111] direction all the combinations are Raman active excepting $\Lambda_1 \times \Lambda_2$. At the zone boundary the Raman inactive combinations are $\Gamma'_{25} \times \Gamma_2'$, $\Gamma'_{25} \times \Gamma'_{12}$, $\Gamma'_{25} \times \Gamma_{25}$, $\Gamma'_{25} \times \Gamma_{15}$, and $\Gamma_2' \times \Gamma'_{25}$.

By the aid of group theory we have been able to evaluate which pairs of phonon modes give rise to the two-phonon Raman scattering, and furthermore to which components of the polarizability tensor they contribute. This is of considerable assistance in the identification of features of the spectrum. The selection rules have been calculated by Johnson and Loudon (*28*) for the germanium structure and by Burstein et al. (*29*) for alkali halides.

IV. ONE-PHONON RAMAN EFFECT

A. Identification of the Phonons

In the preceding sections, the Raman scattering by one-phonon processes has been discussed and its symmetry properties evaluated. In this section we elaborate on these results to describe the way in which different phonon types may be identified with the aid of the selection rules. In Section IV, A, it is assumed that the wavevector transfer, $\mathbf{Q}$, in the scattering is of no importance. Piezoelectric crystals are discussed in Sections IV, B and C, and Brillouin scattering in Section IV, D.

Most Raman scattering experiments are performed by scattering through 90°. A typical experimental arrangement is shown in Fig. 6

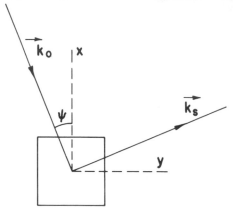

Fig. 6. Schematic diagram of a typical scattering diagram with the Z axis of the crystal perpendicular to the scattering plane.

where the crystal z axis is perpendicular to the plane of the scattering and the x axis is at an angle ψ to the incident light. In Section III, B, we discussed the symmetry of the Raman tensor and showed that in cubic crystals there are three components, I_{xxxx}, I_{xyxy}, and I_{xxyy}. When both the incident and scattered light are polarized in the scattering plane the intensity is given by

$$\tfrac{1}{2}(I_{xxxx} - I_{xxyy}) \sin^2 2\psi + I_{xyxy} \cos^2 2\psi$$

If the incident light is polarized in the scattering plane and the scattered light perpendicularly, the intensity is I_{xyxy}. If the incident light is polarized perpendicularly to the scattering plane, the intensity is I_{xyxy} in the scattering plane and I_{xxxx} perpendicular to it.

An important quantity in many experiments is the depolarization ratio, ρ, which is defined to be the ratio of the scattered intensity polarized perpendicular to the plane of the scattering to that of the intensity polarized in that plane. In this example for unpolarized incident light, it is given by

$$\rho = \frac{I_{xxxx} + I_{xyxy}}{\tfrac{1}{2}(I_{xxxx} - I_{xxyy}) \sin^2 2\psi + I_{xyxy}(1 + \cos^2 2\psi)}$$

The depolarization ratio depends on the crystal orientation.

Let us apply these results to the germanium structure. In Section III, D, we showed that the Γ'_{25} mode was Raman active, and that the polarizability tensor was of the form $P_{\alpha\beta} = C_2(1 - \delta_{\alpha\beta})$. Consequently both I_{xxxx} and I_{xxyy} are zero, and the one-phonon Raman scattering occurs only in the I_{xyxy} component. The depolarization ratio is, therefore, given by $1/(1 + \cos^2 2\psi)$.

It is strictly not possible to apply this method directly to the distorted $BaTiO_3$ structure because the modes are infrared active. It is, however, instructive to do so if only to compare the results with those obtained in the next section. In Table 1 we show the expressions for the intensity of the scattering for various crystal orientations and polarizations of the light.

TABLE 1

Components of the Raman Tensor for Different Orientations of a Crystal with 4 mm Point Group Symmetry

Scattered light	Incident light $\parallel$	Incident light $\perp$
	Crystal Z-axis, Vertical	
$\parallel$	$1/2(I_{xxxx} - I_{xxyy}) \sin^2 2\psi + I_{xyxy} \cos^2 2\psi$	I_{xzxz}
$\perp$	I_{xzxz}	I_{zzzz}
	Crystal Y-axis, Vertical	
$\parallel$	$1/4(I_{xxxx} + I_{zzzz} - 2I_{xxzz}) \sin^2 2\psi + I_{xzxz} \cos^2 2\psi$	$I_{xyxy} \cos^2 \psi + I_{xzxz} \sin^2 \psi$
$\perp$	$I_{xyxy} \sin^2 \psi + I_{xzxz} \cos^2 \psi$	I_{xxxx}

The forms of the polarizability tensors for the optic modes are given by Loudon (3) as:

$$\begin{pmatrix} a & o & o \\ o & a & o \\ o & o & b \end{pmatrix}, \quad \begin{pmatrix} c & o & o \\ o & -c & o \\ o & o & o \end{pmatrix}, \quad \begin{pmatrix} o & o & e \\ o & o & o \\ e & o & o \end{pmatrix}$$

for the Δ_1, Δ_2, and Δ_5 modes respectively. From these results it may be seen that it is possible to distinguish between the modes on the basis of polarization measurements. If the z axis is perpendicular to the scattering plane only the Δ_1 modes are obtained if both the incident and scattered light are polarized along the z axis, only the Δ_2 modes are observed when the light is polarized in the scattering plane, and the Δ_5 modes are seen when the incident light is polarized in the plane and scattered light perpendicular to it. With the y axis vertical, however, it is not possible to distinguish the Δ_1 and Δ_2 modes.

The one-phonon Raman scattering enables the frequencies and the symmetry assignments of the long wavelength phonon modes to be obtained. This information may then be compared with that obtained from other experimental techniques and used to deduce models for the interatomic forces in crystals. It is not our object to review the many experimental results now available. It is perhaps worth mentioning however, that by determining the number and symmetry of the phonons, Baumann and Porto (30) were able to assign the structure of the rare earth fluorides.

B. Piezoelectric Crystals

In piezoelectric crystals a normal mode may give rise to Raman scattering and also contribute to the dielectric properties. Modes which have an electric polarization couple with the photons in the crystal and their frequencies are very different depending whether their wavevector is smaller or greater than the wavevector of light of the same frequency. This phenomena is discussed by Born and Huang (5) for cubic diatomic crystals and has since been generalized by Loudon (3) and others (31). We shall follow the treatment of Born and Huang (5) but extend it to more complex crystals.

The dielectric polarization per unit volume set up in a crystal by the motion of the ions is the sum of the effective charges times the displacements of the atoms

$$\mathbf{M} = \frac{1}{Nv}\sum_{lk} Z_k \mathbf{U}(lk)$$

where $N\varepsilon$ is the volume of the crystal. Since we are concerned with wavelengths much larger than interatomic spacings this expression may be rewritten in terms of the normal modes of zero wavevector as

$$\mathbf{M} = \frac{1}{Nv}\sum_{j} \mathbf{M}(oj)P(oj)$$

where it is convenient to introduce the new normal mode coordinates

$$P(oj) = \left(\frac{\hbar}{2\omega(oj)}\right)^{\frac{1}{2}} A(oj)$$

and

$$\mathbf{M}(oj) = \sum_k Z_k \mathbf{e}(k \mid oj)/(M_k)^{\frac{1}{2}}$$

When an electric field, $\mathbf{E}$, of wavevector, $\mathbf{Q}$, and frequency, ω, is applied to the crystal the response is calculated by writing the equations of motion for the coordinates, $P(oj)$. By analogy with Eq. (11) the result is

$$\ddot{P}(oj) = -\omega(oj)^2 P(oj) + \mathbf{M}(oj) \cdot \mathbf{E} \exp(i\omega t) \tag{42}$$

The dipole moment of the crystal per unit volume, in the direction α is

$$M_\alpha = \frac{1}{Nv} \sum_j M_\alpha(oj)P(oj) + \sum_\beta P^o_{\alpha\beta}E_\beta \exp(i\omega t) \tag{43}$$

where $P^o_{\alpha\beta}$ is the electronic polarizability of the crystal introduced in Section II, Eq. (18). This latter equation may be rewritten in terms of the frequency dependent susceptibility, $\chi_{\alpha\beta}(\omega)$ as

$$M_\alpha = \chi_{\alpha\beta}(\omega)E_\beta \exp(i\omega t)$$

where $\chi_{\alpha\beta}(\omega)$ may be obtained by eliminating $P(oj)$ from Eq. (43) with the aid of Eq. (42) to give

$$\chi_{\alpha\beta}(\omega) = P^o_{\alpha\beta} + \frac{1}{Nv} \sum_j \frac{M_\alpha(oj)M_\beta(oj)}{\omega(oj)^2 - \omega^2} \tag{44}$$

A relation between the dielectric polarization and the electric field may also be obtained from Maxwell's electromagnetic equations. For a wave with wavevector, $\mathbf{Q}$, and frequency, ω, the result, in Gaussian units, is

$$\mathbf{E} = -\frac{4\pi[\mathbf{Q}(\mathbf{Q}\cdot\mathbf{M}) - \omega^2\vec{\mathbf{M}}/c^2]}{Q^2 - \omega^2/c^2}$$

Now eliminating $\mathbf{M}$ with Eq. (44) gives

$$\frac{4\pi Q_\alpha \sum_{\gamma\beta} Q_\beta \chi_{\beta\gamma}(\omega)E_\gamma - \omega^2 \sum \chi_{\alpha\beta}(\omega)E_\beta/c^2}{Q^2 - \omega^2/c^2} = -E_\alpha \tag{45}$$

The frequencies of the normal modes are given by the frequencies ω for which the matrix

$$\delta_{\alpha\beta} + \frac{4\pi Q_\alpha \sum_\gamma Q_\gamma \chi_{\gamma\beta}(\omega) - \omega^2 \chi_{\alpha\beta}(\omega)}{Q^2 - \omega^2/c^2} \tag{46}$$

has zero eigenvalues, and the different components of the electric vector are given by its eigenvectors. These results are applicable for any crystal symmetry; however, it is of interest to discuss them in a few special cases.

1. Cubic Crystals

In a cubic crystal, e.g., the perovskites, the susceptibility is isotropic and we may quite generally take Q in the α direction. The solution for the α component or longitudinal waves is then

$$1 + 4\pi\chi(\omega) = 0 \qquad (47)$$

which is equivalent to the electric displacement, **D** being zero but the electric field, **E**, finite. The longitudinal modes have frequencies independent of **Q** and given by the Eq. (47) and denoted by ω_L. The β component of the matrix gives

$$1 - \frac{\omega^2}{c^2}\chi(\omega)\Big/\left(Q^2 - \frac{\omega^2}{c^2}\right) = 0$$

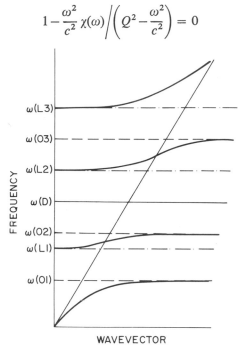

WAVEVECTOR

Fig. 7. The frequency of the modes of oscillation at long wavelengths in the perovskite structure. The frequencies $\omega(L1)\ldots\omega(L3)$ are the frequencies of the longitudinal modes, $\omega(O1)\ldots\omega(O3)$ of the transverse modes. The solid lines show the frequencies of the mixed transverse phonon-photon modes. $\omega(D)$ is the frequency of the triply degenerate mode. The maximum wavevector in this diagram is about 10^{-3} of the maximum wavevector within the Brillouin zone.

For small wavevectors, $Q < (\omega/c)L$, this has solutions $\omega = \omega_L$, and $\omega = Qc$. At large wavevectors, $Q \gg \omega/c$, the solutions are the poles of $\chi(\omega)$, namely $\omega(oj)$. The solution for all Q is shown in Fig. 7 for the perovskite structure. In the intermediate Q range the modes are mixed photon–phonon modes and were called polaritons by Hopfield (32). For these modes the electric field, $\mathbf{E}$, is zero. The difference in frequency between ω_L and $\omega(oj)$ arises because of the electric fields associated with the former modes.

In Fig. 7 it is seen that the symmetry of the optic modes is reduced away from $Q = 0$. At $Q = 0$ the group theory discussion is strictly correct and the three branches of the phonon modes are degenerate at the frequencies $\omega(L1) - \omega(L3)$. However, once the wavevector transfer is finite the symmetry is reduced and the discussion must be modified to include the extra photon modes and the finite wavevector. In a Raman scattering experiment $Q > \omega/c$, and, hence, the number of modes is obtained correctly by discussing only the phonon modes and using the reduced symmetry appropriate for the wavevector, $\mathbf{Q}$.

2. UNIAXIAL CRYSTALS

In tetragonal crystals, such as the distorted $BaTiO_3$ structure, and in hexagonal crystals, there is a unique axis and the susceptibility is of the form $\chi_{xx}(\omega) = \chi_{yy}(\omega) \neq \chi_{zz}(\omega)$. When the wavevector, $\mathbf{Q}$, lies along the z direction, the longitudinal modes are given by the equation

$$1 + 4\pi\chi_{zz}(\omega) = 0$$

and the transverse modes by

$$1 - \frac{\omega^2}{c^2}\chi_{xx}(\omega)\bigg/\left(Q^2 - \frac{\omega^2}{c^2}\right) = 0 \tag{48}$$

When the wavevector is in the X direction there are three different types of mode. The frequency of one of these is given by Eq. (48) and the others by the solutions of

$$1 + 4\pi\chi_{xx}(\omega) = 0$$

$$1 - \frac{\omega^2}{c^2}\chi_{zz}(\omega)\bigg/\left(Q^2 - \frac{\omega^2}{c^2}\right) = 0$$

The solutions of these equations for the case of the distorted $BaTiO_3$ structure are shown in Fig. 8, for the two cases discussed above.

These considerations may be extended to less symmetric crystals by the use of the general Eq. (46); we shall not, however, pursue this further here.

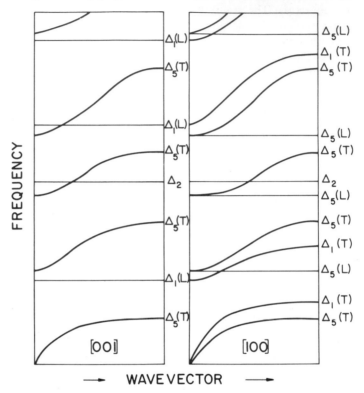

Fig. 8. The dispersion relation of the photon-phonon modes in the distorted $BaTiO_3$ structure. The Δ_1 modes are polarized along the Z axis and the Δ_5 perpendicular to it. The Δ_2 modes are not infrared active. The maximum wavevector is about 10^{-3}, the maximum wavevector within the Brillouin zone.

3. EXPERIMENTAL RESULTS

The first manifestations of the photon–phonon interaction was observed in experiments with large scattering angles. The wavevector transfer, **Q**, was correspondingly much larger than ω/c, and the frequencies observed were the $\omega(Lj)$ and $\omega(oj)$ of Figs. 7 and 8. In the cubic diatomic crystal, ZnS, two modes were observed by Couture–Mathieu and Mathieu (33) instead of the one predicted by the theory when the photons are neglected. These measurements were subsequently explained by Poulet (34).

Now let us consider the influence of these effects on the Raman scattering by the distorted perovskite structure described in the previous section. If the Z axis is perpendicular to the scattering plane and if both incident and scattered light are polarized parallel to one another the modes

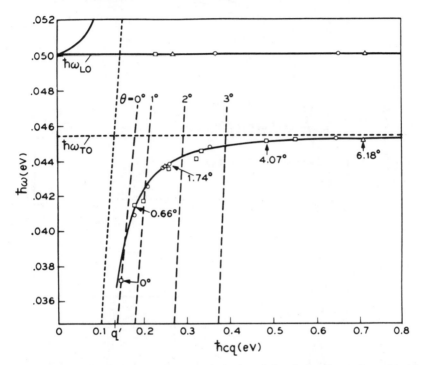

Fig. 9. The polariton spectrum of GaP (*35*). A plot of the observed energies and wave vectors of the polaritons and of the *LO* phonons; the theoretical dispersion curves are shown by the solid lines. The dispersion curves for the uncoupled photons and phonons are shown by short-dashed lines. The values of energies and wave vectors which are kinematically possible at θ are shown by longdashed lines. Some of the experimental angles θ are indicated next to the data points. $\square$ k_L = in 111 direction; $\triangle$ k_L = in 100 direction; $\bigcirc$ = polycrstaline sample. (Reproduced from Ref. *35*, p. 965.)

observed are $\Delta_1(T)$ and Δ_2 of Fig. 8. When the incident and scattered light are polarized perpendicularly to one-another $\Delta_5(L)$ and $\Delta_5(T)$ are observed simultaneously. When the Y axis is perpendicular to the scattering plane the frequencies vary with the orientations of the specimen. However, if $\mathbf{Q}$ is chosen to be either along the X or Z axis the frequencies of Fig. 8 are obtained. In the former case $\Delta_1(T)$, Δ_2, $\Delta_5(T)$, and $\Delta_5(L)$

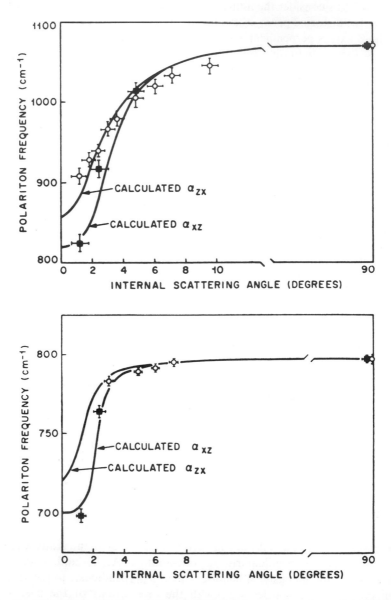

Fig. 10. Comparison of theoretical and observed frequencies of coupled phonon-photon modes in α-quartz: ○ = observed α_{zx}; ■ = observed α_{xz}. (Reprinted from Ref. *36*, p. 839.)

are observed, while in the latter case $\Delta_1(L)$, Δ_2, and $\Delta_5(T)$. These results show that it is possible to determine the different frequencies with Raman scattering, and as before to identify the symmetry by measurements with different polarizations of the light and orientations of the specimen.

One further feature was demonstrated by Poulet (34). Not only is the frequency of the mode modified by the interaction with the photons but also the Raman scattering efficiency. This arises because the electric field associated with the longitudinal modes strongly influences the coupling of the mode with the electron-hole pairs. Consequently, the Raman scattering efficiency is enhanced for the longitudinal modes.

This modification is incorporated into the theory by altering the magnitude of the coefficients $P_{\alpha\beta}(\mathbf{q}j)$ of Eq. (17) depending upon whether j is a longitudinal or transversely polarized mode. This modification is readily incorporated in the direct method of calculating the coefficients, Section II, D, and in the shell model procedure. Poulet (34) modified the expansion technique by adding terms to Eq. (23) which depend on the macroscopic electric field. These terms may then be related to the linear electrooptic coefficients. The importance of the different scattering efficiencies of longitudinal and transverse modes was first demonstrated experimentally for zinc blende (33).

The photon–phonon mixing has received attention more recently in experiments at small scattering angles when the momentum transfer $|\mathbf{Q}|$ is comparable with ω/c. It is then possible to follow the behavior of the transverse modes to small wavevector as illustrated in Fig. 9 for GaP (35). Recently measurements on quartz have shown the influence of polariton effects on the higher optic modes (36) as shown in Fig. 10. These measurements have strikingly confirmed the predictions of the theory described above.

C. Doped Semiconductors

If free carriers are introduced into an ionic semiconductor they modify the interatomic forces. This is particularly the case for the longitudinal optic modes because they are associated with the macroscopic electric field. The free carriers will move in such a way as to screen out this electric field. This screening may be computed within the self-consistent field approximation and represented by dividing the field by the dielectric constant of the free electrons as described, for example, by Pines (37).

If the carrier density is such that the distance between the electrons is smaller than ω/c but greater than interatomic distances then the theory of the preceding section is directly applicable. Suppose we consider a particular mode j and rewrite the condition for the longitudinal modes, Eq. (47), with the aid of Eq. (44) for the susceptibility. The result is

$$1+4\pi P_{\alpha\beta}^{o}+4\pi \sum_{j'\neq j}\chi_{j'}(\omega_L)+\frac{4\pi M_{\alpha}(oj)M_{\beta}(oj)}{Nv(\omega(oj)^2-\omega_L^{2})}=0$$

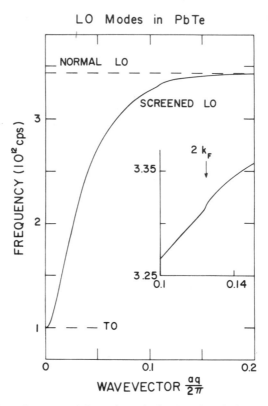

Fig. 11. The dispersion curve of the optic modes in PbTe doped with 2×10^{19} carriers/cc. The inset shows the discontinuity when the wavevector equals the Fermi surface diameter. (Reprinted from Ref. *38*, p. 550.)

where $\chi_{j'}(\omega_L)$ is the contribution to the susceptibility at frequency, ω_L, from all the other modes. This equation may be rewritten for cubic crystals as

$$\omega_L^{2}-\omega(oj)^2=\frac{4\pi M(oj^2)}{Nv\varepsilon'(\omega_L)} \qquad (49)$$

where $\varepsilon'(\omega_L)$ is the dielectric constant resulting from all processes other than the mode j. The term $4\pi M(oj)^2$ corresponds to the change in frequency due to the electric field and the only change in Eq. (49) in a doped semiconductor is that the dielectric constant has an additional term resulting from the free carriers. This latter contribution depends on both the wavevector and frequency of the phonons and, in principle, is dependent on the band structure and the exchange and correlation effects in the dielectric constant.

DISPERSION CURVES OF TIN TELLURIDE AT 100°K

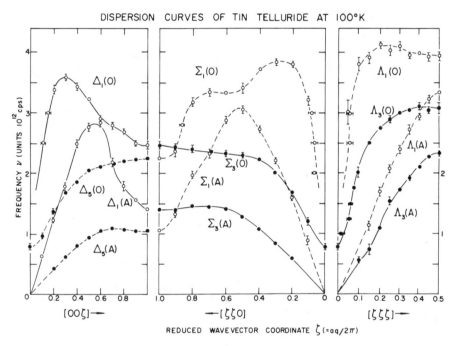

Fig. 12. The dispersion relations for SnTe (40), as measured with neutron scattering techniques. Note the decrease in the frequency of the LO modes as $Q \to 0$.

There are only two cases of interest experimentally; the first is a heavily doped crystal such that the plasma frequency of the electrons is much greater than the lattice frequencies. The dielectric constant of the free electrons is then given adequately by the Thomas–Fermi approximation (37) as

$$\varepsilon(q, \omega) = 1 + k_s^2/q^2$$

and for a diatomic crystal

$$\omega_L{}^2 = \omega_T{}^2 + (\omega_L{}^2 - \omega_T{}^2)/(1 + k_s^2/q^2) \tag{50}$$

Calculations based on a slight modification of this expression for 2×10^{19} carriers/cc in PbTe arc shown in Fig. 11 (38). This is the case of interest in a neutron scattering experiment in which the wavevector resolution is poor (one-sixtieth of the Brillouin zone) and the screening length, k_s, must be comparable. Measurements of the longitudinal optic branch show a decrease in frequency as first found in PbTe (38), and subsequently in PbS (39), and SnTe (40) as shown in Fig. 12.

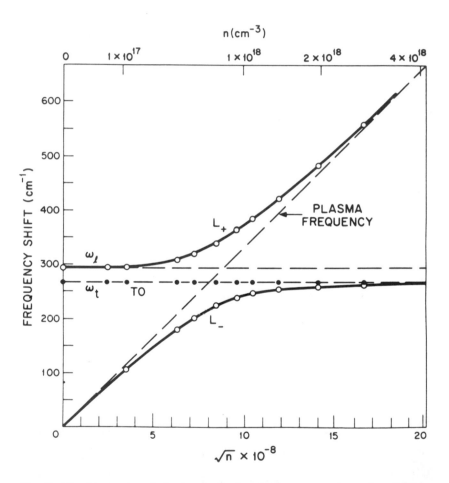

Fig. 13. The frequencies of the longitudinal and transverse optic modes of GaAs, measured by Raman scattering techniques as a function of carrier density (42). (Reprinted from Ref. 42, p. 849.)

The other approximation of interest is that of small wavevector and variable carrier density. This was examined by Yokota (41) and the dielectric constant in this approximation is

$$\varepsilon(o, \omega) = 1 - \omega^2/\omega_p^2$$

where the plasma frequency is

$$\omega_p^2 = \frac{4\pi n e^2}{m^* \varepsilon^\infty}$$

where m^* is the effective mass of the electrons and n is their density. In a cubic diatomic material the frequencies of the coupled phonon–plasmon modes are given by (41)

$$\omega^2 = \frac{\omega_p^2 + \omega_L^2}{2} \pm \frac{1}{2}\left((\omega_p^2 + \omega_L^2)^2 - 4\omega_T^2 \omega_p^2 \right)^{\frac{1}{2}}$$

This expression has been very elegantly verified by the Raman scattering measurements of Mooradian and collaborators (42,43) as shown for GaAs in Fig. 13.

It is possible to perform more detailed calculations as described by Varga (44) and by Cochran et al. (45). However, it is difficult to verify these predictions because with the neutron scattering technique the wavevector resolution is so poor, that only heavily doped materials can be studied, while in Raman scattering the wavevector transfer is so small it never becomes comparable with the distance between the carriers.

D. Brillouin Scattering

Brillouin scattering is the Raman scattering by the acoustic modes in the crystal. The theory of this scattering is developed in exactly the same manner as for the optic modes, but the notation used is frequently quite different. The frequencies of the acoustic modes in a crystal satisfy for small wavevectors the equation

$$\omega(\mathbf{q}j) = C(\mathbf{q}j)|\,\mathbf{q}\,| \tag{51}$$

where the velocity $C(\mathbf{q}j)$ is dependent on the direction of the wavevector and the branch index j. Conservation of energy and momentum then lead to the condition for scattering as

$$c\omega = 2\omega_0 \sin \phi/2C(\mathbf{q}j) \tag{52}$$

where c is the velocity of light, ω_o the frequency of the incident light, and ω has been neglected in comparison with ω_o. The scattering angle is ϕ. Equation (52) shows that the frequency transfer is related to the incident frequency by the ratio of the velocity of sound to the velocity of light. This is about 10^{-4} and consequently the frequency transfers in Brillouin scattering are a maximum of 10^{11} Hz and usually considerably less. In this region Eq. (51) is a very good description of the modes. Since the frequency transfers depend on the direction of the momentum transfer, Q, the Raman scattering has the symmetry of the little group of Q, rather than the full point group of the crystal.

In this long wavelength region, it is frequently convenient to discuss the normal modes in terms of strains, rather than the individual displacements of the different atoms. The strain parameter $\eta_{\alpha\beta}$ is defined in terms of the displacements of the atoms in a crystal due to the strain by

$$\eta_{\alpha\beta} = \frac{\delta U_\alpha(lk)}{\delta R_\beta(lk)}$$

The Raman scattering may be calculated (5) by expanding the polarizability in terms of these strains (cf. Eq. 18) as

$$P_{\alpha\beta} = P_{\alpha\beta} + \sum_{\gamma\delta} P_{\alpha\beta\gamma\delta}\eta_{\gamma\delta} + \cdots \tag{53}$$

Now to obtain the one-phonon coefficients of Eq. (17) and the cross-section through Eq. (21), we need the relationship between the strain and the normal mode coordinates $A(\mathbf{q}j)$ for the acoustic modes. In the acoustic modes, all of the polarization vectors of the different atoms are in the same direction and can be reduced to

$$\mathbf{e}(k \mid \mathbf{q}j) = M_k(\sum_k M_k)^{-\frac{1}{2}}\mathbf{e}(\mathbf{q}i)$$

where $\mathbf{e}(\mathbf{q}j)$ is the normalized eigenvector for the branch, and the mass factors arise from the different normalization of the eigenvectors, $\mathbf{e}(k \mid \mathbf{q}j)$. It is then seen from the definition of the strain parameters that

$$\eta_{\alpha\beta} = \left(\frac{V}{\rho}\right)^{\frac{1}{2}} \sum_{\mathbf{q}j=1} \left(\frac{\hbar}{2\omega(\mathbf{q}j)N}\right)^{\frac{1}{2}} e_\alpha(\mathbf{q}j)q_\beta \exp\left(i\mathbf{q}\cdot\mathbf{R}\binom{l}{k}\right)A\binom{\mathbf{q}}{j} \tag{54}$$

where ρ is the density of the crystal and V its volume. The expression for the polarizability of a single acoustic mode in terms of coefficients of Eq. (53) is given by

$$P_{\alpha\beta}(\mathbf{q}j) = \sum_{\gamma\delta} \left(\frac{V\hbar}{\rho 2\omega(\mathbf{q}j)N}\right)^{\frac{1}{2}} P_{\alpha\beta\gamma\delta}e_\gamma(\mathbf{q}j)q_\delta \tag{55}$$

The advantage of this procedure over that used for optic mode Raman scattering, which could equally well have been applied here, is that the $P_{\alpha\beta\gamma\delta}$ may be obtained from the elasto-optic coefficients. These coefficients which express the change in optical dielectric constant, ε^∞, when a strain is applied to a crystal, may be measured directly, and used to calculate the magnitude of the Raman scattering.

The elasto-optic coefficients, $k_{\alpha\beta\gamma\delta}$, are defined by the relation

$$\delta(\varepsilon^\infty)_{\alpha\beta}^{-1} = \sum_{\gamma\delta} k_{\alpha\beta\gamma\delta}\eta_{\gamma\delta}$$

In terms of these quantities the polarizability is

$$P_{\alpha\beta\gamma\delta} = -\frac{1}{4\pi} \sum_{\mu\nu} \varepsilon_{\alpha\mu}^\infty k_{\mu\nu\gamma\delta}\varepsilon_{\nu\beta}^\infty \tag{56}$$

Since the frequency change in Brillouin scattering is so small, $\hbar\omega \ll k_\beta T$ and the intensity of both Stokes and anti-Stokes processes (Section II) is the same. The intensity for a particular acoustic mode is given by the tensor $I_{\alpha\beta\gamma\delta}$ as

$$I_{\alpha\beta\gamma\delta} = \frac{k_B T V}{2\rho N C(\mathbf{q}j)^2} \sum_{\lambda_1\lambda_2\lambda_3\lambda_4} P_{\alpha\beta\lambda_1\lambda_2} P_{\gamma\delta\lambda_3\lambda_4} e_{\lambda_3}(\mathbf{q}j)e_{\lambda_3}(\mathbf{q}j)\frac{q_{\lambda_2}q_{\lambda}}{|\mathbf{q}|^2}\Delta(\mathbf{q}-\mathbf{Q}) \tag{57}$$

This expression shows that the intensity is dependent on the direction of $\mathbf{Q}$ but does not depend on its magnitude. The factors of $1/\omega$ arising from the population factor and the normal mode normalization are cancelled by the q^2 factor in the expressions for the polarizability.

These results may be applied to the case of a cubic crystal, when $\varepsilon_{\alpha\beta}^\infty = \varepsilon^\infty \delta_{\alpha\beta}$ and the only nonzero elasto-optic coefficients are k_{1111}, k_{1212}, and k_{1122}. A typical scattering geometry is shown in Fig. 5(c) with the momentum transfer along the [100] direction. One of the three acoustic modes is longitudinally polarized and the other two are transversely polarized and degenerate. The incident and scattered light may be polarized either in the z direction, or in the scattering plane, the p direction. The intensity from the longitudinal mode is given by

$$I_{zzzz} = \frac{k_B T V}{8\pi(C_{11})^2} (\varepsilon^\infty)^4 (k_{1122})^2$$

$$I_{pppp} = \frac{k_B T V}{16\pi(C_{11})^2} (\varepsilon^\infty)^4 (k_{1111}^2 + k_{1122}^2)$$

and for the transverse modes

$$I_{pppp} = \frac{k_B T V}{16\pi (C_{44})^2} (\varepsilon^\infty)^4 (k_{1212})^2$$

$$I_{pzpz} = \frac{k_B T V}{16\pi (C_{44})^2} (\varepsilon^\infty)^4 (k_{1212})^2$$

where C_{11} and C_{44} are the elastic constants of the crystal. These results show that it is possible to measure the elastic constants, identify the different branches and also to obtain the elasto-optic coefficients using Brillouin scattering.

V. THE TWO-PHONON RAMAN EFFECT

A. Van Hove Singularities

The expression for the two-phonon Raman scattering was given in Eq. (22) as $I_{\alpha\beta\gamma\delta}^{II}$, and depends upon the frequencies of two phonons through the delta functions $\delta(\omega \pm \omega(\mathbf{q} j_1) \pm \omega(\mathbf{q} j_2))$. One of the features which most determines the two-phonon spectrum is the density of states for the different two-phonon processes. This density of states may be calculated once the phonon dispersion curves are known.

One of the features of the joint density of states which is of interest is the occurrence of singularities, when the joint frequencies are a maximum, minimum, or saddle point. These occur (see Fig. 14) when $\mathbf{q}$ is either zero or a zone boundary wavevector or may occur by accident for an intermediate wavevector. The form of these singularities was first examined by Van Hove (46). The four types of singularity are illustrated in Fig. 15. $P_o \rightarrow P_3$ are the different types of critical point where $j = 0 \rightarrow 3$ is the number of directions in which the frequency surface is a maximum in frequency as a function of $\mathbf{q}$. Several of the critical points such as those arising from the $q = 0$ modes and the zone boundary modes are a consequence of the symmetry of the crystal structure, and frequently, the type of critical point is also determined by the symmetry. In other cases the occurrence and type of critical point is dependent on the particular interatomic forces. In some cases, the frequency dispersion curve does not have zero derivative but a finite slope at the zone boundary (the X point in the germanium structure is an example, shown in Fig. 1). This behavior can inhibit the occurrence of some of the critical points (28).

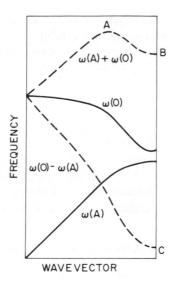

Fig. 14. A schematic diagram showing the occurrence of singularities in the two-phonon density of states. The singularities at B and C are imposed by the symmetry of the dispersion curves but that at A is a result of the particular shape assumed for the curves.

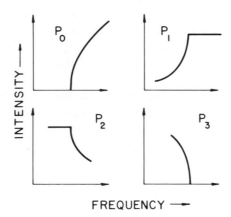

Fig. 15. The shapes of the two-phonon critical points. P_j is the shape when the point is a maximum in frequency in j different directions (28).

The two-phonon Raman spectrum will be large where there is a large density in the two-phonon states and exhibit the Van Hove singularities at the frequencies of the critical points in the two-phonon density of states.

B. Symmetry Conditions

The symmetry of the two-phonon processes were discussed in Section III.D. In that section we discussed the case of the perovskite structure and the contribution of the two-phonon states from phonons propagating along the [001] direction. The symmetry properties of the singularities may be deduced from the results obtained above. If a singularity occurs from phonons with a wavevector q at a general point in the [001] direction the singularities

$$(\Delta_1\Delta_1), (\Delta_1\Delta_2), (\Delta_2\Delta_2), (\Delta_5\Delta_5)$$

occur in the I_{xxxx} and I_{xxyy} contributions to the intensity while $(\Delta_1\Delta_5)$ and $(\Delta_2\Delta_5)$ singularities occur in the I_{xyxy} contribution. For the singularities arising from the phonons with zone boundary wavevectors the corresponding results are;

$$(M_1\,M_1), (M_3\,M_3), (M_4{}'\,M_4{}'), (M_5\,M_5)$$

$(M_5{}'\,M_5{}')$ and $(M_1\,M_3)$ pairs contribute to I_{xxxx} and I_{xxyy} while $(M_5\,M_5)$, $(M_5{}'\,M_5{}')$, $(M_3\,M_5)$, and $(M_4{}'\,M_5{}')$ pairs contribute to I_{xyxy}. It is therefore possible to distinguish between the singularities partly on the basis of their shape, and partly by observing in which Raman spectra they occur, as pointed out by Loudon and Johnson (28) and by Kleinman (47).

There have been many attempts to interpret the two-phonon Raman spectrum in terms of the phonon dispersion relations. Frequently the frequencies of the zone boundary modes are obtained from the peaks in the spectra with little regard for the polarizations or the singularities. This procedure is very unreliable unless the phonon dispersion curves are available from other experimental techniques.

More reliable results can be obtained by measuring the frequency and type of Van Hove singularity in each different component of the Raman tensor. The results are then interpreted in terms of the frequencies of the zone boundary phonons. Even in these circumstances, however, the results must only be tentative unless some prior information is available from other techniques. This is well illustrated by the case of diamond for which the singularities were wrongly interpreted (28,13) until detailed neutron scattering measurements were performed (48). Once the singularities are identified their frequencies can be used to improve the accuracy with which certain phonons are known, as illustrated very elegantly by Loudon and Johnson (28) for the two-phonon infrared spectrum of germanium and silicon.

C. Calculations of Two-Phonon Scattering

Before the two-phonon Raman scattering can be calculated, both the phonon frequencies, $\omega(\mathbf{q}j)$, and the polarizability coefficients, $P_{\alpha\beta}\begin{pmatrix} \mathbf{q} - \mathbf{q} \\ j \quad j' \end{pmatrix}$, must be known. Until recently both of these were unknown, but the development of neutron scattering techniques has enabled the phonon dispersion curves of many materials to be measured. It is now possible to perform these calculations with reasonable confidence in these frequencies, leaving any large discrepancy in the result to be ascribed to errors in the polarizability.

The first calculation of the two-phonon spectrum was by Smith in 1948 (49) of the spectrum for diamond. She used a very crude model for the lattice dynamics of diamond and drastic simplifications in the polarizability. Despite these deficiencies, however, few calculations have been performed which are any improvement on this early work.

A considerable amount of computation by Karo and Hardy (50) has evaluated the two-phonon density of states of various alkali halides. The Raman spectrum was calculated by putting the polarizability, $P_{\alpha\beta}\begin{pmatrix} \mathbf{q} - \mathbf{q} \\ j \quad j' \end{pmatrix} = 1$. This approximation ignores the selection rules discussed in Section III.D and above. Furthermore, there is no distinction between the different components of the Raman tensor. Despite these deficiencies, considerable agreement between the theoretical calculations and experiment is achieved (51) as shown in Fig. 16.

The two-phonon Raman spectra in germanium, silicon and diamond have been calculated (13) by means of the expansion technique (Section II.D) for the polarizability. The coefficients $P_{\alpha\beta\gamma\sigma}\begin{pmatrix} ll' \\ kk' \end{pmatrix}$ were simplified by symmetry, by assuming only nearest neighbor interactions and further by putting $P_{\alpha\beta\gamma\sigma}\begin{pmatrix} ll' \\ kk' \end{pmatrix} = CR_{\alpha}R_{\beta}R_{\gamma}R_{\delta}$, where C was a constant and $\mathbf{R}$ the distance between the ions. The two-phonon spectra were calculated using the phonon frequencies, as given by shell models whose parameters had been obtained by fitting to the measured dispersion curves in symmetry directions. The results showed qualitative agreement with the measurements on diamond by Krishnan (*52*). They also predicted a considerable dependence of the results on the component of the Raman tensor.

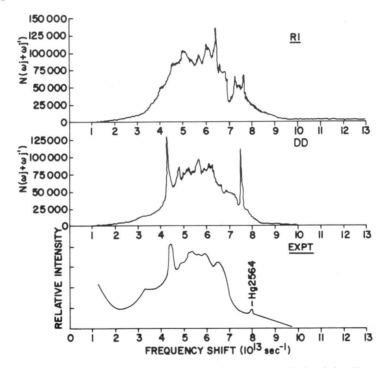

Fig. 16. The two-phonon Raman scattering of NaCl as calculated by Karo and Hardy (*50*) on the rigid ion (*RI*) model and deformation dipole model (*DD*) and as measured by Welsh et al. (*51*). Rigid-ion and *DD* two-phonon densities-of-states curves, together with the observed second order Raman spectrum taken at 300°K. (Reprinted from Ref. *50*, p. 705.)

The two-phonon spectra of the alkali halides have been calculated using the shell model theory of the polarizability (*17*). The anharmonic coefficients were deduced by assuming a Born–Mayer short range potential between nearest neighbors, an approximation which was very satisfactory in other calculations for alkali halides (*53*). The phonon frequencies were obtained by using a shell model. The results show qualitative agreement with experiment, but in many cases strong peaks in the calculated spectra are weak in the experimental spectra, and the calculations seem to be too strongly dependent on orientation; some results are shown in Fig. 17.

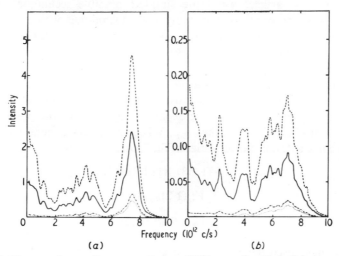

Fig. 17. The two-phonon Raman scattering of KBr as a function of temperature (*17*). The Raman tensor components are (*a*) I_{xxxx} and (*b*) I_{xyxy}, and the temperatures are dashed lines 450°K, solid lines 300°K, dot-dashed lines 90°K and dotted lines 10°K. (Reprinted from Ref. *17*, p. 291.)

None of the calculations described above give good agreement with experiment, and this is clearly due to deficiencies in our models of the polarizability coefficients. Undoubtedly one of the main difficulties in the interpretation of Raman spectra is at this point, and it is to be hoped that further work is forthcoming to resolve these difficulties.

As yet we have not mentioned the three and four-phonon processes. These are very analogous to the two-phonon processes, but are generally weaker, and more temperature dependent. It is possible to derive the properties of Van Hove singularities and of the selection rules, but no detailed application of these has yet been made.

VI. ANHARMONICITY

A. Anharmonic Interactions

In this section we discuss the effect of the anharmonicity of the inter-atomic potential on the Raman spectra. The anharmonicity gives rise to a coupling between the normal modes of vibration, so that if one phonon of a particular mode is excited it will in time decay into other modes. In this section we shall review those features of anharmonic effects which are relevant to this article, using the simplest possible techniques. More comprehensive accounts of the many body techniques which are commonly employed are given in the book by Abrikosov et al. (54) and by Maradudin and Fein (55). These have now been applied to a wide variety of different problems (56,57).

The anharmonic interactions arise from terms in the expansion of the potential energy (Eq. 10) beyond those included in the harmonic approximation. It is useful to rewrite the expansion in terms of the phonon coordinates, $A(\mathbf{q}j)$, and the strains, $\eta_{\alpha\beta}$. When this is done the anharmonic terms become a double power series of the form:

$$
\begin{aligned}
V_{ANH} = {} & \sum_{123} V(1\ 2\ 3)A(1)A(2)A(3) + \cdots \\
& + \sum_{\alpha\beta 12} V_{\alpha\beta}(1\ 2)\eta_{\alpha\beta}A(1)A(2) + \cdots \\
& + \sum_{\alpha\beta\gamma\delta} V_{\alpha\beta\lambda\delta}\eta_{\alpha\beta}\eta_{\gamma\delta} + \cdots
\end{aligned} \tag{58}
$$

where we have used the labels 1, 2, 3 as shorthand for the suffices $(\mathbf{q}_1 j_1)$, $(\mathbf{q}_2 j_2)$, and $(\mathbf{q}_3 j_3)$. The coefficients are given in terms of the expansion coefficients in real space as

$$
\begin{aligned}
V(1\ 2\ 3) = {} & \frac{1}{6}\left(\frac{\hbar^3}{8N\omega_1\omega_2\omega_3}\right)^{\frac{1}{2}} \sum_{\substack{l_2 l_3 \\ k_1 k_2 k_3 \\ \alpha\beta\gamma}} \phi_{\alpha\beta\gamma}\begin{pmatrix} o\ l_2\ l_3 \\ k_1 k_2 k_3 \end{pmatrix} e_\alpha(k_1 \mid 1) \\
& \times e_\beta(k_2 \mid 2)e_\gamma(k_3 \mid 3)\left(\frac{1}{M_{k_1}M_{k_2}M_{k_3}}\right)^{\frac{1}{2}} \exp i\left[\mathbf{q}_1\cdot\mathbf{R}\begin{pmatrix} o \\ k \end{pmatrix}\right. \\
& \left. + \mathbf{q}_2\cdot\mathbf{R}\begin{pmatrix} l_2 \\ k_2 \end{pmatrix} + \mathbf{q}_3\cdot\mathbf{R}\begin{pmatrix} l_3 \\ k_3 \end{pmatrix}\right]\Delta(\mathbf{q}_1 + \mathbf{q}_2 + \mathbf{q}_3)
\end{aligned}
$$

and

$$
\begin{aligned}
V_{\alpha\beta}(1, 2) = {} & \frac{\hbar}{4}\left(\frac{1}{\omega_1\omega_2}\right)^{\frac{1}{2}} \sum_{\substack{l_2 l_3 \\ k_1 k_2 k_3 \\ \gamma\delta}} \phi_{\gamma\delta\alpha}\begin{pmatrix} o\ l_2\ l_3 \\ k_1 k_2 k_3 \end{pmatrix} e_\gamma(k_1 \mid 1) \\
& \times e_\delta(k_2 \mid 2)R_\beta\begin{pmatrix} l_3 \\ k_3 \end{pmatrix}\left(\frac{1}{M_{k_1}M_{k_2}}\right)^{\frac{1}{2}} \exp i\left[\mathbf{q}_1\cdot\mathbf{R}\begin{pmatrix} o \\ k_1 \end{pmatrix}\right. \\
& \left. + \mathbf{q}_2\cdot\mathbf{R}\begin{pmatrix} l_2 \\ k_2 \end{pmatrix}\right]\Delta(\mathbf{q}_1 + \mathbf{q}_2)
\end{aligned}
$$

The delta functions in these expressions ensure conservation of crystal momentum. Once an interatomic potential is assumed, these expressions may be calculated to obtain the coefficients in Eq. (58). Unfortunately the potentials are rarely known, and various drastic simplifications are employed to reduce the number of arbitrary parameters. These simplifications are very similar to those entering into the calculation of the polarizability of the crystal, as described in Section II.D.

B. Frequencies and Lifetimes of the Phonons

One of the main effects of anharmonic interactions on the Raman spectra is on the one-phonon spectrum. The peaks are broadened as a result of the finite lifetimes of the modes and also change frequency as the temperature is altered. In an experiment, energy conservation is applicable only between the photons and the initial and final states of the crystal (Eq. 1). In an anharmonic crystal in which the Raman active phonon decays into pairs of phonons, we need to study the crystal response for a range of different frequencies, ω, corresponding to the energies of the final pairs of phonons.

The lifetimes of the phonons may be calculated by second-order perturbation theory and the first term of the expansion (*58*). The result may be expressed in terms of a quantity

$$\Gamma(ojj', \omega) = \frac{18\pi}{\hbar^2} \sum_{12} V \begin{pmatrix} o \\ j \end{pmatrix} 1\ 2 \end{pmatrix} V \begin{pmatrix} o \\ j' \end{pmatrix} 2\ 1 \end{pmatrix}$$

$$\{(n_1 + n_2 + 1) \times [\delta(\omega_1 + \omega_2 - \omega) - \delta(\omega_1 + \omega_2 + \omega)]$$
$$+ (n_2 - n_1) \times [\delta(\omega_1 - \omega_2 - \omega) - \delta(\omega_1 - \omega_2 + \omega)]\} \qquad (59)$$

When $j = j'$ this expression is the standard perturbation theory result for the inverse lifetime or half-width of a normal mode. The extension to $j \neq j'$ is necessary when there is more than one Raman active mode in the crystal. We have restricted the calculation to phonons of zero wavevector and hence $\mathbf{q}_2 = -\mathbf{q}_1$. This is adequate for the discussion of anharmonicity of the Raman active modes because the wavevector transfer is very small compared with $\mathbf{q}_1$. We may take account of the coupling with the photon modes in piezoelectric crystals by allowing $\omega(oj)$ to vary with momentum transfer, $\mathbf{Q}$, but the Γ and Δ functions to a good approximation do not vary. Pathak (private communication) has shown that for small wavevector transfers the photon–phonon coupling slightly alters the anharmonic coefficients.

The corresponding change in the frequency of the normal mode is obtained by using second order perturbation theory on the first term of the expansion (58), and first-order perturbation on the terms having four phonon coordinates and the strain. The result is

$$\Delta(ojj', \omega) = -\frac{18}{\hbar^2} \sum_{12} V\begin{pmatrix} o \\ j \end{pmatrix} 1 \ 2 \end{pmatrix} V\begin{pmatrix} o \\ j' \end{pmatrix} 1 \ 2 \end{pmatrix} \frac{n_1+n_2+1}{(\omega_1+\omega_2+\omega)_p}$$

$$\times \frac{n_1+n_2+1}{(\omega_1+\omega_2-\omega)_p} + \frac{n_2-n_1}{(\omega_1-\omega_2+\omega)_p} + \frac{n_2-n_1}{(\omega_1-\omega_2-\omega)_p}$$

$$+ \frac{12}{\hbar} \sum_{1} V\begin{pmatrix} o & o \\ j & j' \end{pmatrix} 1 \ 1 \end{pmatrix} (2n_1+l) + 2 \sum_{\alpha\beta} V_{\alpha\beta}\begin{pmatrix} o & o \\ j & j' \end{pmatrix} \eta_{\alpha\beta}^T \qquad (60)$$

where $\eta_{\alpha\beta}^T$ is the thermal strain of the crystal.

Now let us consider the case of a single Raman active mode so that

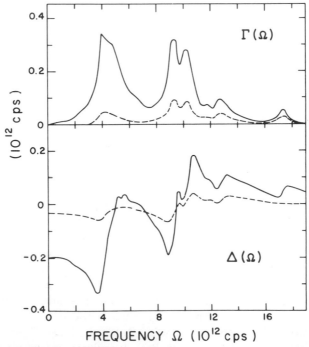

Fig. 18. The width $\Gamma(\Omega)$ and frequency shift $\Delta(\Omega)$ as functions of the applied frequency for the Raman active mode of germanium (13). Full curve is 300°K, broken curve 10°K. (Reprinted from Ref. 13, p. 485.)

$j = j'$ in Eqs. (59) and (60). It is then apparent that the response of the mode to an applied frequency, ω, is as if the mode had a frequency $\omega(oj) + \Delta(ojj, \omega)$ and a half-width of $\Gamma(ojj, \omega)$. The discussion leading up to Eq. (20) for the one-phonon Raman scattering must now be modified and the result becomes

$$I^I_{\alpha\gamma\beta\delta} = P_{\alpha\gamma}(oj)_\gamma P_{\beta\delta}(oj) Im[G(ojj, \omega)]/(1 - \exp(-\beta\hbar\omega)) \qquad (61)$$

where the response function, $G(ojj, \omega)$, is given by

$$G(ojj, \omega) = \frac{2\omega(oj)}{\omega(oj)^2 + 2\omega(oj)(\Delta(ojj, \omega) + i\Gamma(ojj, \omega)) - \omega^2} \qquad (62)$$

If in these expressions Δ and Γ are small compared with $\omega(oj)$ and do not vary rapidly with ω, the effect of anharmonicity is to alter the measured frequencies by $\Delta(ojj, \omega(oj))$ and to give peaks of a Lorenzian shape and half-width, $\Gamma(ojj, \omega(oj))$. This is indeed a good approximation to the results of many experiments. The dependence of both Δ and Γ on the frequency may modify this conclusion however. In Fig. 18 are shown calculations of Δ and Γ for the Raman active mode in germanium (13). The shape of these curves is a reflection of the two-phonon density of states and the coefficients of the anharmonic expansion. The shape is quite different from that of the two phonon Raman scattering.

The frequency dependence of Δ and Γ causes the cross-sections to depart from a Lorenzian shape. This is shown most strikingly by calculations of the shape of the response function for the longitudinal optic mode of sodium iodide, as illustrated in Fig. 19 (53), and less dramatically by the calculated shapes of the spectra for the Raman active mode of germanium, Fig. 20 (13).

When there is more than one Raman active mode the theory must be modified (55,56). The response function is given by the matrix equation

$$\sum_{j'} \{[\omega(oj)^2 - \omega^2]\delta_{jj'} + 2\omega(oj)[\Delta(ojj', \omega) + i\Gamma(ojj', \omega)]\}G(oj' j'', \omega)$$

$$= 2\omega(oj)\delta_{jj''} \qquad (63)$$

and the one-phonon Raman scattering is given by

$$I^I_{\alpha\beta\gamma\delta} = \sum_{jj'} P_{\alpha\gamma}(oj)P_{\beta\delta}(oj') Im[G(ojj', \omega)]/(1 - \exp(-\beta\hbar\omega)) \qquad (64)$$

The importance of the coupling between the modes may be seen by evaluating $G(oj'j'', \omega)$ from Eq. (63) by perturbation theory as

$$G(ojj', \omega) = G(ojj, \omega)[\Delta(ojj', \omega) + i\Gamma(ojj', \omega)]G(oj'j', \omega) \qquad (65)$$

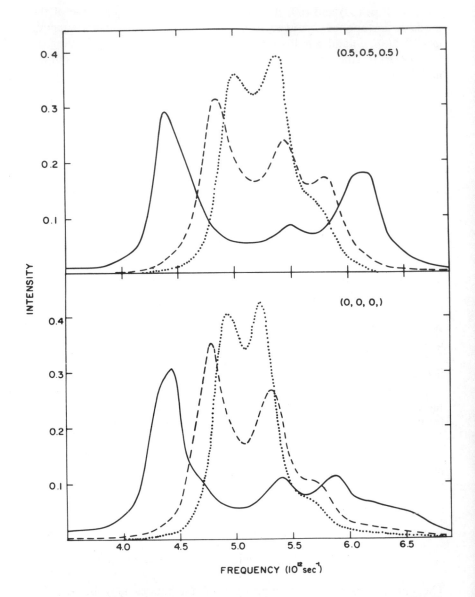

Fig. 19. The shapes of the response functions for the zone boundary (*111*) direction and $q = 0$ longitudinal optic modes in NaI: ..... = 5°K; –––– = 90°K; ––––– = 300°K. (Reprinted from Ref. *53*, p. 271.)

The terms $Im[G(ojj, \omega)]$ give a contribution to the Raman scattering which is roughly Lorentzian in shape about $\omega(oj) + \Delta[ojj, \omega(oj)]$. The cross product terms give a similar contribution from

$$Im[G(ojj, \omega)]\{\Delta(ojj', \omega)Re[G(oj'j', \omega)] - \Gamma(ojj', \omega)Im[G(oj'j', \omega)]\}$$

but a term which is asymmetric with respect to that frequency from the terms

$$Re[G(ojj, \omega)]\{\Delta(ojj', \omega)Im[G(oj'j', \omega)] + \Gamma(ojj', \omega)Re[G(oj'j', \omega)]\}$$

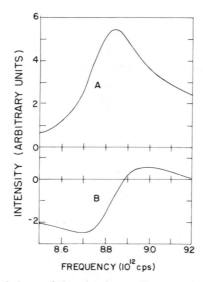

Fig. 20. The calculated shape of the one-phonon Raman scattering in germanium at 300°K. *A* is the one-phonon part and *B* arises from the mixing between one and two phonon processes. The scales for the different contributions are arbitrary. (Reprinted from Ref. *13*, p. 487.)

This term will act so as to alter the observed frequency of the peak and also its shape.

The response function enters into the calculation of the response of the mode, no matter what probe is used to study the crystal. When only one mode is Raman active the shape of the peak is identical with the shape observed by neutron scattering or by measurement of the imaginary part of the dielectric constant. When mixing between the modes j and j' is important, this is no longer the case, because the amplitude of the mixing depends on the relative sizes of the polarizability tensors for the different modes.

Symmetry shows that the modes will couple only if they belong to the same irreducible representation of the space group. The coupling occurs only between modes belonging to the same part of the Raman tensor, and there is no mixing between modes which contribute to different components of the Raman tensor.

C. Coupling between One and Two-Phonon Processes

In Section II.C we distinguished between one and two-phonon processes. In an anharmonic crystal this distinction becomes less meaningful, because it is possible to have processes in which one phonon is excited but then decays by the anharmonic interactions into two, which then interact with the photons again. The contribution of this term to the scattering was evaluated using standard techniques (17) as

$$
-\frac{6}{(1-\exp(-\beta\hbar\omega))} \sum_{jj'12} P_{\alpha\gamma}\binom{o}{j} P_{\beta\delta}(1\ 2) V\binom{o}{j'}, 1\ 2)
$$

$$
\times \left\{ Re[G(ojj', \omega)][(n_1+n_2+1)(\delta(\omega_1+\omega_2+\omega)-\delta(\omega_1+\omega_2-\omega)) \right.
$$

$$
+(n_2-n_1)(\delta(\omega_1-\omega_2+\omega)-\delta(\omega_1-\omega_2-\omega))]
$$

$$
+Im[G(ojj', \omega)]\left[\frac{n_1+n_2+1}{(\omega_1+\omega_2+\omega)_p} + \frac{n_1+n_2+1}{(\omega_1+\omega_2-\omega)_p} + \frac{n_2-n_1}{(\omega_1-\omega_2+\omega)_p} \right.
$$

$$
\left. \left. + \frac{n_2-n_1}{(\omega_1-\omega_2-\omega)_p} \right] \right\} \tag{66}
$$

The important feature of this term is that it contains a contribution which is asymmetric with respect to the peak of the one-phonon spectrum and another which is symmetric about that frequency. In an exactly similar manner to the case of mixing between the modes, the asymmetric term acts so as to shift the observed frequencies and to alter the shape of the spectrum in a manner which is dependent upon the polarizability and is therefore technique dependent. The spectra observed with different experimental techniques are therefore expected to give slightly different frequencies and shapes for the one-phonon peaks.

The contribution of the asymmetric term to the Raman active mode in germanium has been calculated (13) and is shown in Fig. 20. It is perhaps worth commenting that the importance of the mixing both among the phonons of zero wavevector and also with the multiphonon background increases as the temperature is increased.

The effect of anharmonicity on the two-phonon spectrum is less dramatic. It alters the locations of the critical points and tends to smooth out the discontinuities. It is very difficult to obtain information about anharmonic effects from the two-phonon spectra.

D. Experimental Results

The results of the calculations described above show that the widths of the one-phonon peaks are expected to be proportional to temperature, at high temperatures, and that the squares of the frequencies is likewise proportional to temperature. These predictions have been verified in a considerable number of experiments. Despite this qualitative agreement few quantitative calculations have been made of anharmonic effects which may be compared with Raman scattering results. The half-width of the optic mode in the diamond type of semiconductors has been studied and in Table 2 we compare the experimental results (58,59) with the

TABLE 2

Half-width (10^{12} Hz) of the Raman Active Mode in the Germanium Structure

Temp.	Experiment	Theory (60)	Theory (13)
Ge 300°K	0.069 (59)	0.123	0.21
Si 300°K	0.081 (59)	0.066	0.25
C 300°K	0.051 (58)		0.045
C 500°K	0.063 (58)		0.056
C 700°K	0.072 (58)		0.068
C 970°K	0.108 (58)		0.091

calculations of Klemens (60), and Dolling and Cowley (13). In the former calculations, the frequency spectrum is approximated to take account of the scattering only to the longitudinal acoustic modes and the anharmonic coefficient obtained by examining a linear chain with the aid of Gruneisen's approximation (5). In the latter calculations, a shell model was used to calculate the lattice frequencies and the anharmonic forces obtained by a comparison with the thermal expansion coefficient. The agreement between experiment and theory is somewhat worse than that obtained for the calculations of anharmonic effects in other crystals (53).

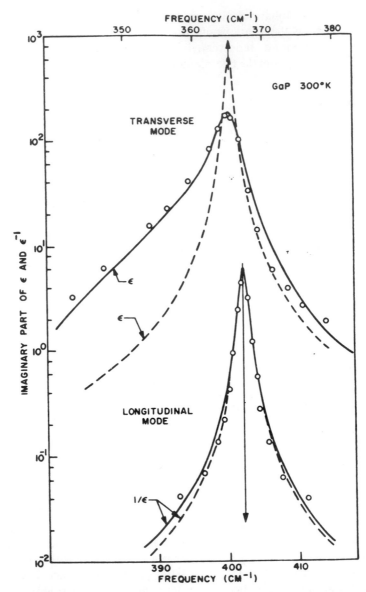

Fig. 21. The shapes of the Raman active modes of GaP at 300°K as measured (*35*) and calculated (*61*) using Γ and Δ independent of frequency, dotted line, and frequency dependent solid line: $\bigcirc$ = Raman data; $---$ = oscillator 2; $\underline{\quad\quad}$ = oscillator 3. (Reprinted from Ref. *61*, p. 919.)

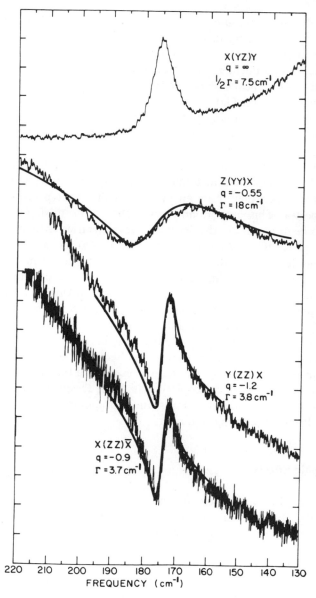

Fig. 22. The shape of the Raman scattering near one of the optic modes of $BaTiO_3$ for different polarizations of the light (62). The different tensor components are described by the symbols in brackets and are I_{yzyz}, I_{yyyy}, I_{zzzz} and I_{zzzz} respectively. (Reproduced from Ref. 62, p. 1356.)

Most likely this is because of the uncertainty in the nature of the inter-atomic forces in these crystals.

Some experimental evidence is now available which supports the need for frequency dependent Γ and Δ functions to explain the detailed shape of the one-phonon peaks. Barker (61) has interpreted the results of Henry and Hopfield (35) on GaP as evidence for the necessity of using a frequency dependent damping function, as shown in Fig. 21. The asymmetries arising from the mixing of the different one-phonon modes or from the mixing of the one- and two-phonon processes have been observed in $BaTiO_3$ by Rousseau and Porto (62), as shown in Fig. 22. These authors account for their results in terms of the one- and two-phonon mixing process for which they draw an analogy with Auger processes in electronic spectra. This author, however, believes the mixing between the modes to be important in the perovskite ferroelectrics as found in $SrTiO_3$ (63) and in $KTaO_3$ (64). Very recently Scott (65) has shown that some anomalous features of the Raman scattering in quartz may be understood on the basis of mixing between the one- and two-phonon processes. A particularly clear example of the anharmonic mixing of different one-phonon processes has been found in $AlPO_4$ by Scott (65a) and interpreted by Zawadowski and Ruvalds (65b).

The interpretation of the fine structure in the one-phonon Raman spectra is difficult. It may arise from the frequency dependence of the Δ and Γ functions or from the mixing processes, and the origin can only be settled by a detailed microscopic calculation. Despite these difficulties, the measurement of this structure is one of the more interesting developments in Raman scattering at present.

E. Morphic Effects

Morphic effects are the change in the Raman spectrum as a result of a force being applied to a crystal. The two most common types of forces are strains described by the strain parameters $\eta_{\alpha\beta}$, and electric fields described by E. There are two important effects which occur as a result of applying these forces. The first is the change in the frequencies of the normal modes which can then be studied with the aid of one-phonon scattering processes. The second arises when the force reduces the symmetry of the crystal so that modes which were not Raman active are now able to scatter photons.

The first of these effects is readily treated by the techniques already described. If a strain $\eta_{\alpha\beta}$, is applied to a crystal the change in the self-energy of a mode $(\mathbf{q}j)$ is given by

$$\Delta'(\mathbf{q}jj', \omega) = 2\left[V_{\alpha\beta}\begin{pmatrix} \mathbf{q} & -\mathbf{q} \\ j & j' \end{pmatrix} + \frac{3}{\hbar}\sum_{j''} V_{\alpha\beta}\begin{pmatrix} o \\ j'' \end{pmatrix} G(oj''j'', \omega) V\begin{pmatrix} o & \mathbf{q} & -\mathbf{q} \\ j'' & j & j' \end{pmatrix}\right]\eta_{\alpha\beta}$$
(67)

where the coefficients $V_{\alpha\beta}$ were defined in Eq. (58). The first term in Eq. (67) is a direct interaction of the strain with the modes, while in the second term the strain interacts with an optic mode which then influences the modes through anharmonicity. The second term is only present in piezo-electric crystals. Since the strains are usually sufficiently small that the effects are very small, it is adequate to neglect the off-diagonal terms in the self-energy.

A measurement of the change in the frequency with the applied stress is a direct measure of the coefficients and hence of the anharmonic parameters. More measurements of this type would be extremely useful in determining these largely unknown parameters. A further feature of the distortions is that they may split the degeneracy of certain modes of vibration. For example in germanium the triply degenerate Raman active mode is split by a η_{zz} strain into a doubly degenerate mode and a single mode and by a strain η_{xy} into three distinct modes. Furthermore these different modes may be distinguished by measuring the polarization of the scattered spectra.

The theory is similar for an applied electric field. The self-energy is given by

$$\Delta'(\mathbf{q}jj', \omega) = 2\sum_{\alpha}\left[M_{\alpha}\begin{pmatrix} \mathbf{q} & -\mathbf{q} \\ j & j' \end{pmatrix} + \frac{3}{\hbar}\sum_{j''} M_{\alpha}\begin{pmatrix} o \\ j'' \end{pmatrix} G(oj''j'', \omega) V\begin{pmatrix} o & \mathbf{q} & -\mathbf{q} \\ j'' & j & j' \end{pmatrix}\right]E$$
(68)

where the M coefficients are the expansion of the dielectric polarization in terms of the phonon coordinates. This term is only nonzero however for pyroelectric crystals. In the more symmetric crystals commonly studied there is no self-energy effect which is linear in the electric field. The self-energy in these cases is given by

$$\Delta'(\mathbf{q}jj, \omega) = \frac{24}{\hbar^2}\sum_{\alpha\beta j_1 j_2} G(oj_1 j_1, \omega) G(oj_2 j_2, \omega) M_{\alpha}\begin{pmatrix} o \\ j_1 \end{pmatrix} M_{\beta}\begin{pmatrix} o \\ j_2 \end{pmatrix}$$

$$\times V\begin{pmatrix} o & o & \mathbf{q} & -\mathbf{q} \\ j_1 & j_1 & j & j \end{pmatrix} E_{\alpha}E_{\beta}$$
(69)

where we have neglected the nonlinear dipole moments.

The alteration of the polarizabilities on applying a force is more difficult to calculate in detail. Despite this it is possible to deduce the effects by the use of symmetry. Suppose an electric field is applied to the cubic perovskite structure in the z direction (66). The symmetry of the crystal is lowered from the $m3m$ point group to the 4 mm point group. This is the symmetry of the distorted $BaTiO_3$ structure in which we

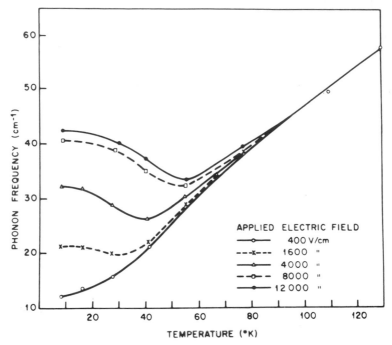

APPLIED ELECTRIC FIELD

──o──	400 V/cm
---x---	1600 "
──△──	4000 "
--o--	8000 "
──●──	12 000 "

Fig. 23. The temperature dependence of the transverse optic mode of lowest frequency in $SrTiO_3$ for various values of the applied electric field (68). (Reprinted from Ref. 68, p. 1178.)

found, Section III, that all the optic modes were Raman active. Consequently an electric field applied to the perovskite structure induces one-phonon Raman processes.

The same techniques may be used for discussing strains. An η_{zz} strain in the perovskite structure reduces the point group symmetry to 4/mmm. Since this is centrosymmetric, strains do not induce one-phonon processes in the perovskite structure.

One of the most elegant uses of morphic effects has been to study the optic modes of the cubic perovskite structure by applying an electric field. In these elegant experiments by Worlock and Fleury (67,68) the frequencies of the optic modes have been measured and their intensities shown to be proportional to the square of the electric field. Furthermore in $SrTiO_3$ at low temperatures they have been able to measure the electric field dependence of the mode of lowest frequency as shown in Fig. 23. This provides a direct measure of the anharmonic coupling coefficients associated with this mode. In summary morphic effects provide a way of studying modes which are not usually Raman active and also of determining anharmonic parameters directly.

F. Brillouin Scattering

The effect of anharmonicity on the Brillouin scattering region requires some careful consideration. This is because it is necessary to take account of the finite wavevector transfer and the small frequency transfer. Consider the limit as both frequency transfer, ω, and wavevector transfer, $\mathbf{Q}$, approach zero, of both the two-phonon cross-section (Eq. 22) and also of the one-phonon self-energy (Eq. 59 and 60). In the former there are terms of the form

$$(n_1+n_2+1)[\delta(\omega_1+\omega_2-\omega)-\delta(\omega_1+\omega_2+\omega)]+(n_2-n_1)[\delta(\omega_1-\omega_2-\omega)$$
$$-\delta(\omega_1-\omega_2+\omega)] \tag{70}$$

where the suffix (1) denotes $(\mathbf{q}_1 j_1)$ and (2) denotes $(\mathbf{q}_2 j_2)$ where $\mathbf{q}_2 = -\mathbf{q}_1 + \mathbf{Q}$. The contribution of these terms when both $\mathbf{Q}$ and ω are small can now be evaluated. The phonon summation term gives a small contribution because ω_1 and $\omega_2 \gg \omega$ for most of the phonons. The second term, however, gives a large contribution if $j_1 = j_2$. The contribution is

$$\beta\hbar n_1(n_1+1)C_1(\mathbf{Q})[\delta(C_1(\mathbf{Q})-v(\mathbf{Q}))-\delta(C_1(\mathbf{Q})+v(\mathbf{Q}))] \tag{71}$$

where $C_1(\mathbf{Q})$ is the gradient with respect to the direction of the momentum transfer, $\mathbf{Q} \cdot \nabla\omega(\mathbf{q}_1 j_1)/|\mathbf{Q}|$ and $v(\mathbf{Q})$ is the velocity of the probe which in Raman scattering is $\omega/|\mathbf{Q}|$. This result and the corresponding result for the self-energy of the phonons are dependent on the probe velocity, and alter with the ratio $\omega/|\mathbf{Q}|$, even as ω and $|\mathbf{Q}|$ tend to zero. This is clearly an unphysical result since the cross-section will have a unique value in this limit. The difficulty arises because, in the derivation of the two-phonon cross-section and of the self-energies, no account was taken of the lifetime of the phonons $(\mathbf{q}_1 j_1)$ and $(\mathbf{q}_2 j_2)$. The result therefore is valid only so long as $\omega \gg \Gamma(\mathbf{q}_1 j_1)$ and $\Gamma(\mathbf{q}_2 j_2)$ where Γ is the half-width or inverse lifetime of the modes. The results we have developed above are valid only in the collisionless régime in which the frequency, ω, is sufficiently small that few collisions occur between the phonons within one period, $1/\omega$.

In this collisionless régime it is of interest to point out some of the features. The two-phonon scattering is probe velocity dependent and also direction dependent, since $\nabla\omega(\mathbf{q}_1 j_1)$ is directional. The self-energy of the phonons is similarly singular as ω and $|\mathbf{Q}|$ become small. This leads to the elastic waves having only the point group symmetry of the crystal and not the further symmetry imposed by the fourth rank tensor properties of the macroscopic elastic constants (69). The width of the sound waves is proportional to temperature but does not depend on their frequency, in agreement with the result of Landau and Rumer (70).

When the frequency, ω, becomes much less then the inverse lifetime of the thermal phonons, $\Gamma(\mathbf{q}_1 j_1)$, many collisions occur within each period of the wave, and the propagation is known as thermodynamic or collision dominated. When approached from our point of view there are two effects which occur in this region. One is a modification of Eq. 71 to take account of the finite lifetime, while the other is the effect of the oscillations in the local temperature. The theory has been developed (71,72) to treat these both as arising from phonon collisions, but since these results are obtained only by summing a set of ladder diagrams to produce the phonon Boltzmann equation, we shall assume the Boltzmann equation and follow the approach of Guyer, Krumhansl and Cowley (73,69).

The modification to the results of Eq. (70) to incorporate the finite width $\Gamma(\mathbf{q}_1 j_1)$ may be obtained by the use of many body techniques to give

$$\frac{\beta\hbar\omega}{\pi} n_1(n_1+1)/\Gamma(\mathbf{q}_1 j_1) \tag{72}$$

This result shows that the width of the elastic wave is independent of temperature at high temperatures and proportional to ω, as found initially by Akhiezer (74). Notice the contrast with the results for the collisionless region. The corresponding contribution to the real part of the self-energy, Δ, is zero, showing that there is a difference between the velocities of sound in the collisionless and collision dominated regimes (67). This difference has recently been found experimentally (75) in potassium bromide with neutron scattering techniques, as shown in Fig. 24. It is also worth noting that the symmetry of Eq. (72) is consistent with the symmetry of the elastic constants.

The inclusion of the width of the phonons removes the difficulties with the two-phonon scattering. In the collisionless region it was velocity dependent and inversely proportional to ω for constant velocity, whereas in the thermodynamic region the singular behavior is removed and the intensity is independent of probe velocity.

So far in these considerations we have neglected the effect of the local temperature changes in the thermodynamic régime. The results therefore refer to crystals under isothermal conditions. The thermal strain, $\eta_{\alpha\beta}$, of a crystal arises from the leading term in the expansion (58) in terms of strains and phonon coordinates. The contribution to the free energy is

$$\sum_{\alpha\beta} \sum_{1} V_{\alpha\beta}(1\ 1)(2n_1+1)\eta_{\alpha\beta} \tag{73}$$

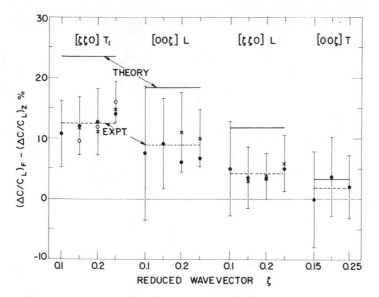

Fig. 24. The difference between the temperature dependence of the velocities of sound in the thermodynamic régime and in the collisionless régime (75) for different elastic waves in KBr.

If the local temperature changes by T_1 due to a strain $\eta_{\gamma\delta}$ the extra contribution to the free energy,

$$2\sum_{\alpha\beta} \sum_{1} V_{\alpha\beta}(1\ 1)n_1(n_1+1)\frac{\hbar\omega_1}{k_B T^2}T_1\eta_{\alpha\beta} \tag{74}$$

is quadratic in the strain parameters and so contributes to the elastic constants. The change in temperature, T_1, must be expressed in terms of the strains by the use of the phonon Boltzmann equation,

$$\frac{\delta n_1}{\delta t} + \nabla \omega_1 \cdot \nabla n_1 = (N+R)n_1$$

where N and R are the momentum conserving and nonmomentum conserving collision operators. The phonon density is expanded in terms of the strain, local temperature, and net flow of phonons as

$$n_1 = [\exp\{(\hbar\omega_1 - \lambda \cdot \hbar\mathbf{q}_1 + 2\sum_{\alpha\beta} V_{\alpha\beta}(1\,1)\eta_{\alpha\beta})/k_B(T+T_1)\} - 1]^{-1}$$

This equation is substituted into the phonon Boltzmann equation and the result linearized and used to derive the equations for local conservation of energy and momentum as

$$i\omega C_V T_1 - i\mathbf{Q} \cdot \lambda L = i\omega \sum_{\alpha\beta} M_{\alpha\beta}\eta_{\alpha\beta} \tag{75}$$

$$-i\mathbf{Q} R T_1 + \left(i\omega Y + \frac{1}{\tau}\right)\lambda = -i\mathbf{Q} \sum_{\alpha\beta} Z_{\alpha\beta}\eta_{\alpha\beta} \tag{76}$$

respectively.

C_V is the specific heat of the crystal, τ is a function of the collision operators (73) and the other constants have been simplified to apply only to cubic crystals and are

$$L = \sum n(n+1)\beta\hbar^2\omega q_\alpha \frac{\delta\omega}{\delta q_\alpha}$$

$$R = \frac{1}{T}\sum n(n+1)\beta\hbar^2\omega q_\alpha \frac{\delta\omega}{\delta q_\alpha}$$

$$Y = \sum n(n+1)\beta\hbar^2 q_\alpha^2$$

$$M_{\alpha\beta} = 2\sum n(n+1)\beta\hbar^2\omega V_{\alpha\beta}(1\,1)$$

$$Z_{\alpha\beta} = 2\sum n(n+1)\beta\hbar^2 q_\gamma \frac{\delta\omega}{\delta q\gamma} V_{\alpha\beta}(1\,1)$$

where we have dropped the suffices denoting the mode (1) on n, ω, and q. Equations (75) and (76) can now be solved to obtain an equation for T_1 in terms of $\eta_{\alpha\beta}$ which may be substituted back into Eq. (74) to obtain the change in the elastic constants due to the temperature fluctuations. The result for a longitudinal mode in a cubic centrosymmetric crystal is

$$\frac{M_{\alpha\alpha}}{T}\left[\frac{i\omega M_{\alpha\alpha}\left(i\omega Y + \frac{1}{\tau}\right) + Q^2 L Z_{\alpha\alpha}}{Q^2 L R - C_V Y \omega^2 + i\omega C_V/\tau}\right] \tag{77}$$

This term gives rise to both a change in the velocity and the attenuation. When the frequency is small and Q correspondingly small the change in the velocity is

$$\frac{1}{T} M_{\alpha\alpha}^2 / C_V$$

which is the well known difference between the adiabatic and isothermal elastic constants, and the attenuation of the sound wave arises from the thermal conductivity of the medium.

The denominator of Eq. (77) has some interesting properties. At large Q but small ω it gives rise to a Lorentzian peak τ about $\omega = 0$ with a half-width given by $LR\tau/C_V$. In thermodynamic terms this is the thermal conductivity divided by the specific heat and is the diffusion peak, well known in the theory of liquids. It may be shown to have an intensity of order $(C_p/C_V - 1)$ compared with the intensity of the elastic waves. At larger frequencies it may happen that $\omega Y \gg 1/\tau$. The denominator then has a singularity when the velocity is $(LR/C_V Y)^{\frac{1}{2}}$, and gives rise to the second sound mode which also has an intensity proportional to $(C_p/C_V - 1)$. The possibility of detecting this mode by Raman scattering was first pointed out by Griffin (76).

As yet we have said nothing about the size of the different regions. The $\Gamma(\mathbf{q}_1 j_1)$ is typically about 10^9 Hz at helium temperatures and 10^{11} Hz at several Debye temperatures. Brillouin scattering is, therefore, an excellent tool for studying the difference between the velocities in the zero and first sound regions. As yet neither the second sound mode nor the diffusive peak have been detected by Brillouin scattering in crystals. Both experiments are very difficult as it is necessary to suppress the elastically scattered light from imperfections as much as possible. Also the second sound mode requires low temperatures, so that $1/\tau$ is small (few Umklapp processes), but also high ω without destroying the local thermodynamic equilibrium. In practice it has been detected only by heat pulse techniques in solid helium (77). Despite these difficulties Brillouin scattering should play a very important role in studying these phenomena and also of investigating the interesting intermediate region.

Recently Griffin (78) has pointed out that the intensity of light scattered by the Stokes and anti-Stokes lines in Brillouin scattering should be altered when heat is flowing down a specimen. The result of thermodynamic effects might be even more pronounced in the two-phonon Raman scattering in the Brillouin scattering region. No experiments have as yet been reported on either of these topics.

G. Ferroelectricity

A ferroelectric crystal is one which shows a spontaneous electric polarization which is easily reversed by application of an electric field. Most ferroelectrics have a phase transition below which they are ferroelectric but above which they are paraelectric. The static dielectric constant of the crystal has an anomalous behavior above the transition as given by

$$\varepsilon = \frac{C}{T - T_c} \tag{78}$$

where C is the Curie constant and T_c the transition temperature. Anderson (79) and Cochran (80) pointed out this behavior may be understood as an instability of the crystal against an optic mode of long wavelength the square of whose frequency is given by

$$\omega_T^2 = K(T - T_c) \tag{79}$$

with K a constant. At the phase transition the crystal becomes unstable against this mode of vibration and distorts to a new structure. Many experiments have now been performed which have verified Eq. (79). In particular for the perovskites, $SrTiO_3$ and $KTaO_3$, experiments have been performed by neutron scattering (81,82), infrared spectroscopy (83,84), and Raman scattering (67,68). The latter applied an electric field to induce one-phonon Raman activity in the perovskite structure as described above in Section E.

The behavior of this mode in $SrTiO_3$ has been understood in terms of the anharmonic interactions. It is seen from Eq. (60) that the shift, Δ, increases at high temperatures proportionally with temperature. Consequently the observed square of the frequency is given by

$$\omega(oj)^2 + 2\omega(oj)\Delta(ojj, \omega(oj))$$

from which we find that if $\Delta(ojj, \omega(oj)) = \delta T$, then

$$K = 2\delta\omega(oj)$$

$$T_c = -\frac{\omega(oj)}{2\delta}$$

This theory has been tested in a semiquantitative manner (63) and found to give a reasonable description of $SrTiO_3$.

More recently studies have been made of materials with higher Curie temperatures. Not surprisingly the widths, Γ, are then much larger and the form of the Raman scattering is quite different. At frequency

$$\omega \ll \frac{k_\beta T}{\hbar}$$

the Raman scattering cross-section is given approximately by Eq. (64).

$$\sum_j P_{\alpha\gamma}(oj)P_{\beta\delta}(oj)\frac{k_\beta T}{\hbar\omega}I_m[G(ojj, \omega)]$$

At low frequencies and high temperatures the width of the phonons is proportional to ω,

$$\Gamma(ojj, \omega) = \gamma\omega,$$

The cross section then becomes for a single mode

$$P_{\alpha\gamma}(oj)P_{\beta\delta}(oj)\frac{k_\beta T}{\hbar}\frac{4\omega(oj)^2\gamma}{(\omega(oj)^2+2\omega(oj)\Delta(ojj, o)-\omega^2)^2+4\omega^2\gamma^2}$$

This result shows that if γ is sufficiently large that $\omega^4 \ll \omega^2\gamma^2$ the intensity becomes

$$P_{\alpha\gamma}(oj)P_{\beta\delta}(oj)\frac{k_\beta T}{\hbar}\frac{4\omega(oj)^2\gamma}{k^2(T-T_c)^2+4\omega^2\gamma^2} \tag{80}$$

This expression describes a Lorentzian curve whose width at half height is $K(T-T_c)/\gamma$, and decreases as $T \to T_c$. This decrease in width is the critical slowing down of the fluctuations on approaching the transition. This result, Eq. 80, has been used to describe the Raman scattering results on $BaTiO_3$ (85,86) and on KDP (87); the result for KDP is shown in Fig. 25.

The Brillouin scattering of piezoelectric crystals is also modified near a ferroelectric phase transition. Well above the transition the electric polarization responds rapidly to the elastic wave and follows it so as to modify its frequency. However, close to the ferroelectric transitions the fluctuations in the electric polarization slow down and are no longer able to follow the elastic wave. The velocity of the wave then alters as found by Gammon and Cummins (88) in Tri Glycine Sulphate, and as shown in Fig. 26 (pages 163 and 164).

Raman scattering has also been used to study phase transitions in which the mode in the high temperature phase is not Raman active. In the distorted phase the crystal symmetry is decreased and a new, strongly temperature-dependent mode appears. In this way the unstable mode at the antiferroelectric transition of $SrTiO_3$ (89) has been identified.

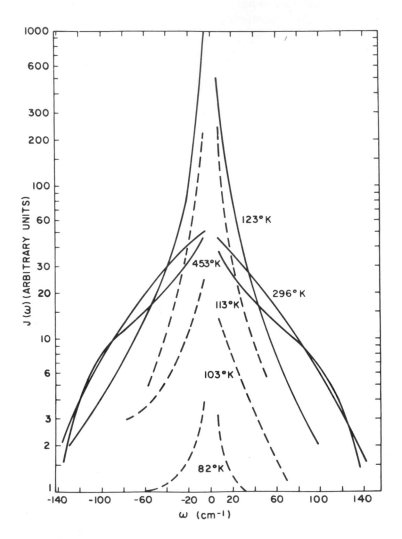

Fig. 25. The I_{xyxy} component of the Raman tensor in KH_2PO_4 as a function of temperature (86). Note the narrowing and increase in the intensity at $\omega - 0$ as the transition 122°K is approached —— $= T > T_c$; $- - - - = T < T_c$. (Reproduced from Ref. 87, p. 1105.)

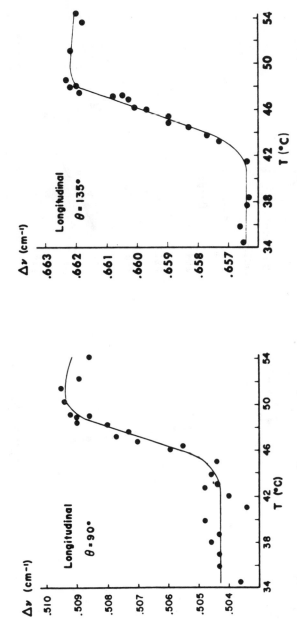

Fig. 26. The change in the frequency of the Brillouin scattered radiation as a function of temperature in TGS (87) longitudinal and transverse components at scattering angles of 90° and 135°. (Reproduced from Ref. 88, p. 194.)

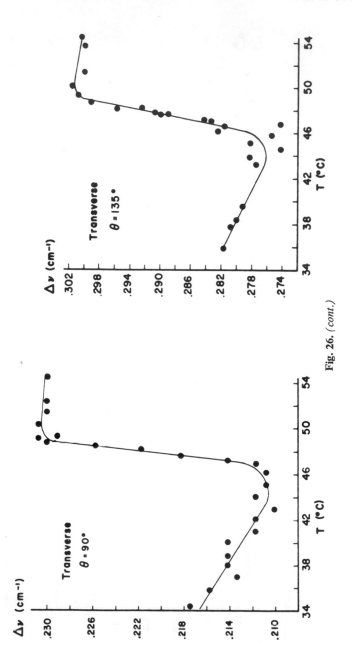

Fig. 26. (cont.)

VII. DEFECTS IN CRYSTALS

A. Theory of Lattice Vibrations

The introduction of defects into crystals considerably modifies the properties of the normal modes of vibration. The changes have been the subject of several excellent reviews, the most recent of which is by Maradudin (90), and so we shall only briefly review the results here. In Section VI.B we introduced the response function of a normal mode $(\mathbf{q}j)$. We shall use similar techniques to evaluate the change in self-energy of the mode due to the defect. There is one large difference, however, and this arises because a defect is localized at a particular lattice site. The wavevector is not conserved and so the perturbation is written as

$$\sum_{\substack{\mathbf{q}_1\mathbf{q}_2 \\ j_1 j_2}} C\left(\frac{\mathbf{q}_1\mathbf{q}_2}{j_1 j_2}\right) A(\mathbf{q}_1 j_1) A(\mathbf{q}_2 j_2) \tag{81}$$

where C is the change in the Hamiltonian due to the defect, and we have restricted consideration to the harmonic approximation. If we consider a single defect, then the coefficients may be directly evaluated and for a mass change of δM at the site (lk)

$$C(12) = \frac{1}{N}\left(\frac{\hbar^2}{4\omega_1\omega_2}\right)^{\frac{1}{2}} \frac{\delta M\omega^2}{M_k} \, e(k \mid 1)\cdot e(k \mid 2) \exp i\,(\mathbf{q}_1+\mathbf{q}_2)\cdot\mathbf{R}\,(lk)$$

whereas for a force change $\Delta\phi_{\alpha\beta}$ between the ions $(l_1 k_1)$ and $(l_2 k_2)$ the coefficient is

$$C(12) = \frac{1}{N}\left(\frac{\hbar^2}{4\omega_1\omega_2 M_{k_1}M_{k_2}}\right)^{\frac{1}{2}} \sum_{\alpha\beta}\Delta\phi_{\alpha\beta}e_\alpha(k_1\mid l_1)e_\beta(k_2\mid l_2)$$

$$\exp\,(i\mathbf{q}_1\cdot\mathbf{R}(l_1 k_1)+i\mathbf{q}_2\cdot\mathbf{R}(l_2 k_2))$$

The self-energy of the phonon arising from this perturbation can be evaluated from the equation of motion of the harmonic response function. The result is shown schematically in Fig. 27 for a single defect, and given explicitly by Maradudin (90) and by Elliott and Taylor (91), for example. Fortunately, for a mass defect in a cubic monatomic crystal, the result for the self-energy is relatively simple

$$\sum (\mathbf{q}jj, \omega) = \frac{\delta M\omega^2}{2M\omega(\mathbf{q}j)[1+\delta M\omega^2 K(\omega)]} \tag{82}$$

where

$$K(\omega) = \frac{1}{MN} \sum \frac{1}{\omega^2 - \omega(\mathbf{q}j)^2} \qquad (83)$$

and M is the host mass. The change in the real and imaginary parts of the self-energy, Δ and Γ in the notation used above, are obtained by allowing ω to be complex and taking the limit as ω approaches the real axis.

Most of the features of interest are exhibited by Eq. (82). If there is a very light mass defect, δM is negative and the denominator of Eq. (82) is singular at the frequency defined by

$$1 = -\delta M\omega^2 K(\omega)$$

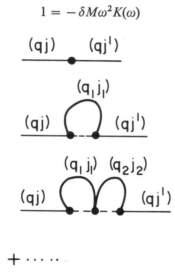

Fig. 27. A schematic diagram showing the self-energy $\Sigma(\mathbf{q}jj', \omega)$ resulting from the introduction of a single defect. The terms show successive orders of perturbation theory.

This is the local mode frequency and there will be a response or contribution to the scattering at this frequency. Besides this contribution, the response function, $G(\mathbf{q}jj, \omega)$, has an imaginary part whenever $K(\omega)$ has an imaginary part. The imaginary part of $K(\omega)$ is dependent on the frequency distribution of the host crystal. The one-phonon Raman scattering consists in this case of the normal one-phonon Raman scattering and superimposed on that the scattering from the local mode and induced scattering from all of the other phonons.

If the mass defect is heavier than the host crystal, δM is positive, and Eq. (82) has a smaller denominator when ω lies within the spectrum of the host crystal. This enhancement is known as a resonant mode because the self-energy goes through a resonance at this frequency. The one-phonon Raman scattering under these circumstances does not show a local mode but a very much enhanced induced one-phonon effect at the frequency of the resonant mode.

The extension of the theory to include a finite concentration of defects is straightforward if only those terms linear in the concentration are required (*91*). Beyond this approximation little work has been performed, and the theory becomes exceedingly cumbersome.

B. Raman Scattering

The discussion of Section VII,A deduced the self-energy and hence the expression for the one-phonon response functions, $G(\mathbf{q}jj', \omega)$ of Eq. (63). If the defect does not alter the polarizability of the crystal the Raman scattering is given by Eq. (61) as for the anharmonic effects. This theory is applicable directly to the case of isotopic defects; however, since $\delta M/M$ is normally small for isotopic defects, these examples give small effects. In practice it is more usual to substitute a different ion in which case the mass, force constants, and polarizability alter. The force constant change is readily incorporated, at least formally into the discussion above, but the polarizability change requires further discussion. Suppose the defect introduces an additional polarizability $\delta P_{\alpha\beta}$. This additional polarizability may be expanded in atomic displacements to give rise to one-phonon Raman scattering dependent on the correlations of the defect atom (ok) with all the others

$$I_{\alpha\gamma\beta\sigma} = \sum_{\substack{l'k' \\ \lambda_1\lambda_2}} \delta P_{\alpha\gamma,\lambda_1}\binom{o}{k} P_{\beta\sigma,\lambda_2}\binom{l'}{k'} \langle\langle U_{\lambda_1}(ok)U_{\lambda_2}(l'k')\rangle\rangle$$

and on the correlation of the defect atom with itself

$$\sum_{\lambda_1\lambda_2} \delta P_{\alpha\gamma,\lambda_1}\binom{o}{k} \delta P_{\alpha\gamma,\lambda_2}\binom{l'}{k'} \langle\langle U_{\lambda_1}(ok)U_{\lambda_2}(ok)\rangle\rangle$$

Whereas in the calculation of the response functions performed above all of the atoms were treated on an equal basis, these new correlation functions select out the defect atoms. When this additional polarizability is included, the cross-section is modified, and the final result for $I_{\alpha\alpha\alpha\alpha}$ in a cubic monatomic crystal with concentration c of mass defects may be written schematically as (91)

$$Im\left[\left(P+\frac{c\delta P}{1+\delta M\omega^2 K(\omega)}\right)^2 G(ojj, \omega)\right]+Im\left[\left(\frac{c\delta P^2}{1+\delta M\omega^2 K(\omega)}\right)K(\omega)\right]$$

This expression shows that the change in the polarizability further enhances the scattering in the region of the local modes or resonant modes. This modification alters the shape of the induced one-phonon spectrum considerably.

C. Theoretical Calculations

The introduction of defects into two systems has been extensively discussed theoretically. In the case of alkali halides the introduction of a mass defect does not give rise to any change in the one-phonon Raman scattering. This is because the defect is at a center of symmetry, and so its vibrations cannot influence the Raman tensor, while the electronic structure of the neighbors is unaltered. In practice a substitutional defect in the alkali halides alters the neighboring ions, because the polarizability coefficients $P_{\alpha\beta,\gamma}\begin{pmatrix}l\\k\end{pmatrix}$ of the neighbors are then nonzero. This gives rise to induced one-phonon Raman scattering. However the local mode, if it exists, has Γ_{25} symmetry and so is not Raman active. The induced one-phonon scattering has been calculated for H^- ions in KCl by Nguyen Xuan Xinh et al. (92). It is worth commenting that the spectra are different for the different components of the Raman tensor. A measurement of the different components enables many of the features to be assigned to particular features in the host lattice spectrum; group theory is of considerable assistance in this.

In the diamond structure the crystals have one-phonon processes allowed in the absence of defects. Nguyen Xuan Xinh (90) has computed the spectrum expected from defects in Si. The results show a considerable amount of structure which it would be interesting to observe experimentally. Recently Maradudin et al. (93) have shown that Raman scattering measurements combined with the application of electric fields or strains to a crystal containing defects can give useful information about the coupling of the defects to the lattice.

VIII. SCATTERING BY ELECTRONIC EXCITATIONS

A. Free Electrons

The polarizability of a single free electron is determined by the classical radius of the electron

$$P_{\alpha\beta} = r_o \delta_{\alpha\beta}$$

where

$$r_o = e^2/mc^2$$

The electronic scattering by many electrons may be calculated in a similar manner to that employed for the phonon case as (94)

$$I_{\alpha\gamma\beta\delta} = \delta_{\alpha\gamma}\,\delta_{\beta\delta}r_o^2 \int_{-\infty}^{\infty} \exp\,(i\omega t)\,\langle\langle\rho(\mathbf{Q},\,t)\rho^+(\mathbf{Q},\,o)\rangle\rangle\,dt$$

where $\rho(\mathbf{Q})$ is the electron density operator. The electron density operator may be calculated using the techniques described by Pines (37) and the result for free electrons is

$$I_{\alpha\gamma\beta\delta} = \delta_{\alpha\gamma}\delta_{\beta\delta}\,\frac{r_o^2|\,\mathbf{Q}^2\,|}{4\pi e^2}\,Im\left[\frac{1}{\varepsilon(\mathbf{Q},\,\omega)}\right]\Big/(\exp\,(\beta\hbar\omega)-1) \qquad (84)$$

The expressions for the dielectric constant are given by Pines (37) and for the cases of $\varepsilon(o,\,\omega)$ and $\varepsilon(\mathbf{Q},\,o)$ are given in Section IV,C.

Numerical estimates of the size of these expressions suggests that they are very small. Considerable enhancement may occur in practice under conditions of an almost resonant Raman effect. The cross section is then enhanced by a factor (95)

$$\frac{E_G^2}{E_G^2 - (\hbar\omega_o)^2}$$

where E_G is the band gap. For suitable choices of laser radiation and semiconductors this can be made very large. In practice it is also necessary to allow for the real band structure of the electrons in the lightly doped semiconductors and for the coupling between the lattice and the electrons as described in Section IV,C. The results of this have been given by Mooradian and McWhorter (43) and are shown to give agreement with their experiments on GaAs. The coupled phonon–plasmon modes shown in Fig. 12, are expected on the basis of the phonon polarizability to have $I_{xxxx} = 0$, and I_{xyxy} finite. However the electronic polarizability has I_{xxxx} finite and $I_{xyxy} = 0$. In their experiments they observe the coupled phonon–plasmon modes in both the I_{xxxx} and I_{xyxy} components showing that both mechanisms are important. Furthermore, they show that the cross sections agree qualitatively with those predicted theoretically.

More recently Mooradian (*96*) has extended these measurements to study the single-particle excitations and their contribution to the $Im(1/\varepsilon(\mathbf{Q}, \omega))$. These excitations correspond to exciting an electron from just below the Fermi surface to just above, and occur for all frequencies less than QV_F, where V_F is the Fermi velocity. The results of Mooradian's experiment confirms the presence of these excitations, but the scattering appears to be several orders of magnitude stronger than expected.

When a large magnetic field is applied to the semiconductors at low temperature, the free electrons alter their energy, so that the area of the electron orbit perpendicular to the magnetic field satisfies the quantization condition (*97*). The energy of the electron is then dependent on the Landau level number, λ, the momentum parallel to the magnetic field, p_z, and the spin direction, S_z. For free electrons the energy is given by

$$\varepsilon(P_z, \lambda, S_z) = (\lambda + \tfrac{1}{2})\hbar\omega_c + P_z^2/2m + \mu_\beta g S_z H$$

where ω_c is the cyclotron frequency, μ_β is the Bohr magneton and g the gyromagnetic factor. The scattering from a crystal in an applied magnetic field may be calculated by evaluating the dielectric constant and substituting the result into Eq. (84). The dielectric constant for free electrons in a magnetic field has been evaluated by Blank and Kaner (*98*). Fortunately, however, the qualitative aspects are fairly easily seen (*95*). The photons are able to scatter the electrons from one Landau level to the next or from one spin level to the same Landau level but with opposite spin. The frequency transfers are given by

$$\omega = \pm m\omega_c$$

$$\omega = \pm 2\mu_\beta g H$$

where m is any positive integer. Slusher, Patel, and Fleury (*99*) have observed this type of scattering involving transitions in InSb corresponding to $\omega = \omega_c$, $2\omega_c$ and $2\mu_\beta g H$; results are shown in Fig. 28. These measurements enable the cyclotron resonance frequency and the effective g values of the electrons to be measured. The advantage of using Raman scattering techniques over the conventional resonance techniques is that the frequencies may be much higher and consequently the purity of the sample is less critical and the temperature need not be so low.

The dielectric constant is also altered when a metal becomes superconducting. An energy gap in the spectrum of the single particle excitations occurs and may be observed in the far infrared spectrum (*100*). The theory of the Raman scattering has been worked out for this case by Abrikosov and Fal'kovskii (*101*) and Khaikin and Bykov (*102*) made an unsuccessful attempt to look for it in lead. However, laser techniques make the experiment well worth repeating, possibly with a semiconducting superconductor.

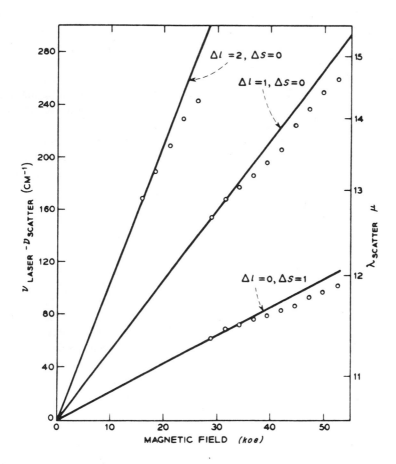

Fig. 28. The magnetic field dependence of the frequencies of the light scattered by electrons in Landau levels (*99*). The experiments were conducted at 30°K with *n* type InSb. The Δl change is the change in Landau level and Δs the change in spin; magnetic field dependence of wavelength of scattered light for the spin-flip, $\Delta l = 1$, and $\Delta l = 2$ process, taken in *n*-InSb ($n_e = 5 \times 10^{16} \text{cm}^{-3}$,. (Reproduced from Ref. *99*, p. 78.)

B. Magnons

Raman scattering by magnons was first discussed in 1960 by Bass and Kaganov (*103*) and is excellently reviewed by Fleury and Loudon (*104*).

There has been considerable discussion of the mechanism of the process ever since that time, although the basic phenomenology has been clear. An excellent review of magnons is given by Kittel (*105*). In a one-magnon process the frequency change, ω, of the light is equal to that of a long wavelength magnon. In ferromagnetic materials in which the anisotropy is low, the magnon dispersion curve is rapidly varying with wavevector at wavevectors of the order of the momentum transfer. The scattering is then analogous to Brillouin scattering. In most antiferromagnetic crystals the anisotropy is sufficiently large that one-magnon Raman scattering gives the frequency of the $q = 0$ magnon, which may also be measured by infrared or neutron scattering techniques.

In crystals with more than one type of magnetic excitation, either ferromagnets or crystals such as Co^{2+} salts having low lying orbital states, the Raman scattering can in principle measure the frequencies of all of the $q = 0$ excitations, unless the scattering is forbidden by the symmetry. Group theory may be used as in the phonon case to assist with the assignment of the observed Raman lines. The two-magnon scattering occurs in an exactly similar manner to that for phonons at the frequencies of pairs of magnons of equal but opposite wavevectors.

The original mechanism proposed by Bass and Kaganov (*103*) was that the spins of the ions are coupled to the magnetic fields of the incident and scattered light waves. Symmetry shows that in the case of one-magnon processes in simple magnetic materials the magnetic polarizability is zero except for the (xz) and (yz) components. The spin direction of the wholly aligned crystal is the z direction. Later a different mechanism was suggested by Elliott and Loudon (*106*) and is more analogous to the phonon mechanism. The electric vector of the light creates transitions from the ground orbital state to an excited orbital state; this then decays to the excited magnon state. Symmetry in this case shows the electric polarizability to be nonzero only for the P_{xz} and P_{yz} components.

The one-magnon Raman scattering has been observed in FeF_2 as shown in Fig. 29 (*107*). The symmetry of the scattering was measured in this experiment and found to be consistent with the mechanism proposed by Elliott and Loudon (*106*), and furthermore, order of magnitude estimates (*104*) suggest that this latter mechanism gives cross sections of about 10^3 times greater than the direct magnetic coupling.

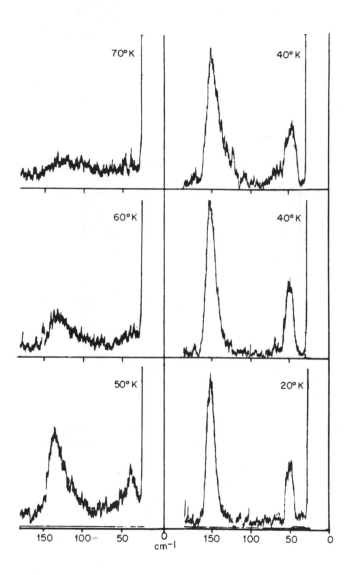

Fig. 29. The Raman scattering from FeF_2 as a function of temperature (*107*). Recorder traces show frequency shifts of Stokes scattered light in the (*zy*) experimental geometry for various temperatures in FeF_2. The lines at ~ 52 and $\sim 154\,cm^{-1}$ are due to photons scattered by one and two magnons, respectively. (Reproduced from Ref. *107*, p. 85.)

A surprising feature of the scattering in FeF_2, Fig. 29, is that the two-magnon peak is stronger than the one-magnon peak. This is very different from the behavior of phonons, and a new mechanism has been proposed (*108*) to explain this and the analogous result in the infrared spectrum. An electron on one magnetic ion is excited by the light to an excited orbital state. There is an exchange interaction by which the electron returns to an excited spin wave state and an electron on a neighboring ion is

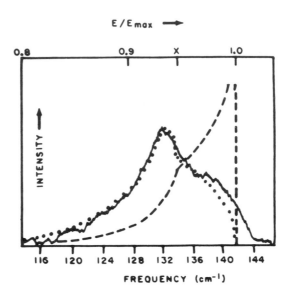

Fig. 30. Two-magnon scattering in $RbMnF_3$ at 10°K (*110*). The solid line shows the experimental results. The dashed curve is a calculation made neglecting magnon-magnon interactions while the dotted curve included them. (Reproduced from Ref. *110*, p. 151.)

excited. The light is then emitted and the second electron returns to another spin wave state. The polarizability on this theory has been parameterized and used to calculate the two-magnon spectrum of $RbMnF_3$ as shown in Fig. 30 (*109*). This mechanism is certainly consistent with the symmetry of the scattering, and also explains its enhanced magnitude.

The shape of the two-magnon spectrum in $RbMnF_3$ as calculated by the above theory is not very satisfactory when compared with the experimental results (*110*). The origin of this discrepancy has been pointed out by

Elliott et al. (*111*). The two magnons are created on neighboring sites which interact with each other because the exchange coupling is of a local nature and is not quadratic in the spin wave variables. The magnon–magnon interaction then modifies the shape of the spectrum to give the result shown in Fig. 30 which is in excellent agreement with experiment.

In short, Raman scattering by magnons has clarified the origin of the interaction, and now experiments should be done to study both the one and two-magnon processes. This would provide information both about magnon frequencies and about magnon–magnon coupling.

C. Excitons

Elliott and Loudon (*106*) have shown that Raman scattering may be used to study the properties of excitons in crystals; the theory of excitons is reviewed by Knox (*112*). The scattering arises in a very similar manner to that described for magnons. Since in most experiments the frequency change, ω, is much smaller than the energies of excitons, the experiments are limited to those materials with low energy electronic excitations. These are rare earth crystals in which the rare earth ion has many excited states and is only weakly coupled to the neighboring ions. Hougen and Singh (*113*) have studied Pr^{3+} ions in $PrCl_3$ crystals and determined the energy levels with Raman scattering. Another type of system with low energy excitons is that of certain transition metal ions. For example, in Co^{2+} salts there are usually a number of energy levels whose frequencies could be determined by Raman scattering. Further details will be found in the chapter by Koningstein and Mortensen (Volume 2).

The selection rules and the symmetry of the scattered light gives information about the symmetry of the excitons. Measurements as a function of temperature in magnetic crystals give information about the effect of the magnetic ordering on the excitons. Further measurements are needed before it is possible to assess the utility of this type of measurement.

Although we have discussed the scattering by electronic excitations only briefly, experiments have been performed to study the line width, line shape and temperature dependence of the scattering. The theory of these effects may be understood in a similar way to those described for phonons, and the results show very similar effects. Likewise the introduction of defects has enabled localized magnons to be studied.

IX. CONCLUSION AND SUMMARY

A. Comparison with Other Techniques

In this review we have shown that Raman scattering provides precise information about the low energy excitations in solids. It is interesting to compare this information with that provided by other experimental techniques. In Section II we showed that the one-phonon Raman scattering was given by a correlation function of the form

$$I_{\alpha\beta\gamma\delta} = \frac{1}{2\pi} \sum_{jj'} P_{\alpha\beta}\begin{pmatrix} o \\ j \end{pmatrix} P_{\gamma\delta}\begin{pmatrix} o \\ j' \end{pmatrix} \int_{-\infty}^{\infty} \exp(i\omega t) \langle\langle A(\mathbf{Q}j, t)A^+(\mathbf{Q}j', o)\rangle\rangle \, dt$$

(85)

where $\mathbf{Q}$ is the momentum transfer vector.

One of the other techniques by which excitations may be measured is that of far-infrared absorption. With this technique, a beam of far infrared radiation falls on a crystal and the reflectivity and transmission are measured as the incident wavelength is varied. The one-phonon contribution to the imaginary part of the dielectric constant is

$$\varepsilon''_{\alpha\beta}(\omega) = \frac{4\pi}{Nv} \sum_{jj'} M_{\alpha}\begin{pmatrix} o \\ j \end{pmatrix} M_{\beta}\begin{pmatrix} o \\ j' \end{pmatrix} (\exp(\beta\hbar\omega) - 1)$$
$$\int_{-\infty}^{\infty} \exp(i\omega t) \langle\langle A(oj, t)A^+(oj', o)\rangle\rangle \, dt$$

(86)

A comparison of Eq. (85) with (86) shows that apart from the coefficients and the population factor the cross sections are very similar. However, as commented in Section III, the two techniques are quite complementary since the selection rules are different. Furthermore the Raman scattering has the advantage that there are more components to the scattering, and it is, therefore, possible to obtain more information about the symmetry.

In the Raman scattering experiment, it is also possible to alter the momentum transfer, unlike the infrared experiment. In fact, in the latter case the wavevector is not well determined and there is some question as to the influence of surface effects which are not well understood at present. These complications do not appear to beset Raman scattering because the interaction of the light with the crystal is much weaker. Both techniques are most useful for crystals which have only a very small electrical conductivity.

One of the other main techniques is that of inelastic scattering of slow neutrons (*114*). The one-phonon scattering cross section is given by

$$\sum_{jj'} F(\mathbf{Q}, \mathbf{q}j)F(\mathbf{Q}, \mathbf{q}j') \int_{-\infty}^{\infty} \exp{(i\omega t)}\langle\langle A(\mathbf{q}j, t)A^{+}(\mathbf{q}j', o)\rangle\rangle \, dt$$

where $F(\mathbf{Q}, \mathbf{q}j)$ is the one-phonon structure factor which depends on the phonon eigenvectors and the neutron coherent scattering cross section of the nuclei. In principle the technique is more flexible than Raman scattering because the momentum transfer, $\mathbf{Q}$, can be varied over the whole Brillouin zone. Furthermore, since the scattering is a nuclear process, the technique may be used in all types of crystals. Neutron scattering may be used to determine all the phonon frequencies in the crystal and not just those of a particular symmetry. The disadvantage of the technique is that the scattering efficiency is small, and the intensity of neutron sources low. Consequently it may only be used when large single crystals are available. The energy and wavevector resolution is much worse than that obtained in Raman scattering. A good illustration of the different limits is given in Section IV,C, where the plasmon–phonon coupling was shown to give rise to an effect which could not be studied completely by Raman scattering, because the momentum transfers available were too small. However, the momentum transfers available with neutrons were too large; the experiments are therefore quite complementary.

The magnetic moment of the neutrons also permits the scattering from the electronic excitations to be observed with neutron scattering. It appears as if the observation of magnons is somewhat easier with neutron scattering than with Raman scattering, but the situation is reversed for the other electronic excitations.

Other techniques, e.g., X-ray scattering and superconducting tunneling, give less detailed information about crystals or alternatively are restricted in their application to a few special crystals. We shall, therefore, not discuss them in detail.

B. Conclusions

We have described the Raman effect in crystals in some detail. It has been shown that experiments on single crystals with well collimated polarized beams of light enable the frequencies and symmetries of the low frequency excitations in solids to be determined. Since the experiments may be performed with readily available equipment, Raman scattering experiments are expected to play a very important role in the study of excitations.

The basic properties of the one-phonon Raman scattering are now understood. Extensive measurements have been made of the frequencies of the phonons in many crystals and of the coupling between the phonons and photons. It is expected that further measurements will study the effect of anharmonicity on the shape of the one-phonon scattering, the effect on the scattering of phase transitions and that of adding defects to the crystals. In all of these fields some preliminary work has been performed, but there are many interesting experiments which have not yet been attempted. Comparatively little progress has been made on the quantitative study of the magnitude of the scattering. Calculations are still only at a semi-quantitative stage and much more work is needed before this complex problem is well understood.

The two-phonon scattering is less well understood. Although features such as Van Hove singularities have been identified, no quantitative calculations have as yet given good agreement with the experimental results. No doubt this largely reflects our inadequate understanding of the polarizability, but may also be due to the neglect of phonon–phonon coupling. In the two-magnon spectrum magnon–magnon coupling has been shown to drastically alter the shape of the spectra. Further work of both a theoretical and experimental nature is needed to settle this point.

Less work has been done on the Raman scattering by electronic excitations. However, the experiments which have been performed so far show this will likely blossom into a very profitable way of studying electrons in solids. Further theoretical work will be needed to develop results which are valid for real materials instead of the simple models used so far.

Until recently Raman scattering was limited to insulating crystals. However, over the last few years it has been extended to semiconductors and recently the first measurement on a metal has been made (115). These results show that Raman scattering techniques may in time be applied to most types of crystals.

In contrast to the situation just several years ago when few experiments and little theoretical work were in progress, the field of Raman scattering has now expanded greatly. In a large part this is due to development of the laser. In the future we can expect the field to continue to expand and to provide interesting results which will greatly enhance our knowledge of solids.

Acknowledgment

The author is grateful to Dr. G. Dolling for a careful reading of the manuscript.

REFERENCES

1. G. Landsberg and L. Mandelstam, *Naturwiss*, **16**, 557 (1928).
2. E. Fermi and F. Rasetti, *Z. Phys.*, **71**, 689 (1931).
3. R. Loudon, *Adv. Phys.*, **13**, 423 (1964).
4. B. Kursunoglu, *Modern Quantum Theory*, W. H. Freeman and Co., San Francisco, 1962.
5. M. Born and K. Huang, *Dynamical Theory of Crystal Lattices*, Oxford Univ. Press, Oxford, 1954.
6. A. A. Maradudin, E. W. Montroll, and G. H. Weiss, *Theory of Lattice Dynamics in the Harmonic Approximation*, "Solid State Physics," Supplement 3, Academic, New York, 1963.
7. W. Cochran and R. A. Cowley, *Handbuch Phys.*, **XXV/2a**, 59 (1967).
8. R. Loudon, *Proc. Roy. Soc.* (*London*), **A275**, 218 (1963).
9. L. N. Ovander, *Opt. Spectrosc.*, **9**, 302 (1960).
10. A. K. Ganguly and J. L. Birman, *Phys. Rev.*, **162**, 806 (1967).
11. R. C. C. Leite and S. P. S. Porto, *Phys. Rev. Letters*, **17**, 10 (1966).
12. M. Born and M. Bradburn, *Proc. Roy. Soc.* (*London*), **A188**, 161 (1947).
13. G. Dolling and R. A. Cowley, *Proc. Phys. Soc.* (*London*), **88**, 463 (1966).
14. B. J. Dick and A. W. Overhauser, *Phys. Rev.*, **112**, 90 (1958).
15. W. Cochran, *Proc. Roy. Soc.* (*London*), **A.253**, 260 (1960).
16. A. D. B. Woods, W. Cochran and B. N. Brockhouse, *Phys. Rev.*, **119**, 980 (1960).
17. R. A. Cowley, *Proc. Phys. Soc.* (*London*), **84**, 281 (1964).
18. V. Heine, *Group Theory in Quantum Mechanics*, Pergamon, New York, 1960.
19. M. Tinkham, *Group Theory and Quantum Mechanics*, McGraw-Hill, New York, 1964.
20. G. F. Koster, *Solid State Physics, V.* Academic, New York, 1957.
21. O. Theimer, *Can. J. Phys.*, **34**, 312 (1956).
22. M. Lax, *Symmetry Principles in Solid State Physics*, (unpublished).
23. S. H. Chen, *Phys. Rev.*, **163**, 532 (1967).
24. A. A. Maradudin and S. H. Vosko, *Rev. Mod. Phys.*, **40**, 1 (1968).
25. J. L. Warren, *Rev. Mod. Phys.*, **40**, 38 (1968).
26. R. A. Cowley, *Phys. Rev.*, **134**, A981 (1964).
27. R. J. Elliott and R. Loudon, *J. Phys. Chem. Solids*, **15**, 466 (1960).
28. F. A. Johnson and R. Loudon, *Proc. Roy. Soc.* (*London*), **A281**, 274 (1964).
29. E. Burstein, F. A. Johnson, and R. Loudon, *Phys. Rev.*, **139**, A1239 (1965).
30. R. P. Baumann and S. P. S. Porto, *Phys. Rev.*, **161**, 842 (1967).
31. L. Merten, *Z. Naturforsch*, **A15**, 47 (1960).
32. J. J. Hopfield, *Phys. Rev.*, **112**, 1555 (1958).
33. L. Couture-Mathieu and J. P. Mathieu, *C.R. Acad. Sci.* (*Paris*), **236**, 371 (1953).
34. H. Poulet, *Ann. Phys.* (*Paris*), **10**, 908 (1955).
35. C. H. Henry and J. J. Hopfield, *Phys. Rev. Letters*, **15**, 964 (1965).
36. J. F. Scott, L. H. Cheesman and S. P. S. Porto, *Phys. Rev.*, **162**, 834 (1967).
37. D. Pines, *Elementary Excitations in Solids*, W. A. Benjamin, New York, 1963.
38. R. A. Cowley and G. Dolling, *Phys. Rev. Letters*, **14**, 549 (1965).
39. M. M. Elcombe, *Proc. Roy. Soc.* (*London*), **A300**, 210 (1967).
40. G. S. Pawley, W. Cochran, R. A. Cowley and G. Dolling, *Phys. Rev. Letters*, **17**, 753 (1966).

41. I. Yokota, *J. Phys. Soc. Japan*, **16**, 2075 (1961).
42. A. Mooradian and G. B. Wright, *Phys. Rev. Letters*, **16**, 999 (1966).
43. A. Mooradian and A. L. McWorter, *Phys. Rev. Letters*, **19**, 849 (1967).
44. B. B. Varga, *Phys. Rev.*, **137**, A1896.
45. W. Cochran, R. A. Cowley, G. Dolling, and M. M. Elcombe, *Proc. Roy. Soc. (London)*, **A293**, 433 (1966).
46. L. Van Hove, *Phys. Rev.*, **89**, 1189 (1953).
47. L. Kleinman, *Solid State Commun.*, **3**, 47 (1965).
48. J. L. Warren, J. L. Yarnell, G. Dolling and R. A. Cowley, *Phys. Rev.*, **158**, 805 (1967).
49. H. M. J. Smith, *Phil. Trans. Roy. Soc. (London)*, **241**, 105 (1948).
50. A. M. Karo and J. R. Hardy, *Phys. Rev.*, **141**, 696 (1966).
51. H. L. Welsh, M. F. Crawford, and W. J. Staple, *Nature*, **164**, 737 (1949).
52. R. S. Krishnan, *Proc. Indian Acad. Sci.*, **26**, 399 (1948).
53. E. R. Cowley and R. A. Cowley, *Proc. Roy. Soc. (London)*, **A287**, 259 (1965).
54. A. A. Abrikosov, L. P. Gorkov, and J. E. Dyzaloskinski, *Methods of Quantum Field Theory in Statistical Physics*, London Prentice Hall, 1963.
55. A. A. Maradudin and A. E. Fein, *Phys. Rev.*, **128**, 2589 (1962).
56. R. A. Cowley, *Adv. Phys.* **12**, 421 (1963).
57. R. A. Cowley, *Rept. Progr. Phys.*, **31**, 123 (1968).
58. R. S. Krishnan, *Proc. Indian Acad. Sci.*, **24**, 45 (1946).
59. J. H. Parker, Jr., D. W. Feldman and M. Ashkin, *Phys. Rev.*, **155**, 712 (1967).
60. P. G. Klemens, *Phys. Rev.*, **148**, 845 (1966).
61. A. S. Barker, Jr., *Phys. Rev.*, **165**, 917 (1968).
62. D. L. Rousseau and S. P. S. Porto, *Phys. Rev. Letters*, **20**, 1354 (1968).
63. R. A. Cowley, *Phil. Mag.*, **11**, 673 (1965).
64. A. S. Barker, Jr. and J. J. Hopfield, *Phys. Rev.*, **135**, A1732 (1964).
65. J. F. Scott, *Phys. Rev. Letters*, **21**, 907 (1968).
65a. J. F. Scott, *Phys. Rev. Letters*, **24**, 1107 (1970).
65b. A. Zawadowski and J. Ruvalds, *Phys. Rev. Letters*, **24**, 1111 (1970).
66. V. Dvorak, *Phys. Rev.*, **159**, 652 (1967).
67. P. A. Fleury and J. M. Worlock, *Phys. Rev. Letters*, **18**, 665 (1967).
68. J. M. Worlock and P. A. Fleury, *Phys. Rev. Letters*, **19**, 1176 (1967).
69. R. A. Cowley, *Proc. Phys. Soc. (London)*, 1127 (1967).
70. L. Landau and G. Rumer, *Phys. Z. Sowjet.*, **11**, 18 (1937).
71. L. Sham, *Phys. Rev.*, **156**, 494 (1967).
72. C. P. Enz, *Ann. Phys.*, **46**, 114 (1968).
73. R. A. Guyer and J. A. Krumhansl, *Phys. Rev.*, **133**, A1411 (1964).
74. A. Akheizer, *J. Phys. Moscow*, **1**, 277 (1939).
75. E. C. Svensson and W. J. L. Buyers, *Phys. Rev.*, **165**, 1063 (1968).
76. A. Griffin, *Rev. Mod. Phys.*, **40**, 167 (1968).
77. C. C. Ackerman, B. Bertman, H. A. Fairbank, and R. A. Guyer, *Phys. Rev. Letters*, **16**, 789 (1966).
78. A. Griffin, *Can. J. Phys.*, (to be published).
79. P. W. Anderson, *Fizika Dielektrikov*, G. I. Skanavi, ed., Moscow, Acad. of Sci., 1960.
80. W. Cochran, *Adv. Phys.*, **9**, 387 (1960).
81. R. A. Cowley, *Phys. Rev. Letters*, **9**, 159 (1962).

82. G. Shirane, R. Nathans and V. J. Minkiewicz, *Phys. Rev.*, **157,** 396 (1967).
83. A. S. Barker and M. Tinkham, *Phys. Rev.*, **125,** 1527 (1962).
84. C. H. Perry and T. F. McNelly, *Phys. Rev.*, **154,** 456 (1967).
85. A. Pincuk, W. Taylor, E. Burstein, and I. Lefkowitz, *Solid State Commum.*, **5,** 429 (1967).
86. M. DiDomenico, S. P. S. Porto, and S. H. Wemple, *Phys. Rev. Letters*, **19,** 855 (1967).
87. I. P. Kaminow and T. C. Damen, *Phys. Rev. Letters*, **20,** 1105 (1968).
88. R. W. Gammon and H. Z. Cummins, *Phys. Rev. Letters*, **17,** 193 (1966).
89. P. A. Fleury, J. F. Scott, and J. M. Worlock, *Phys. Rev. Letters,* **21,** 16 (1968).
90. A. A. Maradudin, *Solid State Phys.*, **18,** 273 (1966). Ibid, **19,** 1 (1966).
91. R. J. Elliott and D. W. Taylor, *Proc. Roy. Soc. (London)*, **A296,** 161 (1967).
92. N. X. Xinh, A. A. Maradudin, and R. A. Coldwell-Horsfall, *J. Phys. Radium*, **26,** 717 (1965).
93. A. A. Maradudin, S. Ganesan, and E. Burstein, *Phys. Rev.*, **163,** 882 (1968).
94. P. M. Platzman, *Phys. Rev.*, **139,** A379 (1965).
95. P. A. Wolff, *Phys. Rev. Letters*, **16,** 225 (1966).
96. A. Mooradian, *Phys. Rev. Letters*, **20,** 1102 (1968).
97. J. M. Ziman, *Principles in the Theory of Solids*, Cambridge University Press, 1964.
98. A. Ya Blank and E. A. Kaner, *Sov. Phys. JETP*, **23,** 673 (1966).
99. R. E. Slusher, C. K. N. Patel and P. A. Fleury, *Phys. Rev. Letters*, **18,** 77 (1967).
100. P. L. Richards and M. Tinkham, *Phys. Rev.*, **119,** 575 (1960).
101. A. A. Abrikosov and L. A. Fal'kovskii, *Sov. Phys. JETP*, **13,** 179 (1961).
102. M. S. Khaikin and V. P. Bykov, *Sov. Phys. JETP*, **3,** 119 (1956).
103. F. G. Bass and M. I. Kaganov, *Sov. Phys. JETP*, **10,** 986 (1960).
104. P. A. Fleury and R. Loudon, *Phys. Rev.* **166,** 514 (1968).
105. C. Kittel, *Quantum Theory of Solids*, Wiley–Interscience, New York, 1963.
106. R. J. Elliott and R. Loudon, *Phys. Letters*, **3,** 189 (1963).
107. P. A. Fleury, S. P. S. Porto, L. E. Cheesman, and H. J. Guggenheim, *Phys. Rev. Letters*, **17,** 84 (1966).
108. J. W. Halley and I. Silvera, *Phys. Rev. Letters*, **166,** 514 (1968).
109. P. A. Fleury and R. Loudon, *Phys. Rev.*, **166,** 514 (1968).
110. P. A. Fleury, *Phys. Rev. Letters*, **21,** 151 (1968).
111. R. J. Elliott, M. F. Thorpe, G. F. Imbusch, R. Loudon, and J. B. Parkinson, *Phys. Rev. Letters*, **21,** 147 (1968).
112. R. R. Knox, *Solid State Physics Suppl. V.* Academic, New York, 1963.
113. J. T. Hougen and S. Singh, *Phys. Rev. Letters*, **10,** 406 (1963).
114. P. A. Egelstaff, *Thermal Neutron Scattering*, Academic, New York, 1965.
115. D. W. Feldman, J. H. Parker and M. Ashkin, *Phys. Rev. Letters*, **21,** 607 (1968).
116. F. Jones and G. Shirane, *Ferroelectric Crystals*, Pergamon, New York, 1962.

CHAPTER 4

Raman Instrumentation and Techniques

C. E. HATHAWAY

DEPARTMENT OF PHYSICS
KANSAS STATE UNIVERSITY
MANHATTAN, KANSAS

I. INTRODUCTION

The instrumentation and sampling techniques were simple in the early days of the Raman effect. The sources ranged from filtered sunlight, as used by Raman in the discovery of the phenomenon, to early forms of the mercury arc. The source of radiation was focused into the sample cell or simply placed adjacent to the sample cell, and the scattered radiation was collected at one end of the sample tube and focused on the slits of a moderately fast, low to medium dispersion prism spectrograph; photographic exposure times were measured usually in hours.

The inherent low intensity associated with the second-order Raman scattering phenomenon lead to gradual improvement in the sources and illumination techniques, the monochromators, and the detection systems. Most of these improvements were made by individuals working with self-designed instruments. Several good reviews of these instrumental developments are available (1–4).

Despite the many advances in photoelectric recording instrumentation made up to 1962, many Raman studies of crystalline powders and polymers (5), colored samples (6,7), and high resolution spectra of gases (3) were still obtained with long photographic exposures. In 1962 Porto and Wood (8) of Bell Telephone Laboratories and Stoicheff (3) of the National Research Council of Canada photographed the first Raman spectra using a pulsed ruby laser as the source. These first spectra of organic samples known to be efficient Raman scatterers were not impressive in themselves, but they were indicative of a new and powerful source for Raman excitation. The laser has been developed almost fully as a source of Raman excitation in the span of six years. There are now at least five commercially available laser Raman spectrometers. The current "Renaissance" in the application of Raman scattering to many new problems has been caused to a large extent by the availability of the laser as a source and the development of very sensitive radiation detection systems.

A Raman instrument consists of (1) the source and illumination systems, (2) the spectral analyzer or monochromator, and (3) the radiation detection system. Each of these components will be discussed individually, and the commercially available instrument packages will be described in terms of these discussions.

II. SOURCES AND ILLUMINATION TECHNIQUES

The proper design of a Raman sample illumination system requires consideration of the factors governing the intensity and distribution of the Raman scattered radiation. The Raman scattered light from a sample is proportional to (1) the fourth power of the Raman scattered frequency, (2) the intensity of the exciting light, and (3) the amount of sample (number of scattering centers, e.g., molecules or ions) from which the scattered radiation can be collected. The first two factors are determined by the choice of the Raman exciting source, since the frequency of the Raman scattered light is the sum or difference of the exciting frequency

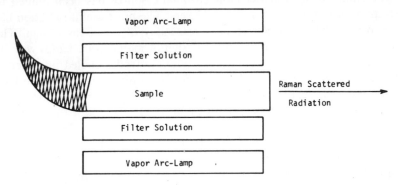

Fig. 1. Simple Raman sample geometry suitable for liquids. The scattered radiation is collected at 90° from the exciting radiation.

and the frequency associated with the energy change in the sample. The third factor is governed by the nature of the sample and the geometry of the illumination system.

Ideally a Raman illumination system consists of a geometrical arrangement which is capable of illuminating a concentrated sample with radiation from an intense, monochromatic source whose wavelength is as short as feasible. The exciting frequency for nonresonance Raman scattering must not be so high that it will be absorbed by electronic transitions. That is, the energy associated with the exciting frequency must be less than the forbidden electronic energy gap characteristic of the sample. This is not the case for resonance Raman scattering, where the Raman intensity is enhanced for excitation in the neighborhood of absorption bands (9–11).

The illumination system, including the optics for collecting the scattered light, should appreciably diminish the Rayleigh scattered exciting radiation prior to its entry into the monochromator. If the Rayleigh scattered radiation cannot be decreased, it is extremely difficult to observe Raman shifts below 80 cm^{-1} even with the most efficient monochromator systems. Observation at right angles to the source illumination decreases the amount of exciting light reaching the monochromator. A typical extended-source illumination system favored in Raman spectroscopy is shown in Fig. 1.

A. Arc-Lamp Sources

The choice of an intense, monochromatic source has been limited to arc-lamps until the recent advent of lasers. The most useful radiation has been provided by cooled mercury arcs, many of ingenious design. The most significant advancement in the design of mercury-arc lamps was the "Toronto lamp," which has mercury pool electrodes cooled by water to reduce the vapor pressure of the mercury (12). A direct current of 8 to 12 A is used normally with the Toronto arc when the discharge section of the lamp is air cooled. Current as high as 30 A may be used if the discharge section of the lamp is water cooled. The intensity of the lamp tends to increase linearly with the current (13). The Pyrex discharge tube becomes darkened by electron and ion bombardment (13), usually limiting the useful life of the Toronto arc to the order of 300 hr. Stoicheff (2) has recommended the use of Corning glass No. 1720 in the discharge section of the lamp to decrease this darkening effect. These lamps may be constructed of Pyrex or quartz in various shapes and sizes as shown in Fig. 2.

The mercury-arc lamp provides several intense lines in its spectrum; the most intense lines are at 2537, 4046, 4358, and 5461 Å. The 2537 Å line due to its shorter wavelength possesses a factor of approximately nine in Raman exciting efficiency over the 4358 Å line for equal illumination intensity. Furthermore, since the 2537 Å line arises from a resonance transition, the Rayleigh scattered line is eliminated easily by absorption in a Hg-vapor cell. The 2537 Å line has been widely used for Raman excitation because of these advantages. However, special magnetically controlled, quartz-mercury lamps may be needed to prevent appreciable absorption of the line in the lamp (14). Low pressure, quartz Toronto lamps may be used with currents as high as 5 A before self-reversal of the 2537 Å radiation becomes appreciable (15). Excitation by the 2537 Å line has certain distinct disadvantages. Quartz optics must be used throughout the illumination system and prism monochromators. Many samples absorb in this spectral region; many samples fluoresce and some samples undergo photodecomposition under 2537 Å illumination. There also are numerous neighboring mercury lines which make it difficult to isolate the 2537 Å line.

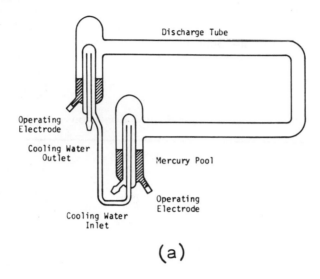

(a)

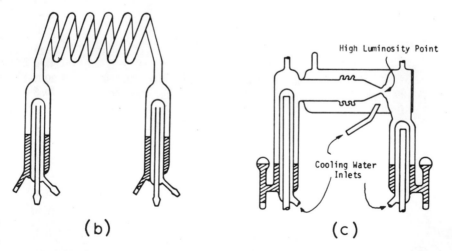

(b)   (c)

Fig. 2. Toronto arcs have been constructed in various forms: (a) modified hair pin discharge tube, (b) helical discharge tube, (c) focal-point lamp.

The lines at 4046 and 4358 Å have been used most commonly for the study of the Raman effect. An emission continuum of Hg_2 is found in the region near 4800 Å of a Hg-spectrum. This continuum tends to obscure the Stokes–Raman bands excited by the 4358 Å line. It is desirable to isolate the 4358 Å line, eliminating both this continuum and other mercury lines. The 4358 Å line can be sharpened and the continuum largely suppressed simply by water cooling the Hg-electrodes as is accomplished by the Toronto lamp. Effective cooling of the electrodes assures that the Hg-vapor pressure remains sufficiently low such that the Hg_2

TABLE 1

Sources for Raman Excitation

Type	Wave-lengths (Å)	Efficiency[a] and typical power (mw)	Detectors	
			Photographic emulsion type[b]	Photoelectric photocathode
Arc-lamp sources				
Argon	8115	0.08	N, M	S–1
	8408	0.07		
Cadmium	2288	13.2	0	S–5
	6439	0.21	E, F	S–20, S–1
Cesium	8521	0.07	N, M	S–1
	8943	0.06		
Helium	3889	1.58	O	S–5, S–20
	5876	0.30	G, D, E, F	S–20
	6678	0.18	E, F, U	S–20
	7065	0.15	U, N	S–20, S–1
	7281	0.13	U, N	S–20, S–1
Krypton	8113	0.08	N, M	S–1
	8298	0.08		
Mercury	2537	8.7	O	S–5
	4047	1.36	O	S–20
	4358	1.0	O	
	5461	0.41	G, D, E	
Rubidium	7800	0.10	N, M	S–1
	7948	0.09		
Sodium	5890	0.30	D, E, F	S–20
	5896	0.30	N, M	S–1
	8195	0.08		
Xenon	8232	0.08	N, M	S–1
	8280	0.08		

TABLE 1—*continued*

Type	Wave-lengths (Å)	Efficiency[a] and typical power (mw)	Detectors Photographic emulsion type[b]	Photoelectric photocathode
Laser sources				
Argon; gas, cw	4579	25	O	
	4658	15	O	
	4765	60	J	
	4727	15	G	S-20
	4880	900	D, F, G	
	4965	60	D, F, G	
	5017	25	F, D, G, J	
	5145	900		
Gallium Arsenide; injection cw	8400		N	S-1
Helium-Neon; gas, cw	6118	5	⎫	
	6328	50	⎬ E, F	S-24
	11,523	20	⎭	
	33,912	15	Z	S-1
Krypton; gas, cw	5280		⎫ D, F, G	⎫
	5390		⎭	
	5682	100	E, F	S-20
	6471		⎫ U, N	
	6764		⎭	⎭
Neon; gas, cw	3324	10	O	S-5
Nitrogen; gas, pulsed	3371	100 (average)	O	S-5
Nd:YAG; cw	10,600	1000 or greater	Z	S-1
Nd:YAG+$Ba_2NaNb_{15}O_{15}$	5300	20% of Nd:YAG	D, G	S-20
Ruby ($Cr:Al_2O_3$); cw and pulsed	6943	100 to 1000 (average)	U, N	S-20 S-1
Xenon; gas, cw	5419		D,F	⎫
	5971	100	D, E, F	S-20
	6271		E, F	⎭

[a] The efficiency is indicated for the arc-lamp sources and represents the fourth power of the frequency dependence relative to Hg-4358 Å; the typical power (mw) is indicated for the laser sources.

[b] Eastman Kodak Emulsion Sensitizing Types.

molecules are not readily formed. However, filtering is still required to further suppress the continuum and to remove other mercury lines. Numerous liquid filters and interference filters have been used to achieve this purpose (*1,13,16*). Similarly, filters have been determined which isolate the 4046 Å and 5461 Å lines of the mercury arc (*1*). Care must be taken to insure that photochemically induced changes in the filtering solutions do not cause exciting radiation intensity changes when attempting to measure relative or absolute Raman intensities.

Exciting radiation in the red or near infrared must be used for samples which absorb in the violet to blue spectral region. Stammreich (*17*) has reviewed discharge lamps using helium (5876, 6678, 7065, 7281 Å), argon (8115, 8408 Å), krypton (8113, 8298 Å), xenon (8232, 8280 Å), rubidium (7800, 7498 Å), and cesium (8521, 8943 Å). A small annular, electrodeless lamp which uses microwave excitation with an alkali metal vapor has been described (*18*). Table 1 lists data on arc lamp sources.

B. Laser Sources

The laser or optical maser became available as a source of intense, monochromatic, coherent radiation in 1960 (*19*). The pulsed ruby laser was followed by the continuous operating (cw) He–Ne gas laser in 1961 (*20*). The development of high-powered, long-lived laser systems has continued rapidly, and laser radiation can be obtained now almost anywhere in the electromagnetic spectrum (*21*). The impact of this source of radiation on Raman spectroscopy may be gauged most easily by the number of papers which have been published using the laser for Raman excitation. It is the author's opinion, certainly not shared by all, that laser systems will completely replace the arc-lamp systems.

Much of the early development of the laser excited Raman system was accomplished at Bell Telephone Laboratories by Porto et al. (*8,22–26*), where a productive program of laser development made such sources easily accessible (*27*). Many other laboratories, too numerous to properly reference, have converted to laser excitation and have contributed to the further development of the technique.

The most commonly used lasers for Raman excitation are the continuously operating helium-neon (6328 Å) and argon-ion (4880, 5145, and 4765 Å) gas lasers, and the pulsed and continuously operating forms of the ruby, $Al_2O_3:Cr^{+++}$ (6943 Å) and the neodymium doped yttrium-aluminum garnet, Nd:YAG (1.06 μ) lasers. Brandmüller (*28*) recently reviewed lasers as Raman excitation sources. It is much too early to predict which lasers will become the most common for Raman illumination, but the perfection of a long-lived, cw krypton-ion laser with exciting lines in both the red and green spectral regions offers a good choice of radiation for Raman excitation. Of course, a general purpose gas laser system which allows any of the noble gases to be used as the active agent is ideal. The Nd:YAG laser has already proven its usefulness as a source for Raman studies of semiconductors (29,30). The development of optically nonlinear crystals, such as barium sodium niobate (31) ($Ba_2NaNb_{15}O_{15}$), which by second harmonic generation at 20% or greater efficiency of the 1.06 μ radiation gives rise to an intense coherent line at 5300 Å (32), allows the Nd:YAG laser to be much more useful as a Raman source. The development of the neon and nitrogen lasers yields lines in the ultraviolet spectral region which more than rival the Hg-2537 Å line. The ultimate, of course, is the continuously tunable laser source. Table 1 indicates a few of the commercially available laser systems which have been used or may be used for Raman sources.

The advantages of the laser system are as follows:

1. There are a variety of exciting lines available with a clear spectral region on each side of the exciting line.

2. The band width of the laser line is usually smaller than a vapor-arc lamp line.

3. The polarization of the laser beam is defined and may be controlled to within 0.1%.

4. The energy is concentrated in a narrow beam and the illumination geometry may be designed to take advantage of this concentration.

5. The intensity may be easily controlled.

6. Since many samples tend to fluoresce less when illuminated in the red spectral region, the commonly used He–Ne laser has an additional advantage.

The disadvantages of laser excitation systems are primarily the initial cost and the short-lived character of the noble-gas ion lasers. Both of these are offset by the convenience and efficiency, and these inconveniences are tending to disappear with time. Several manufacturers (Spectra Physics, Coherent Radiation, Carson Laboratories) have announced argon-ion lasers with total outputs of the order of one-quarter to one-half watt at costs comparable to high quality He–Ne lasers.

C. Illumination Geometries and Special Sample Cells

The proper design of the sampling system requires efficient illumination of a minimal amount of sample, and efficient collection of the scattered radiation by the spectral analyzer system (2,3,4). The mercury-arc system is basically an extended geometry, while the laser system is a confined geometry. The techniques of illuminating the sample are distinctly different for the two systems. In any case, certain precautions must be taken and experimental factors considered. Quite frequently the success of obtaining a high quality spectrum depends upon the proper preparation of the sample. For both gases and liquids it is well to filter the sample to remove all particulate matter which may cause Tyndall scattering of the exciting radiation. Various micropore filters (0.01 μ) are available which aid in cleaning samples. Liquids also may be distilled into the sample tubes, effecting both a cleaning and purifying of the sample.

Solid samples ideally should be transparent and without imperfections, however, most solids do not fall into this category and many are available only as crystalline powders. The crystalline powder has been one of the greatest challenges in obtaining Raman data. Many advances were made in this area prior to the advent of the laser and excellent reviews are available (33–35). In working with solids, the order of preference is (1) single crystal, (2) polycrystalline, and (3) compressed powder tablet. Considerable success has been had by placing powdered samples in pressed alkali halide discs (4,36) and either back or side illuminating the sample. A number of materials, including KBr, NaCl, KCl, and KI may be used as the halide host matrix. Ideally the index of refraction should be chosen to be close to that of the sample. However, care must be taken to insure (1) no exchanges take place between the sample and the host matrix, (2) no structural changes occur in the sample during grinding or pressing, and (3) no electronic effects occur in the sample due to being surrounded by an ionic matrix.

A high percentage of the incident radiation may be reflected into the spectrometer by the multiple reflections occurring in polycrystalline and powdered samples. The incident illumination must be as spectrally clean as possible, and secondary filtering between the sample and monochromator is usually required to reduce the intensity of the scattered exciting line. The intensity of the Rayleigh scattered light will determine the intensity of grating "ghosts." Such spectral anomalies can be an extreme nuisance when studying low-frequency Raman shifts (e.g., lattice vibrations of molecular crystals). Several schemes have been devised which fairly efficiently remove the scattered exciting radiation (*13,33,34,35*), but these techniques do not generally allow low frequency (less than 100 cm^{-1}) Raman shifts to be measured.

Many polymer samples and organic powders fluoresce under the conditions of Raman excitation, but quite frequently this fluorescence arises from impurities; such fluorescence can obscure the Raman shifts. In many cases these samples can be further purified by recrystallizing procedures or simply soaking. For example, polyethylene when soaked in hexane loses almost all its fluorescence (*37*).

The problem associated with efficiently coupling the illumination system to the collimator of the monochromator has been extensively discussed (*38,39,40,49,53*). The problem of efficiently coupling the scattered radiation from the typical samples needed for extended sources is formidable. However, the use of an image slicer makes it possible to use the scattered radiation from such a cylindrical sample tube to illuminate the slit of the monochromator quite efficiently. The front of the sample tube is optically sliced into linear segments which are focused then on the slit, one above the other (*41*). The problem of coupling the scattered light from a laser illumination system to a monochromator may be handled much more easily (*49,53*).

1. MERCURY-ARC ILLUMINATION

The mercury-arc systems with an input of 2.5 kw can radiate up to 50 W of energy in the 4358 Å line, but because of the extended geometry of the system only the order of a watt is made available for Raman excitation of gases and liquids. Light furnaces have been designed to allow the maximum effective flux from these lamps to illuminate the minimal amount of sample. The lamp (or lamps) is usually designed to completely surround the sample tube, and the lamp housing may be coated with magnesium oxide in order to achieve maximum diffuse reflectance (*42*).

Liquids have been the easiest sample form to study and most illumination systems for liquids have been similar to those shown in Figs. 1 and 3(a). The sample is held in a cylindrical tube surrounded by a number of lamps or a single helical lamp. A liquid filter is placed between the lamp and the sample to isolate the required mercury line. The liquid filter chamber may be built as an integral part of the sample tube, and a thermostated circulating filter solution can serve also as a temperature control. Polarization measurements (See Section VI, B) may be made easily by

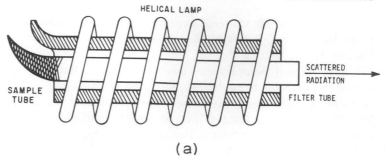

(a)

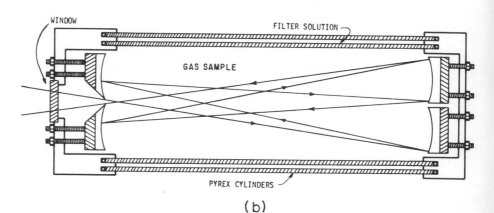

(b)

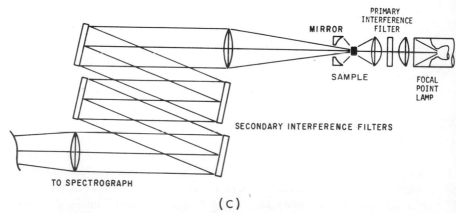

(c)

Fig. 3. Illumination systems for extended vapor arc-lamps: (a) simple liquid sample tube with helical Toronto arc, (b) multiple reflection gas cell for use with helical or extended discharge tube Toronto arcs, (c) focal point lamp system for crystalline powders.

wrapping the sample tube with polarizing sheets; typical sample volumes may vary between 100 ml and 0.2 ml.

Since the intensity of the Raman scattering depends on the number of scattering molecules, special multiple-reflection cells have been constructed [(see Fig. 3(b)] for the study of gases. These cells can achieve up to the order of 40 reflection paths and when operated at increased pressures yield intensity gains of the order of 40 over a single reflection cell. Several such cells have been described (2,40,41,43) and detailed instructions of the construction and alignment have been given by Stoicheff (2).

The extended mercury-arc system is particularly inefficient for solids but is still used in some cases (4). The focal-point, Toronto lamp illumination system (13,35) as shown in Fig. 3(c) has proven quite successful, even for translucent polymer samples (5) and powder samples (13). The intense radiation at the constricted point in the lamp is collected by an $f/1.0$ condenser lens, passed through a primary interference filter, and then focused onto the back side of the sample disk. The thickness of the disk is made equal to $(1/k)$, where k is the apparent extinction coefficient (13,34,35). The scattered radiation is reflected from several interference filters (13,34), each of which transmits the exciting radiation, removing up to 92% of the exciting line before the radiation is focused on the slits of the monochromator. Chemical filters as primary and secondary filters are not very satisfactory since they lack the necessary sharp cutoff. If 2537 Å radiation is used with a quartz version of the focal-point lamp (44), the exciting radiation can be removed by absorption in a mercury-vapor cell placed in the optical path.

When single crystals are studied, it is important to obtain the polarization data (see Section VI, B) in terms of the crystal orientation. Couture (45) has described a system in which the incident light is concentrated by a lens in a designated crystal direction, and the scattering angle is limited by baffles. However, the convergent geometry can lead to anomalous depolarization data (46).

2. LASER ILLUMINATION

Several methods of illuminating Raman samples with a laser beam have been used (8,22–27,29,47–50). There are basically two types of laser irradiation systems. The first techniques made use of the highly collimated, unfocused laser beam (22,23,24,27). Later studies have shown the increased radiance of the focused laser beam to yield high quality Raman spectra of extremely small volumes (26,49). A variety of illumination schemes are illustrated in Fig. 4.

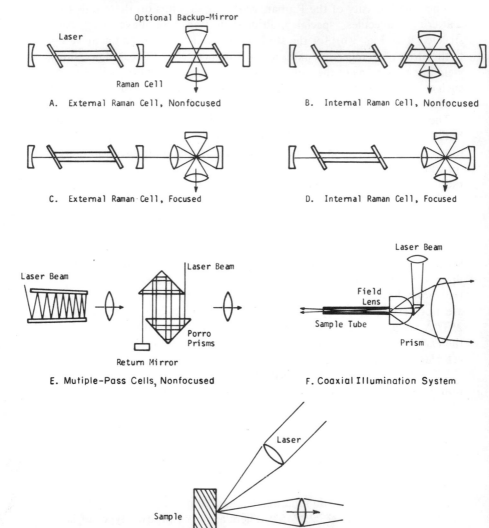

A. External Raman Cell, Nonfocused

B. Internal Raman Cell, Nonfocused

C. External Raman Cell, Focused

D. Internal Raman Cell, Focused

E. Mutiple-Pass Cells, Nonfocused

F. Coaxial Illumination System

G. Backscatter Illumination System for Opaque Solids

Fig. 4. Laser Raman illumination systems. The arrow through the collecting lens indicates the direction of the monochromator.

The well-defined polarization of the laser beam may be used to decrease the Rayleigh scattered exciting line (26). The scattered radiation should be observed at 90° to the laser beam, and the plane of polarization should be parallel to the observation direction. The Rayleigh line is caused predominately by isotropic scattering so that if the scattered radiation is observed in a direction that coincides with the direction of vibration of the electric vector of the exciting radiation, the Rayleigh line will vanish to a degree described by the depolarization ratio (see Section VI, B).

The laser system is usually equipped with an optional interference filter to eliminate spurious nonlasing lines when necessary, and a half-wave plate for rotation of the plane of polarization. Figure 5 shows the schematic of the Spex illumination scheme and single crystal goniometer which may be mounted in the sample illuminator system. A polarization analyzer may be placed between the sample and the spectrometer, and it is advisable to place a calcite or quartz wedge as a polarization scrambler in front of the slit of the monochromator (see Section III).

Clear samples, such as liquids and gases, may be located inside the cavity (22,23,26,49). Weber et al. (26) have designed several elaborate multiple-pass cells which may be used inside the cavity to obtain very respectable gas spectra for pressures of 1 atm. It is esssential to use Brewster angle windows on sample cells which are used internal to the laser, since normal windows create a loss through reflection which may adversely affect the laser performance. The high transmission of Brewster angle windows for a given polarization may also be used to advantage on sample cells used external to the laser. The Brewster windows may be placed in an opposite sense to one another so as to counteract the lateral displacement of the laser beam. While a gain in power is achieved by placing the sample in the cavity, the technique requires more care, and the external cavity is usually the most convenient and is often quite adequate for liquids.

The schemes shown in Fig. 4(a, b, c, d) cause the laser beam to traverse the cell in a horizontal manner, which makes it difficult to efficiently illuminate the normally vertical slits of a monochromator. A Dove prism in the optical path between the cell and the monochromator allows the image to be rotated to match the entrance slits (26). An alternative technique is to deflect the laser vertically through an external cell (26).

The laser beam may be multiple-passed through an external cell consisting of two highly reflecting surfaces making a slight angle with respect to one another as shown in Fig. 4(e) (50). Two Porro prisms also may be combined to yield a multiple-pass cell (51).

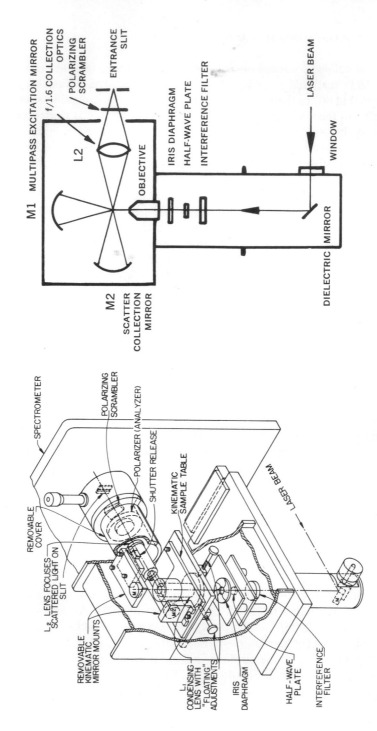

Fig. 5. The Spex Industries, Inc. Model 1430 Laser Raman sample illuminator.

All of the schemes for multiple-passing the laser beam through the sample require carefully optical coupling of an extended Raman source to the entrance slits and collimator of the monochromator. This technique possesses some of the same difficulties of collecting Raman radiation from a large solid angle and transmitting it through the entrance slits of the monochromator as encountered in the extended mercury-arc systems.

An alternative method involves focusing the laser beam into the sample (26,49,52,53). This method allows the use of extremely small-volume Raman samples, since the disadvantage of the decrease in the number of scattering molecules is offset by the increased radiance produced by focusing the laser beam. Atwood (52) first suggested that a spectrometer will transmit a larger Raman signal from a laser-illuminated sample if the laser beam is focused down to a greater degree. Benedek and Fritsch (53) used diffraction theory to study the problem of collecting scattered light from the focal region and determined the optimum focal length of the lens used to focus the laser in terms of the optical parameters of the collimator and slit system of the monochromator. Barrett and Adams (49) have extended these studies, both theoretically using confocal-resonator theory and experimentally using a focused argon-ion laser and gas samples.

Figure 6 shows the geometry of a focused laser Raman exciting system. The focusing angle of the laser beam, α, is well approximated by $\alpha = d/f$, where d is the diameter of the laser beam and f is the focal length of the lens. The parameter b is the length of the beam between the point of minimum radius, w_o, and the point at which the beam has a radius of $\sqrt{2}w_o$. This minimum radius is given by

$$w_o = \frac{4\lambda}{\pi\alpha} \tag{1}$$

where λ is the wavelength of the radiation. The Raman scattered radiation may be considered to be coming from a source cylinder whose length is $2b$ and whose diameter is $2w_o$. This includes the brightest region of Raman emission and neglects the less bright regions of emission. It can be shown that for a given monochromator slit and collimator geometry, there is an optimum value of the focusing angle, α. Barrett and Adams found the optimum value of α is bound by:

$$4\frac{\lambda M}{\pi W_s} \geq \alpha \geq \sqrt{\left(\frac{16\lambda M}{\pi L_s}\right)} \tag{2}$$

where W_s is the width of the slit, L_s is the length of the slit, and M is the magnification from the source to the slit. The magnification is given by:

$$M^2 = \Omega/\Omega_s \tag{3}$$

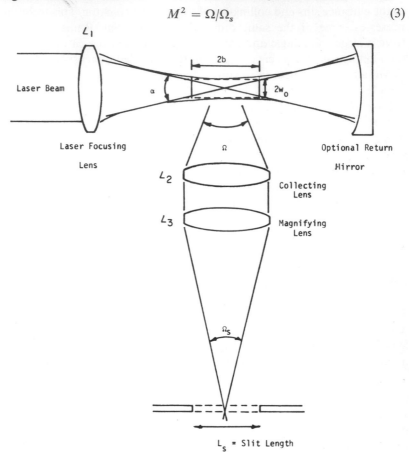

Fig. 6. Geometry involved in optimizing Raman scattered radiation collected by a monochromater. Adapted from Ref. (*49*).

where Ω is the solid angle subtended at the source, and Ω_s is the solid angle associated with the spectrometer. The total useful Raman flux collected increases as the square root of M; therefore, it is desirable to use as large a value of M as practical. The collecting lens L_2 should be chosen to be as fast as possible, $f/1.0$ or smaller, and L_3 may be chosen then to match the solid angle of the spectrometer. The proper choice of L_1 may be chosen by setting α within the bounds dictated by equation (2).

The focusing of the laser beam may be done externally (53) or internally (49) to the laser cavity. Figure 7 shows the vibration–rotation band of N_2 obtained by Barrett and Adams by focusing the 3-mm diameter beam of an argon-ion laser (4880 Å) internal to the cavity with a 3-cm focal length lens. The effective scattering volume was about 10^{-8} cm³, and

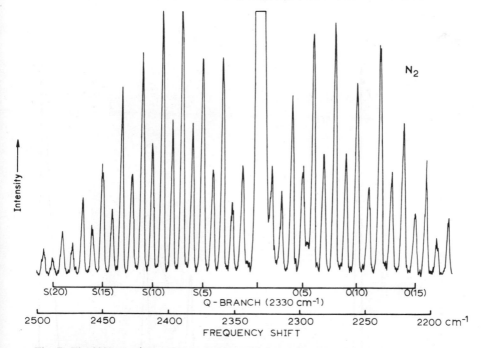

Fig. 7. The 2330 cm^{-1} Raman band of N_2. This spectrum was obtained by focusing the 3-mm diameter beam of an Ar$^+$ laser (4880 A) internal to the cavity with a 3-cm focal length lens. The effective scattering volume was about 10^{-8} cm³, and the number of scattering molecules was about 10^{11}; a PE El monochromator was used in the single pass configuration with a photon counting system. Reprinted from Ref. (49), p. 318, by courtesy of *J. Opt. Soc. of Am.* and the author.

the number of scattering molecules was about 10^{11}. Barrett (54), more recently, has reported the Raman spectra of gaseous discharges at a pressure corresponding to scattering from an effective volume containing only 10^9 molecules.

The technique of focusing the laser beam into the sample has been used also for liquids and solids (55–57) and has been particularly successful for polymers and powdered samples (58–60). Figure 8 shows a Raman spectrum of polytetrafluorethylene obtained by R. F. Schaufele using the focused laser technique and photoelectric recording. This may be compared against a 15 and 72 hr photographic exposure using mercury-arc excitation (5). Figure 9 shows polarization data between 1000 and 1200 cm^{-1} obtained on a 0.3 mm thick piece of translucent, oriented polyethylene. Repeated efforts to obtain these data using mercury-arc excitation were not successful.

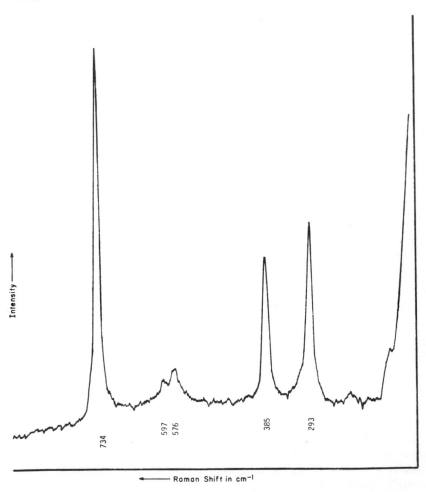

Fig. 8. The Raman spectrum of the polytetrafluoroethylene polymer Teflon as obtained by R. F. Schaufele using a focused He-Ne laser, double monochromator and phase sensitive detection. The Raman shifts are indicated in cm^{-1} below each band.

Bailey et al. (*61*) have reported the Raman spectra of liquid samples as small as 50 μl by using a focused He–Ne laser. Figure 10 shows the spectrum of linalyl methyl ether plus a terpene impurity taken by focusing a He–Ne laser into a single-pass cell whose volume is less than 1.0 μl. Murphy and Bernstein (*62*) have reported Raman spectra of vapors of

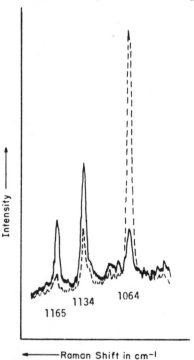

Fig. 9. Raman spectrum of oriented polyethylene obtained with a focused He-Ne laser and the Spex Raman Spectrometer operating in the photon counting mode. The incident radiation was polarized perpendicular to the polyethylene chains. The dashed curve represents the scattered light polarized parallel to the chains, and the solid curve represents the scattered light polarized perpendicular to the chains.

common organic solvents at room temperature. In particular, they have reported the Raman spectrum of 5 torr pressure of carbon tetrachloride obtained with an externally focused argon-ion laser (4880 Å at 250 to 500 mw). They also reported the Raman spectrum of benzene in a carbon tetrachloride solution at a concentration by volume of 5×10^{-5} of C_6H_6 to CCl_4. Based on the work of Barrett (*49,54*), it may be possible to obtain a spectrum of a liquid sample as small as 0.01 μl.

The use of pulsed laser illumination in rapid scan Raman spectroscopy will be discussed in Section VII.

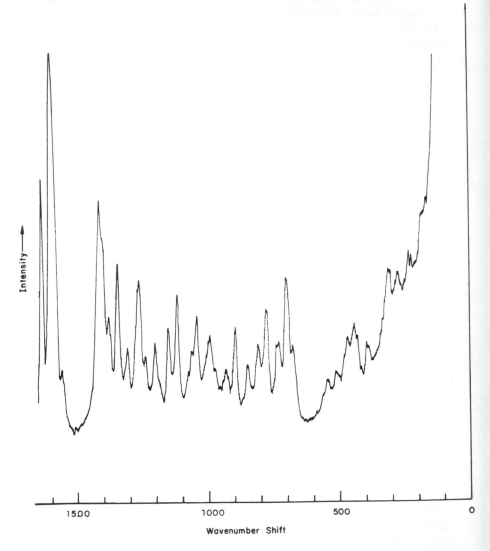

Fig. 10. The Raman spectrum of linalyl methyl ether plus a terpene impurity obtained by focusing a He-Ne laser into a single-pass cell whose volume is of the order of 1.0 μl. The instrument used was a Spex Raman Spectrometer operating in the photon counting mode.

3. Temperature Controlled Cells

Numerous sample cells have been designed which allow Raman spectra to be obtained over the range of temperatures from 4°K to approximately 1300°K. Moderate cooling (~0°C) and heating (~100°C) may be achieved by simply surrounding the convential sample tube with a concentric jacket through which a temperature controlled fluid may be circulated. In spite of the many difficulties of instrumental geometry, many sample dewars using liquified or cooled gases have been designed for use with extended mercury-arc sources (63–70). The focal point mercury-arc lamp allows the use of a simplified optical dewar (71) to study solids.

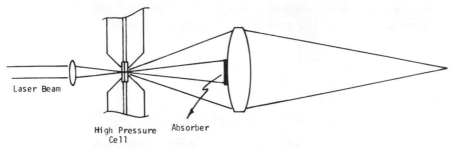

Laser Beam

High Pressure   Absorber
Cell

Fig. 11. The laser beam may be focused into a high pressure cell containing a sample and the Raman radiation may be collected in the forward scattered direction.

Temperatures up to 200°C may be obtained by wrapping the sample tube with a nichrome heater, but higher temperatures require careful cell design (72–74). Pyrex glass may be used for temperatures up to 550°C and quartz up to 1200°C.

High pressure Raman work, except for gases, has been quite limited. Walrafen has described a cell for use with liquids at pressures as high as 1400 atm (75).

The confined geometry of laser illumination makes the design of temperature cells much easier. Ordinary optical dewars (76) may be used for temperatures down to 4°K, and numerous studies have been made on crystals at reduced temperatures using simple optical dewars (55,57). A small sample furnace for temperatures up to 1200°C has been designed for studying molten salts with a focused laser geometry (77).

A design which may be used for obtaining the Raman scattering from a diamond-anvil, high-pressure cell (78) is shown in Fig. 11. The laser is focused into the high-pressure region and the scattering is observed in the forward direction (*78a*). The forward scattered laser beam may be absorbed. Recently a high hydrostatic pressure cell has been used to measure the pressure dependence of Raman-active phonons (*78b,c*).

Several other examples of specialized sample cells are shown in the various chapters of this book.

III. MONOCHROMATORS

A conventional spectral analyzer is composed of an entrance slit, a dispersive system such as a prism or a grating, and an exit slit or a lens system which forms chromatic images of the entrance slit in the focal plane (see Fig. 12). The general requirements for Raman spectral instru-

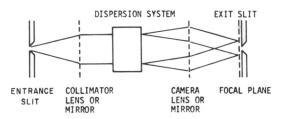

Fig. 12. Block diagram of a simple monochromator.

ments have been high speed and moderate resolution. The recent improvement in sources and detection techniques now allows higher resolving power instruments with only moderate speeds to be used for Raman studies. Raman spectrographs, in addition, must be free of stray light because of the weakness of the Raman radiation compared to the exciting radiation. Stray light may arise from any of the following causes:

1. Leakage of light through the instrument housing.
2. Leakage of light through the slits which does not come from the sample.
3. Reflection and scattering of light at the surfaces of the optics.
4. Reflection and scattering of light from the walls and from the mountings of the optics.
5. Scattering of light and fluorescence within the optics.

Care in design can minimize most of these problems, and the use of double monochromators reduces the problems even further.

Spectroscopic instruments for Raman spectroscopy may be divided into two classes according to the final method of recording the data, either photographic or photoelectric. Prior to the introduction of the photoelectric recording spectrometer by Rank (79), all Raman data were recorded using photographic emulsions. The advantages and disadvantages of these methods of detection will be discussed in Section IV. Obviously the photoelectric recording system is to be preferred because of its convenience provided it yields as much information as the photographic technique.

A. Photographic Instruments

The design philosophy of a spectroscopic instrument to be used with a photoelectric detector is different from one which is to be used with a photographic emulsion. The photographic speed depends on the total power per unit area in the spectra line image (80,81),

$$I = B_\lambda T_\lambda (A/f^2) \tag{4}$$

where B_λ is the source brightness, T_λ is the transmission function of the optical system, A is the area of the limiting aperture, and f is the focal length of the camera lens. It is advantageous to use a camera of short focal length or high angular aperture ratio. The speed of the instrument is independent of the collimator focal length; the only requirement of the collimator is that it be of sufficient size to fully illuminate the camera lens. Most spectrographs are asymmetrical in that the focal length of the collimator lens is greater than the focal length of the camera lens. A larger slit may be used with a collimator lens of long focal length to give the same size spectral line as that obtained by a more narrow slit with a collimator lens of short focal length. Furthermore, a longer slit may be used to advantage with a photographic instrument by placing a cylindrical lens of short focal length in front of the photographic plate. The image may be reduced in length by a factor of ten to twenty with a corresponding increase in intensity (2).

Most photographic instruments use a prism as the dispersion system, and most Raman instruments use multiple prism systems to achieve the necessary dispersion. The angular dispersion of a prism depends on the change of the index of refraction of the prism as a function of the wavelength and is not linear in either wavelength or wave number. The image of a straight slit produced by an instrument is curved, and curved entrance slits are often used to compensate for this image curvature. A comparison spectrum must be placed on the photographic plate in order to measure the Raman data, and care must be taken when comparing the spectra because of the curved image.

Photographic Raman instruments have often been used with long time exposures. Variations in the temperature may lead to loss in definition and resolving power caused by changes in the index of refraction of the optical elements and slight structural changes in the instrument caused by thermal expansion. The shift is of the order of 0.5 to 1 Å per degree centigrade for a typical glass prism instrument. Temperature controlled housings are essential for long photographic exposures. A complete treatment of prism instruments has been given by Sawyer (*80*).

B. Photoelectric Instruments

The speed of a photoelectric instrument depends on the total energy incident on the detector (*41*),

$$E_\lambda = B_\lambda T_\lambda A D (\Delta\lambda)^2 (h/f) \tag{5}$$

where B_λ, T_λ, and A were defined previously, $\Delta\lambda$ is the spectral slit width, D is the angular dispersion, and f is the focal length of the collimator. Photoelectric instruments depend on the speed of the collimator and should have a short focal length collimator lens or mirror. For an extended Raman source (mercury-arc excitation), the slit should be as long as is possible to fully illuminate. Optical image slicers have been designed which allow long slits to be filled efficiently (*41*). Long slits are not necessary for focused laser illumination techniques.

Most instruments designed for photoelectric detection use gratings as the dispersive system. The image position for a reflection grating (see Fig. 13) will be dictated by the basic grating equation,

$$n\lambda = d(\sin i + \sin r) \tag{6}$$

where n is the diffraction order, i is the angle of incidence, r is the diffraction angle, and d is the grating spacing. One disadvantage of a grating is the overlapping of different diffraction orders. The nth order position for a wavelength λ_1 coincides with the $(n+1)$th order position for a wavelength λ_2, when $n\lambda_1 = (n+1)\lambda_2$. The first-order position for λ_1 will coincide with the second-order position of $(\lambda_1/2)$. There is overlapping of the first-order extreme red (8000 Å) of the visible spectrum with the second-order violet (4000 Å). As the order of the diffraction increases, the overlapping becomes more severe.

A second problem associated with the grating is the small percentage of radiation which is concentrated in any one diffraction order. However, modern "blazed" gratings are constructed to place as much as 70% of the incident radiation in a given order for a particular wavelength region (82).

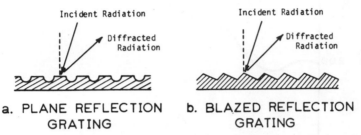

Fig. 13. Comparison of the plane and blazed reflection gratings. The plane reflection grating has decreasing intensity in each higher order of diffraction, but the angle of a blazed grating may be chosen so as to concentrate the radiation in a particular diffraction order.

The transmission factor, or efficiency of a grating, varies with the polarization of the incident light (82). Figure 14 shows a plot of the ratio of the diffracted intensity for incident light polarized perpendicular to the gratings spacings to the diffracted intensity of the incident light polarized parallel to the gratings spacings. These data were obtained on a Perkin–Elmer LR-1 Raman spectrometer for the spectral region of Stokes–Raman shifts excited by a helium-neon laser (83). This effect causes problems in obtaining Raman polarization data. The raw data must be corrected for the grating transmission factor or a polarization "scrambler" must be placed prior to the slits (26). A polarization scrambler consists of a quartz or calcite wedge, which rotates the plane of polarization of a given wavelength different amounts for each point on the slit. The net affect is to change the incident, well-defined polarized light into light of a mixture of polarizations.

Errors which occur in the production of diffraction gratings can cause a general degradation of their performance. Random errors and surface irregularities reduce the resolving power and cause general scattering. Periodic errors, by far the most troublesome and difficult to correct, cause ghost or spurious lines to appear in the spectrum. If the periodic

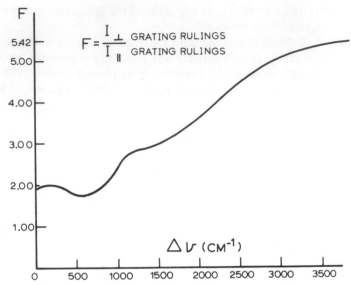

Fig. 14. The ratio of intensities transmitted in the PE LR-1 Raman Spectrometer when the incident radiation is polarized perpendicular and parallel to the grating rulings. Courtesy of the Perkin-Elmer Corporation.

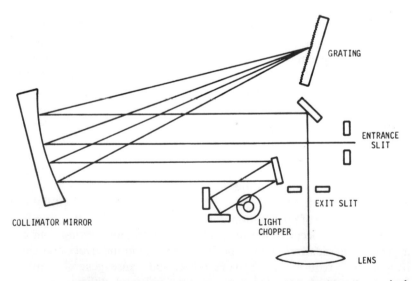

Fig. 15. Optical diagram of the PE LR-1 monochromator which double passes a single grating for double dispersion.

error is such that the grating width contains approximately one cycle, the ghosts are symmetrical about the parent line. Such lines are known as Rowland ghosts, and their intensities can be an appreciable fraction of that of the parent line. Rowland ghosts make it quite difficult to work near the Raman exciting line when studying crystalline powders or samples of poor quality. Interferometrically ruled gratings, such as those produced by Jarrell–Ash, are relatively free of such ghosts. If there are a number of cycles of error across the grating, the ghost is produced at locations which are simple integrals of the parent line and may occur at appreciable distances from the parent line. Such spurious lines are called Lyman ghosts, and are not as troublesome in Raman spectroscopy as the Rowland ghosts. A Lyman ghost may be used as a wavelength calibration check if its position is known accurately.

Raman lines occurring near a laser exciting line may be checked as possible ghosts with a pair of narrow-band interference filters which pass the laser line. The spectrum should be recorded with both interference filters in the laser beam prior to the sample, and then recorded again with one filter between the sample and the spectrometer and one prior to the sample. The exciting line ghosts should appear equally intense in both spectra, while true Raman lines will not appear in the second spectrum.

The angular dispersion of a grating for a fixed angle of incidence is given by

$$\frac{dr}{dn} = \frac{n}{d \cos r} \tag{7}$$

The dispersion is directly proportional to the diffraction order, n. For normal incidence, and for small values of r, the angular position is proportional to λ. However, scanning monochromators work at incidence angles which deviate from normal, and the wavelength may not be simply linear with the rotation of the grating.

Many types of grating mounts have been devised and have been discussed by several authors (80,84). A Littrow mount is normally used in the double-pass instrument; it makes use of one lens or mirror as the collimator and focusing element by folding the optical path. The optical diagram of the Perkin–Elmer LR-1 monochromator shown in Fig. 15 shows a double-passed Littrow mounted grating. This system is quite compact, but it is difficult to reduce the scattered or stray light to an absolute minimum. In the Ebert (85) and Czerny–Turner (86) mounts, the aberrations which the collimator reflection introduces are corrected by the telescope reflection. A double monochromator, the Spex Model 1400, and a dual monochromator, the Jarrell–Ash, both using the Czerny–Turner mount, as shown in Figs. 16 and 17, respectively.

A grating must be rotated in some fashion in a scanning monochromator in order to present successive spectral intervals at the exit slit. The

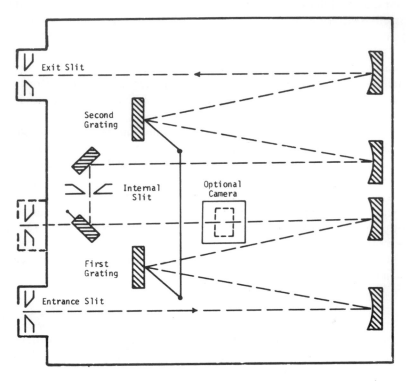

Fig. 16. Optical diagram of the Spex Model 1400 double monochromator using two gratings mounted to yield double dispersion.

frequency of the light emerging from the exit slit is determined by the angle between the undispersed light and the normal to the grating. The grating may be caused to move in such a fashion so as to be linear in either wavelength, λ, or wavenumber, $v = 1/\lambda$, with respect to the lead-screw rotation. Consider the mounting of a grating on a lead screw as shown in Fig. 18. The proper combination of a lead screw and arm mechanism will generate either the $\sin \theta$ or $\csc \theta$ function required to

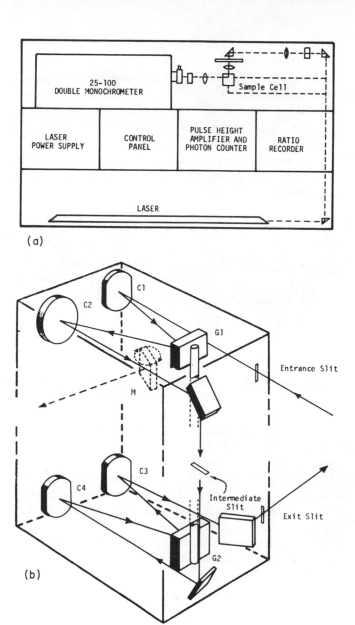

Fig. 17. The Jarrell-Ash Raman Spectrometer using the Model 25–100 double monochromator with the gratings mounted so as to yield only single dispersion; A is the instrumental arrangement and B is the double monochromator optical arrangement. The collimator mirrors are designated C1 and C3, the focusing (exit) mirrors C2 and C4, the gratings G1 and G2; the single monochromator may be used with the optional mirror *M*.

make the system linear in wavelength or wavenumber, respectively. The basic grating equation yields

$$\lambda = \frac{d}{n}(\sin i + \sin r) = \frac{2d}{n}\sin \theta \cos \phi = k \sin \theta \qquad (8)$$

where k is a constant, since $\cos \phi$ may be kept constant. The arm-lead screw movement must generate a cosecant function for a system to be linear in wavenumber.

$$\nu = \frac{1}{\lambda} = \frac{1}{k}\csc \theta \qquad (9)$$

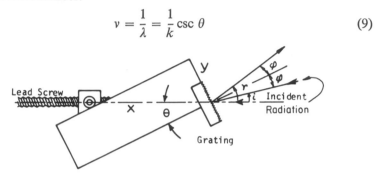

Fig. 18. Simple cosecant drive mechanism to rotate a grating such that the spectral display is linear in wavenumber.

The arm-lead screw arrangement, the cosecant drive, shown in Fig. 18 yields a linear wavenumber drive mechanism, since $\csc \theta = (x/y)$, where y is a constant and x is the position of the follower-nut on the lead screw. The scanning is accomplished by the follower-nut on the lead screw driving against the pivot arm of the grating. A similar arrangement, the sine bar, can be used to achieve a grating drive mechanism which is linear in wavelength.

There are numerous types of monochromator systems which have been used in photoelectric Raman spectroscopy. The several types of monochromators are as follows (87,88):

1. A single monochromator uses one dispersive element only once.

2. A double-pass monochromator uses one dispersive element twice by appropriate optical design to achieve double dispersion.

3. A tandem monochromator uses a pair of single monochromators together by imaging the exit slit of the first monochromator on the entrance slit of the second monochromator. Double the dispersion is obtained.

4. A double monochromator uses a pair of dispersive elements and an internal slit arranged optically such that twice the dispersion is obtained.

5. A dual monochromator uses a pair of dispersive elements and an internal slit arranged optically such that double dispersion does not occur.

Single monochromators are quite common; Fig. 15 shows an example of the double-pass grating monochromator. Reflected and scattered light are much more troublesome in instruments which use the double-passing system (*80*). Single-pass radiation of a wavelength different from the second-pass wavelength may be focused on the exit slit in the double-pass, Littrow system. One technique used to discriminate between the first- and second-pass radiation presented at the exit slit is to arrange the optical path such that the second-pass radiation is chopped and the first-pass radiation is not chopped. A phase sensitive, tuned detection system may be used to detect the alternating second-pass radiation and reject the constant or dc first-pass radiation. However, overloading problems can still arise with highly sensitive photomultiplier tubes. An alternative technique is to block the bottom half of both the entrance and exit slits. The first-pass image of the entrance slit is inverted and is blocked at the bottom half of the exit slit. The second-pass image is upright and passes through the top half of the exit slit. In this manner the double-pass system may be used with an external chopper, with dc detection systems, and perhaps even with photon-counting systems.

The ability of a tandem, dual, or double monochromator to reduce the scattered light within the instrument to a minimum was first utilized by van Cittert (*89*). This type of instrument has been revived in recent years for Raman spectroscopy (*90,91*). Figure 19 shows the scattered light in a single monochromator (f/6.8, Model 1700-II Spex Industries Mono- chromator) and a tandem monochromator consisting of two such single monochromators combined (*90*). Such instruments also reduce the ghost intensities when made with matched gratings. A tandem monochromator may be constructed from two matched single monochromators, but there are problems in making the two dispersive systems track identically. The design of the dual and double monochromator systems makes it easier to synchronize the grating movements (*91,92*). The dual monochromator does not have double dispersion, but the tracking error is virtually eliminated. The advantages of both of these instruments have been well discussed in the literature (*87,88,91,92*). Examples of the double and dual monochromator are shown in Figs. 16 and 17, respectively.

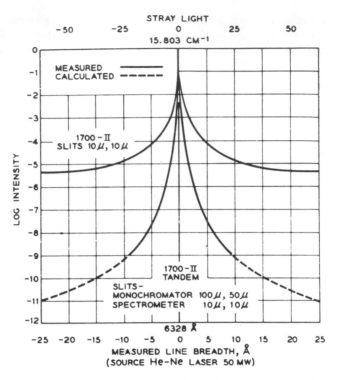

Fig. 19. Stray light measurement for a single Spex Model 1700-II monochromator and two such monochromators used in tandem. Reprinted from Ref. (*90*), p. 762, by courtesy of Applied Optics and the author.

IV. DETECTION TECHNIQUES†

The Raman scattered radiation presented to the detector may range in power from that which may be easily detected to that which is below the level of the best detection techniques available ($\sim 10^{-14}$ W). In the early years of Raman measurements, prior to the availability of commercial photoelectric instruments, the majority of Raman data reported were detected using photographic emulsions. Since the advent of photoelectric recording spectrometers, the reporting of photoelectrically recorded Raman data has increased continually.

† The author recommends *Astronomical Techniques*, University of Chicago Press, 1962, Edited by W. A. Hiltner, Chapters 1, 6, and 7 as a general reference for detection techniques.

There is usually a fundamental distinction in the use of a photographic emulsion and a photoelectric detector. The photographic emulsion is used in a nonscanning system where the whole of the spectral data is presented to the detector during the total time of the measurement. Each spectral element is observed during the total time of the observation, T, in such a multiplex system. The photoelectric detector, excluding the image intensifier, is normally used in a scanning system where only information in a given spectral bandwidth (Δv) is presented to the photomultiplier in a given time interval. That is, when N spectral elements are to be measured during a total time T, each spectral element is observed during a time (T/N). In situations where the fluctuations in the signal have a uniform frequency spectrum (e.g., photon noise) and where the background noise (e.g., stray or scattered light, instrument noise) is not increased by the simultaneous arrival of the whole spectrum, the signal to noise ratio is increased by $\sqrt{N}$ for the multiplexing system over the scanning system. However, photographic emulsions are not ideal quantum detectors and the time integration using a photographic emulsion is limited. Present photoelectric detection systems rival the photographic detection technique. The perfection of a multichannel, photoelectric spectral recording instrument which would allow time integration and correction for photocathode response would remove any advantage of photographic recording over photoelectric recording. The subject of rapid scanning Raman spectroscopy using multiplexing techniques is covered in Section VII.

A. Photographic Detection†

The most common detector of light is the photographic emulsion. However, exact figures as to the quantum efficiencies or sensitivities of various emulsions are not easily measured or stated since the quantum efficiency of the emulsion depends on the conditions under which it is used. The quantum efficiency describes the ability of the detector (emulsion) to record information received. A detector which receives N photons and records n events is said to have a quantum efficiency of (n/N) or $[(n/N) \times 100]\%$. A perfect detector which records each photon received has a quantum efficiency of 1.0 or 100%. The practical quantum efficiency of an emulsion varies with (1) the wavelength of the incident light signal, (2) the length of the exposure, and (3) the photographic density to which

† The author recommends *Experimental Spectroscopy* by Ralph A. Sawyer, Dover Publications, 1963, New York as a general reference for photographic techniques.

the plate is developed. It is estimated that only about 10% of the light
signal incident upon an emulsion is actually absorbed by the photographic
grain, and that approximately 10 quanta must be absorbed before the
grain will become blackened when developed. Thus many more than 100
photons must strike a region before a signal may be recorded. The typical
emulsions used in Raman spectral studies (103aO, 103aE) have quantum
efficiencies in the range between 0.01% to 1.0%. As many as 10,000 to as

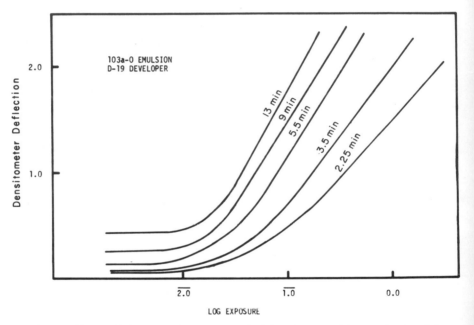

Fig. 20. Characteristic curves for Eastman Kodak 103a-O emulsion as developed in
D-19. Adapted from data taken from Kodak Scientific and Technical Data, p. 9.

few as 100 quanta must strike a grain region in order to record an image of
the incident signal. A new Eastman Kodak Emulsion, formerly known as
081–01 and now known as type IaE, has become available recently for
He–Ne laser excited Raman spectral studies (*26*). The author's limited
use of this plate has shown the IaE emulsion to have a greater sensitivity
and slightly more grain than the 103aE emulsion.

   The standard technique of presenting sensitivity data on an emulsion is a
characteristic curve and a spectral sensitivity curve (*93*). The characteristic
curve is a plot of the response of the emulsion, optical density, versus the

logarithm of the exposure. The exposure is the product of the flux per unit area (illumination) and the length of time and is usually stated in the awkward but standard system of units of photometry as meter-candle-seconds. The characteristic curve for a given emulsion will vary with the development time for the recommended developer. Figure 20 shows the characteristic curves for the Kodak Emulsion 103aO as developed in Kodak D-19 developer for the times indicated. It is preferable that the

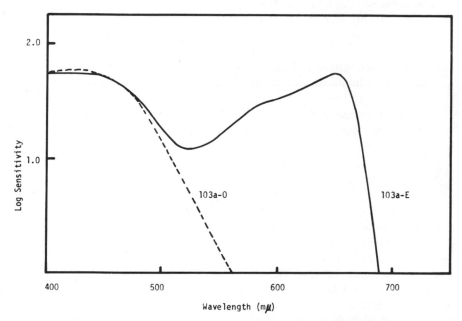

Fig. 21. Sensitivity curves for Eastman Kodak 103a-O and 103a-E emulsions. Adapted from data taken from Kodak Scientific and Technical Data, p. 9.

exposure be such that the information appears on the straight-line portion of the characteristic curve when intensity measurements are to be made. The slope of the straight-line portion of the curve may be determined to some degree by the length of the development time as can be seen in Fig. 20.

The variation of the quantum efficiency of an emulsion with the wavelength is given by the spectral sensitivity curve. The spectral sensitivity is plotted usually in terms of the reciprocal of the exposure (ergs/cm^2) required to produce a given density (signal) above the gross fog (background noise) when the emulsion is developed as recommended by the manufacturer. Figure 21 shows the spectral sensitivity curves for the Kodak 103aO and 103aE emulsions for a signal level of density 0.6 above the background level. As may be seen in Fig. 21, the sensitivity of a photographic emulsion varies sufficiently with wavelength that corrections must be made before comparing darkening of the film in different spectral regions. Table 1 indicates the appropriate Kodak emulsions for use with various Raman excitation sources.

It is generally true in photography that the two factors governing the exposure, the intensity and the time, act independently. This is not true for the low levels of intensity and the corresponding long exposure times (>2 min) encountered in Raman spectral studies. Photographic materials under these conditions suffer a loss in sensitivity. This loss in sensitivity is known as the reciprocity effect and is an important factor in photographic Raman spectroscopy. Correction for the reciprocity effect must be made by additional exposure. It is primarily this factor which limits the time integration advantage of the photographic emulsion. Eastman Kodak emulsions designed for exposure times longer than 2 to 5 min and having a higher sensitivity to low-intensity exposures, such as Types 103aO and IIa, are available (93).

The resolving power and the sensitivity of the emulsion are complementary variables. One must compromise resolving power for sensitivity. The complementary character of the sensitivity and resolving power of an emulsion is easily understood. The larger the grain size, the more probable the required number of photons will be absorbed to allow development of the grain. But the larger the grain the less spatial resolution the plate will possess. Most emulsions used in photographic Raman spectroscopy are capable of spatially revolving 50 to 100 lines/mm and are not usually the limiting factor in resolution.

The contrast or slope of the straight-line portion of the characteristic curve will be determined by the temperature of the development bath and the time of the development. Certain developers tend to increase the sharpness or the ability of the emulsion to give a sharp boundary between areas receiving low and high exposures. This quality is referred to as the acutance. It has been reported that the developer Acufine† is useful in low-level intensity exposures (94), but the author's experience with both Acufine and Eastman Kodak D-19 indicates any advantage of Acufine over D-19 to be very slight for Kodak emulsions.

† Bauman Photo Chemicals, Chicago, Illinois.

B. Photoelectric Detection

1. PHOTOMULTIPLIERS

Photoelectric detection is based usually on a photomultiplier consisting of a photoemissive cathode coupled to a current amplifier, all contained in a compact evacuated envelope. The photocathode is a material with a sufficiently low work-function such that electrons are emitted when light quanta or photons of the proper wavelength are incident on the surface. The number of electrons emitted by the photocathode varies as a linear function of the number of incident photons over a wide range of light levels. Any photon of a given wavelength has the same probability of ejecting a photoelectron as any other photon of the same wavelength, and all the photoelectrons contribute in an equal manner to the cathode current. The probability of a given photon ejecting a photoelectron is called the quantum efficiency, Q. The quantum efficiency varies with the wavelength, the variation being a function of the photocathode material.

The photoelectrons are accelerated by an electric field toward surfaces called dynodes which possess the property of emitting more secondary electrons than received in the incident electron bombardment. The ratio of the average number of secondary electrons emitted by a given dynode to the incident electrons on the dynode is designated as the secondary gain, δ. The specific gain, δ, of a given dynode is an average figure and the total gain, $G = \delta^n$, of a photomultipler with n-dynodes is a statistical average. Hence, the multiplication process taking place within the photomultiplier is statistical and varies considerably for each photoelectron ejected from the cathode. This causes current pulses leaving the anode of the tube to vary in size. While the photomultiplier is basically a pulse device, these current pulses will give rise to an average current,

$$\langle i \rangle = eGQN_p \tag{10}$$

where N_p is the number of photons striking the cathode and e is the charge of one electron; the average gain is of the order of 10^6.

The most common photocathodes for tubes used in Raman spectroscopy are bialkalies [e.g. $(Cs)Na_2KSb$] having what is termed an S-20 response. The S-20 photocathode possesses the highest quantum efficiency over the visible spectrum, peaking at greater than 20% in the 4000 Å region. The Ag–O–Cs photocathode with an S-1 response is useful when it is desirable to detect radiation longer than 8000 Å, such as when using a ruby or a

YAG:Nd laser as a Raman excitation source. Typical spectral response curves are shown for both S-20 and S-1 photomultiplier tubes in Fig. 22.

The configuration of the ITT-FW130 photomultiplier (95) tube commonly used in Raman spectrometers is shown in Fig. 23. This tube possesses 16 box-type dynodes and an S-20 type photocathode. The typical operating conditions for such a tube would be 25°C and 1800 V cathode to anode potential. The ITT-FW130 tube is available with various effective photocathode dimensions to match the exit slit of the monochromator with which it is used.

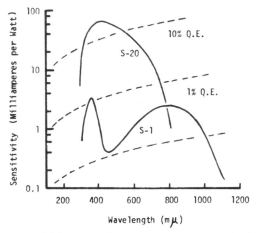

Fig. 22. Sensitivity curves for S-1 and S-20 photocathodes.

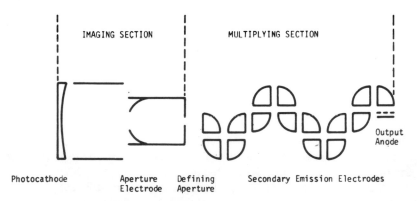

Fig. 23. Diagram of the ITT FW-130 photomultiplier using an electrostatic lens to limit the photocathode aperture. Adapted from material supplied by E. H. Eberhardt of ITT Industrial Laboratories.

It is possible to increase the quantum efficiency of a given photo-cathode by prismatically injecting the light into the photocathode such that multiple reflections occur (96,97), see Fig. 24. Each time the light is reflected from the photocathode there is a probability of causing a photoelectron to be emitted. The net result is a gain in quantum efficiency and an extension of the spectral sensitivity.

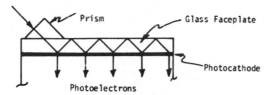

Fig. 24. Prismatic injection of the radiation and internal reflection may be used to increase the effective quantum efficiency of a photomultiplier.

While the photomultiplier is an ingenious and efficient detector of light because of its ability to produce detectable charge bursts in the external anode circuitry for a given single electron emitted from the photocathode, it also suffers from a wide range of noise sources. The term noise is used to designate any fluctuation of the recorded output of the photomultiplier (current or voltage) which limits or interferes with the ability to detect the incident signal radiation (98,99). With no radiation incident on the photomultiplier, the detection system will yield a value of the measured parameter (current or voltage) which is designated as the dark noise. This dark noise may be attributed to noise generated internal and external to the tube. However, external dark noise (e.g., load resistor Johnson noise, amplifier noise, etc.) can be made negligible with proper care. The dark noise generated internal to the tube arises from such processes as thermionic emission from the photocathode and dynodes, leakage currents directly to the anode electrode, cold-field emission from the dynodes, ionic currents caused by the residual gas, residual radio-activity, and cosmic rays. Care is taken in the manufacture of photomultipliers to minimize these causes of noise.

The anode leakage current, all current not originating from electrons passing from the last dynode through free space to the anode, can be an appreciable part of the direct current observed at the anode. This is particularly true in low light level detection where the total current is of the order of 10^{-10} A or less. Assuming the resistance is as high as 10^{13} ohms between the various insulated components of the tube, a potential difference of 1000 V would yield a current of 10^{-10} A in the anode circuit. Furthermore, the leakage current is not strictly ohmic, but is erratic and possesses the high noise content characteristic of sudden discharges. The ITT Industrial Laboratories use an anode guard ring designed to by-pass surface current leakage in the glass stem of the tube directly to ground and have been able to reduce leakage currents to below

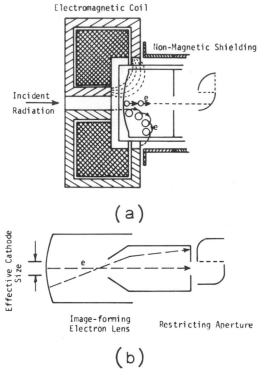

(a)

(b)

Fig. 25. The effective aperture of the photocathode may be reduced by a magnetic lens system (a) or an electrostatic lens system (b). Fig. 25(a) is redrawn from Ref. (*100*), p. 704, by courtesy of *J. Sci. Instruments.*

10^{-12} A (*95*). Even this low level of leakage current may serve to limit the detection of low light levels when the tube is used in a direct current or low frequency alternating current detection system.

The photocathode itself is a source of dark noise primarily because of thermionic emission. The rate at which thermionic electrons will be emitted from the photocathode will follow a Richardson type law (*95*),

$$i = AT^2 \exp\left(-\phi/kT\right) \tag{11}$$

where A is a constant, T is the temperature, k is the Boltzmann constant, and ϕ is the work function. The total number of thermionic electrons which will contribute to the tube current will depend on the effective area of the photocathode and the temperature. The actual area of the photocathode utilized by a Raman spectrometer is usually much smaller than most commercially available photomultiplier photocathodes. One technique used to reduce the photocathode size is the application of a properly shaped magnetic field which causes electrons arising from unwanted portions of the photocathode to miss the first anode (100). A second technique is the use of an image-forming electron lens to generate an electron image of the emitting photocathode in the plane of a small aperture immediately preceding the first dynode. This aperture stops all electrons except those emitted from a restricted area of the photocathode. Both of these techniques, magnetic field reduction and electrostatic lens reduction, yield a comparatively small effective photocathode area, combined with a small bombarded area on the first dynode and effective suppression of the dark emission from the unused portions of the photocathode. These photocathode limiting techniques are illustrated in Fig. 25.

The dark current may be further reduced by cooling the photocathode. The cooling of $S1$ type photocathodes to at least $-20°C$ is recommended for all modes of detection since the dark current falls about one order of magnitude per $10°C$ of cooling near room temperature. Moderate cooling ($-20°C$) of the S-20 type tube is recommended also to improve its performance when used in a photon counting detecting system. Figure 26 demonstrates the decrease of thermionic emission with decreasing temperature for both S-1 and S-20 photocathodes (101). Nakamura and Schwarz (101a) have studied the effect of cooling on photomultiplier tubes and have found the gain in the signal to noise ratio depends on the detection system used.

The dark noise arising from electrons and ions emitted from elsewhere in the tube can be minimized, but not completely eliminated. Such electrons do not in general undergo the full gain of the multiplier section of the tube and may be suppressed by the proper choice of the detection system.

The output of the photomultiplier consists of a dc component and an ac component of current. The ac component commonly is called the shot noise and arises from the emission of electrons from the cathode and dynode surfaces. These shot noise current pulses are of the order of 10^{-9} sec wide and are variable in height. The actual information is carried by both the dc and ac components of the anode output current.

The pulse or ac anode output carries more information than the dc output for low levels of incident light flux. Figure 27 is taken from data supplied by E. H. Eberhardt on an ITT-FW130 photomultiplier tube with an *S*-20 response (*95*). As the level of the incident light flux changes from

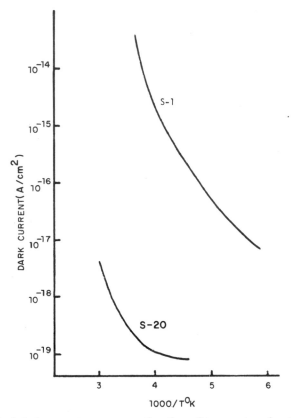

Fig. 26. Typical dark current curves as a function of temperature for *S*-1 and *S*-20 photocathodes.

an extremely low to a moderate level, the output of the tube can be seen to change from essentially a pulsed output to a dc output with superimposed shot noise. These studies very graphically demonstrate the changing character of the output of a photomultiplier tube with the incident light intensity. The scheme used to detect the output of the photomultiplier should be chosen to match the character of the output.

2. DETECTION SYSTEMS

The photomultiplier is normally used in one of four detection schemes:
  1. Direct current amplification
  2. Phase sensitive (lock-in) amplification
  3. Noise-voltage (shot-noise) detection
  4. Electron pulse counting

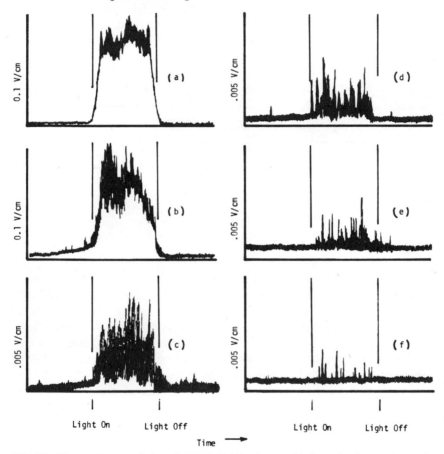

Fig. 27. Output characteristics of ITT FW-130 photomultiplier tube for analog and digital counting modes. (a) Analog operation mode with tube under normal flux intensity with shot noise fluctuations in the signal. (b)–(e) The flux Intensity on the tube is decreased and the shot noise begins to break up into single electron pulses. (f) At the lowest flux intensity only single electron pulses are present, and the tube is operating in the digital mode. These data have been redrawn for reproducibility from ITT Industrial Laboratories Application Note E5.

Direct current amplication is the easiest but also the least sensitive method. When the light signal is of sufficient power to yield photomultiplier currents of the order of 10^{-9} A, the output of the tube may be fed into a high quality direct current amplifier or ammeter as is shown in Fig. 28. The dark current is not discriminated against in such a system and both the signal current, i_s, and dark current, i_d, are amplified and recorded. One must take care to insure that the photomultiplier used in such an amplification scheme possesses a low leakage current. In principle the same sensitivity may be achieved in dc detection as with lock-in detection. However, the dc technique is severely limited by drift caused by anode current leakage and light leakage, and the fact that low level dc amplifiers are less stable and more difficult to construct than ac amplifiers.

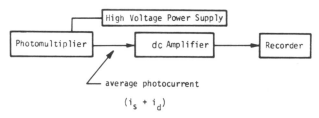

Fig. 28. Block diagram of a simple dc detection system.

For these reasons dc detection is limited usually to high level signal detection, where the signal current is much greater than the dark current.

If the light signal incident upon the photomultiplier is modulated by a mechanical chopper system, an ac amplifier tuned to the modulation frequency, f_s, may be used in the detection system. Such a system has the advantage of higher stability and frequency discrimination over dc detection, but it amplifies all signals of frequency f_s regardless of the phase of the signal. Since the phase of the signal is established by the mechanical chopper, it is feasible to use a lock-in signal processing technique *(102,103)*. The signal from the photomultiplier is fed into a lock-in amplifier *(103)* such as is shown in Fig. 29. The signal usually is preamplified by a low-noise, wide-band amplifier and then increased again in level by an amplifier of moderate bandwidth tuned to the known frequency, f_s, of the signal. The signal at this point is fed into a detector where rectification of the signal occurs. The detector must have as narrow a bandwidth as possible and must be designed such that the centre frequency of the detector does not drift away from the frequency, f_s, of the signal. The synchronous or lock-in detector, the heart of this technique, is essentially a mixer that multiplies the information signal $(f_s + \Delta f)$, by a reference signal at the frequency, f_s, which has a definite phase relationship with respect to the information signal. The reference signal is generated most conveniently by the same mechanical chopper which modulates the incident light flux. The center frequency of this narrow bandwidth detector is locked to the carrier frequency, f_s, and thus avoids drift problems. The mixing produces a lower-side band of frequencies, Δf, about zero frequency and an upperside band as $2f_s$. The upper-side band is eliminated by a simple RC low pass filter immediately following the detector. The output from the low pass filter will be a constant which depends on the level of the information signal and the level of the reference signal multiplied by

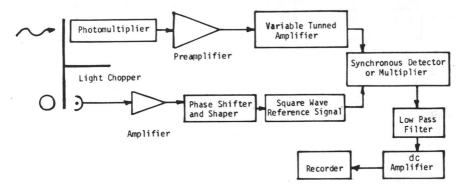

Fig. 29. Block diagram of a phase sensitive detection system.

cos ϕ, where ϕ is the phase angle between the reference and the information signal. When the reference signal and the information signal are in phase, the synchronous rectifier has a maximum dc output. The level of the dc signal at this point is sufficient such that further dc amplification may be used, and the inherent drift of such amplification may be neglected. This detection scheme is the most widely used for low level signal processing and commercial lock-in detection systems are available (103).

Pao et al. (104,105,106) suggested the processing of low level light signals by the detection of the shot noise associated with the signal. Even though the light intensity may be assumed to be constant at low light levels, the output of the photomultiplier fluctuates with time. This fluctuation or "shot noise" is caused by the discrete and random nature of the photoelectric emissions occurring in the multiplication process in the tube as has been discussed in the section on photomultiplier tubes.

(See Fig. 27.) The output current consists of a dc component which is normally called the signal and the associated ac shot noise. For low light levels there is more power in the ac portion of the output than in the dc portion, and the shot noise power varies in a linear manner with the incident light intensity (*107*). In the shot noise detection system the dc portion of the output is eliminated and the shot noise is amplified and detected. The noise–voltage system is shown in Fig. 30. The current from the photomultiplier tube passes through a resistance R to ground and develops the voltage signal to be processed. The average dc power is V^2/R and the average ac power density at a frequency ω is $\langle \delta V(\omega) \rangle^2/R$.

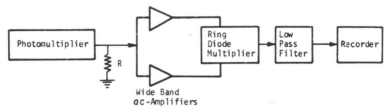

Fig. 30. Block diagram of a shot-noise detection system.

The voltage signal is sent through a high pass filter to eliminate the dc portion of the signal, and the ac portion of the voltage signal is split and sent through two identical wide band amplifiers. The signals from the two amplifiers are fed into a ring diode multiplier or correlator (*108*) to yield $(\delta V)^2$. A low pass filter extracts the dc component of $(\delta V)^2$, which may be fed to a recorder. The use of two identical wide band amplifiers in parallel paths aids in reducing amplifier noise because the noise in one of the paths is uncorrelated with the other and is eliminated to some extent in the correlation mixer system. The same detection system can be used with a single wideband amplifier followed by a simple rectifier or linear detector (*104*). It should be noted that the noise–voltage correlation system is quite economical. Both systems have been used in Raman spectroscopy (*57,104,106,109*).

The fourth method used for the detection of low light levels is a system which has been used for many years in nuclear and x-ray spectroscopy but is only now being used in visible spectroscopy. In this technique, the electron pulses which occur at the anode of the photomultiplier are counted individually by fast electronic circuitry. Since the electron pulses are correlated with the photons striking the cathode, the technique is usually called photon counting (*95,110–113*); a typical photon counting system is shown in Fig. 31.

The pulses of current from the anode are fed into a low noise, pulse shaping preamplifier (e.g., Tennelec Model TCM170, Hammer N-302), which amplifies all current pulses equally and then shapes or broadens the output pulses. The output from this amplifier will include not only the photoelectron pulses (information) but also noise pulses arising in the photomultiplier tube. Those noise pulses arising from ionization of gases in the tube are usually many orders of magnitude greater than photoelectron pulses. Those noise pulses arising from electrons ejected at random from the dynodes will be smaller in height than the photoelectron pulses since they do not travel the full length of the multiplier section. If the output of shaped pulses is fed into a single-channel, pulse-height analyzer, which discriminates against pulses below a preset height, h_1, or against pulses greater than a height, h_2, a significant number of the noise pulses are rejected, and an increase in the signal to noise ratio may be achieved.

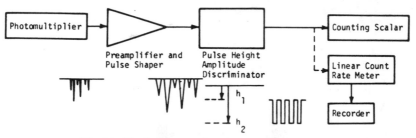

Fig. 31. Block diagram of a photon counting system.

Unfortunately, thermionic electrons emitted from the photocathode will have the appearance of information pulses at the anode and cannot be electronically discriminated against or eliminated. These thermionic noise pulses are best eliminated by limiting the effective size of the photocathode and cooling the photocathode as has been discussed previously. Baum (114) has reported dark counting rates as low as 10 counts/min by cooling to dry ice temperatures.

The output from the discriminator may be fed into a decade scalar which is set to count over a preset time interval, T (1 to 10^4 sec), or the signal may be fed into a linear count rate meter which will extract a dc level from the array of pulses with a variable time constant. The use of a rate meter is not as sensitive as the decade scalar, but the output may be conveniently fed into a strip recorder.

Morton (110) has outlined the technique to maximize the signal to noise ratio (S/N), in photon counting by proper setting of the energy "window" of the discriminator. The photon counting system measures the number of pulses in a time interval T falling in the range between h_1 and h_2 as set on the discriminator. This count consists of the sum of the signal pulses N_s and noise pulses N_d. The average number of noise or dark pulses $\langle N_d \rangle$ can be measured by the dark pulse distribution with the tube

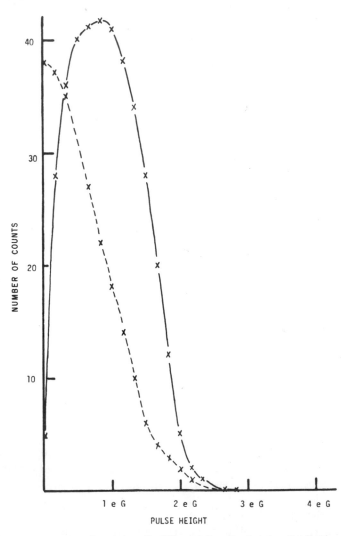

Fig. 32. Single electron integral and differential pulse height distribution curves. RCA type 4501 photocathode, K_2CsSb, counting time 10 minutes. These data redrawn from Ref. (*110*), p. 3, courtesy of Applied Optics and the author.

capped. A number of studies have been made to determine the pulse height distribution in the output of photomultipliers (110,111). The single electron integral and differential dark pulse height distribution curves of an RCA type 4501 photocathode (K_2CsSb) for a 10 min counting interval are shown in Fig. 32. The difference between the total count, $N_s + N_d$, and the dark pulse count represents the signal count. The rms error in the total number of counts is given by $\Delta N_{rms} = (N_s + N_d)^{\frac{1}{2}}$, and the signal to noise ratio is given by

$$R = (S/N) = \frac{(N_s + N_d - N_d)}{(N_s + N_d)^{\frac{1}{2}}} \tag{12}$$

Since both N_s and N_d are functions of h, the signal to noise ratio may be optimized by setting (dR/dh) equal to zero. For the situation where $N_d \gg N_s$, then $R = N_s/\sqrt{N_d}$ and the minimum percentage error is given by

$$\frac{d}{dh} [\ln N_s - \tfrac{1}{2}\ln N_d] = 0 \tag{13}$$

If one plots the single photoelectron pulse height distribution curve and the dark pulse distribution curve on log paper, the proper settings for both h_1 and h_2 may be obtained. Figure 33 shows such curves as obtained by Morton (110) for the RCA-4501 photomultiplier. The dark count for this particular tube is about 2270 pulses per min and the rms deviation is of the order of 48 counts/min. The accuracy of this counting technique improves as the square root of the counting time interval, $\sqrt{T}$. For this particular tube, at the peak of the spectral response ($Q = 30\%$), the minimum detectable signal is of the order of 3 photons/sec.

When N_s is greater than N_d, the pulse height discriminator should be set to a value of h_1 as small as possible to maximize the signal to noise ratio.

The photomultiplier tubes being designed and constructed today have extremely small dark counts when used properly. The photoelectron counts shown in Fig. 27 for a ITT-FW130 photomultiplier give some indication of the quality that may be expected from commercially available tubes. The ITT-FW130 tube used in the author's laboratory at a cathode temperature of $-25°C$ yields a measured dark count of about 1020 counts/min with a rms deviation of 32 counts/min.

Arecchi et al. (113) have designed a system which is a hybrid of photon counting and lock-in detection; such a system is shown in Fig. 34. A high gain photomultiplier is used with a chopped incident light flux in a photon counting system. A gate and switching circuit is triggered by the mechanical chopper such that during a time τ of the on-cycle $(N_s + N_d)$ counts are stored in the (+) or add channel of a bidirectional counter and during a time τ of the off cycle (N_d) counts are stored in the ($-$) or subtraction channel of the counter. The count time τ will be less than or equal to the time t_o of the off- or on-period. The output of the counter is simply $[(N_s+N_d)-N_d]$. With no input signal, the system measures the rms deviation of the dark count during the integration time T. The integration

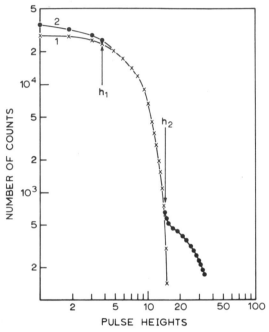

Fig. 33. Single electron response (1) and dark pulse distribution (2) of tube type RCA 4501 (counting time 10 minutes). The proper discriminator settings are given by h_1 and h_2. Reprinted from Ref. (*110*), p. 4, courtesy of Applied Optics and the authors.

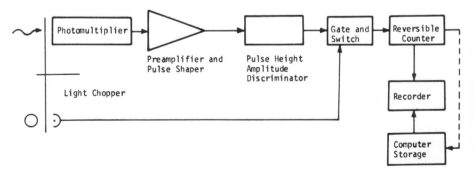

Fig. 34. Block diagram of a synchronous photon counting system.

time of the reversible counter may be set with an electronic timer, or the output may be fed into a two-address computer storage. Using such a technique the integration time T may be greater than the chopping period t_o. The signal to noise ratio is given by ($110,113$)

$$S/N = \frac{[(N_s/t_o)\tau]T}{\left[\left(\frac{2N_d}{t_o}+\frac{N_s}{t_o}\right)\tau T\right]^{\frac{1}{2}}} \tag{14}$$

The signal to noise ratio increases as the square root of the integration time, but will be less than the signal to noise ratio of the common counting system for equal observation times. However, the system does offer a constant measurement of the dark count *in situ*, and a certain degree of ease of measurement.

Photon counting systems have not been used widely but are becoming more common. The major reason is simply that packaged commercial photon counting systems have not been available, although the necessary commercial components may be assembled. Spex Industries now markets the combination ER-3 photon counting and direct current electronic readout system. This system consists of a ITT-FW130 photomultiplier coupled to either a counter system with variable discriminator and rate-meter or a dc picoammeter. The output of either the ratemeter or the picoammeter is fed to a stripchart recorder. In addition, Solid State Radiation Inc. (*114a*) has announced a new photon detection package with both digital and analogue output. This is a system designed specifically for photon counting with a PMT rather than a system constructed from nuclear instrumentation modules. Miller (*114b*) has described an inexpensive circuit utilizing integrated circuits for a photon counting system. The author has constructed this system and is quite pleased with its performance. There are a number of considerations which must be taken into account in the assembly of a photon counting system (*110–112*). The electronic circuitry must have low noise. The photomultiplier should be selected for maximum quantum efficiency and a low dark count. Several manufacturers have photomultiplier tubes which are selected for their photon counting ability, and they are well worth the premium cost.

The comparison of detection techniques is not easy. However, because of the increased interest in the Raman effect and in the detection of low light levels in general, much experience has been gained with the various techniques. Alfano and Ockman (*109*) have undertaken the evaluation of the lock-in, noise-voltage, and photon counting techniques for Raman detection. An EMI 9558 Å photomultiplier operated at 1250 V was used with all three techniques; each associated electronic circuit was of high quality. Since it is well established that the lock-in technique is far superior to the dc detection technique, their results indicate that the order of increasing sensitivity of the techniques is as follows: (1) dc detection, (2) lock-in detection, (3) noise-voltage detection, and (4) photon counting detection. Their results which appear in agreement with other indications (101a,105,110,112) are summarized in Table 2. It should be noted that the values of the photomultiplier signal and dark currents were not measured, but are instead calculated values based on the (s/n) ratios and theoretical expressions based solely on shot noise theory. These theoretical expressions do not include any allowance for other noise contributions, such as $1/f$ noise or noise differences between the different detection systems.

More recently Anderson and Cleary (109a) have measured the signal and dark currents for dc measurement of the photomultiplier anode current, lock-in detection, noise voltage detection, and a combination of the noise voltage and lock-in detection (109b). All detection schemes were examined with the same equivalent noise bandwidth and with a constant light flux within a small band of wavelengths from a standard tungsten source. Their results are summarized in Table 3. The (s/n) ratio of the combined noise voltage and lock-in detection system is not enhanced appreciably over the standard noise voltage detection system, but the combined system is capable of discriminating against nonmodulated background radiation and $(1/f)$ type amplifier noise.

TABLE 2

Experimental Comparison of Detection Techniques[a]

	Lock-in	Noise voltage	Electron pulse counting
$(S/N)_{observed}$ (peak-peak noise)	8.2	27	32
$(S/N)_{observed}$ (rms noise)	41	135	160
Observed signal current	6.0×10^{-11} A	16×10^{-11} A	10.4×10^{-11} A
Collected light power	2.5×10^{-15} W	6.7×10^{-15} A	4.3×10^{-15} W
Dark current	2.3×10^{-10} A	3.1×10^{-10} A	6.4×10^{-12} A
Minimum detectable signal	1.4×10^{-12} A	1.0×10^{-12} A	3.2×10^{-13} A
Minimum detectable light power	5.7×10^{-17} W	4×10^{-17} W	1.3×10^{-17} W

[a] The data presented in this table were obtained from Ref. (109) for the detection of the 992 cm^{-1} Raman band in benzene.

TABLE 3

Experimental Measurement of (S/N) Ratio[a]

Detection technique	RMS (s/n) Ratio at	
	$I_{signal} = 30 \pm 2$ nA $I_{dark} = 90 \pm 2$ nA	7 ± 2 nA 110 ± 2 nA
Theoretical	38	9
DC	4	1
Lock-in	6	2
Noise voltage	16	4
Lock-in plus noise voltage	17	5

[a] The data presented in this table were obtained from Ref. (*109a*). I_{signal} and I_{dark} are the dc photomultiplier anode currents measured with light on and off, respectively.

It should be noted that the photon counting technique is not applicable to moderate level light intensities when the photomultiplier output has the majority of the signal power in the dc component rather than in the pulsed component. The ideal Raman detection system is apparently a photon counting system for low light levels and a simple direct current detection system for moderate and high light levels. The lock-in technique offers a single system which is applicable over the widest range of light intensities but falls short in ultimate sensitivity at the low intensity level.

In selecting or designing the electronics to be used in a low-level light detection system there is no substitute for a thorough knowledge of the characteristics of the primary detector, such as the pulse height distribution and the manner in which this distribution varies with cathode temperature and dynode voltages.

Future improvements may come from some combination of noise-voltage and photon counting systems (*109*), but it is more likely that the greatest improvement will be due to increased sensitivity in the primary detector. It is expected eventually that photoconducting devices, e.g., the photodiode, will replace the photoemissive device. The primary reasons are that photoconductive devices can cover a wider region of the spectrum, and the quantum efficiency of the photoconductor can be made to approach unity over a wide spectral band almost anywhere in the spectrum. The reader is referred to the article on photon counting by Morton (*110*) and the references contained therein for detailed information on the future of photoconductive devices in the detection of low level light intensities. Fisher (*113a*) has compared several popular photomultiplier tubes and P-I-N photodiodes. He has concluded the photodiodes have smaller noise equivalent power and higher quantum efficiencies for the 0.8 μ to 1.0 μ spectral region.

V. COMMERCIAL RAMAN SPECTROMETERS

Instrumentation had to be assembled from components in the early years following the discovery of the Raman effect. The components (source, monochromator, detection system) often had to be home-built if high quality work was to be accomplished. Today many laboratories have Raman instrumentation which has been tailored by the ingenuity

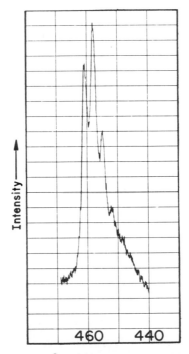

Fig. 35. The 459 cm^{-1} band of CCl$_4$ showing the isotope structure. This spectrum was obtained from a 25 μl cell with a Cary Model 81 Raman Spectrometer using a He-Ne laser and scanning at 0.05 cm^{-1}/sec with a 4 sec time constant. Reprinted courtesy of Cary Instruments.

of the individual investigator, but it is possible to purchase as a complete unit or to assemble commercial components of a state-of-the-art Raman spectrometer. Several commercial Raman spectrometers were available prior to the introduction of the laser as a source, but several others have become available since that time. These instruments all have some common features and certain differences, but any of the available high quality laser-Raman spectrometers may be expected to perform sufficiently well to accomplish any of the following:

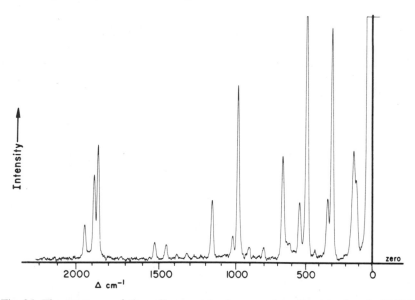

Fig. 36. The spectrum of the yellow powder benzene-chromium-tricarboxyl, (C_6H_6) $(CO)_3$, obtained with a PE LR-1 Spectrometer. This compound fluoresces and decomposes when exposed to the 4358A-Hg line. Reprinted courtesy of the Perkin-Elmer Corporation.

1. Resolve at least three of the peaks corresponding to the chlorine isotope structure of the 459 cm^{-1} band of carbon tetrachloride. (See Fig. 35.)

2. Obtain spectra from colored samples not possible with mercury-excitation. (See Fig. 36.)

3. Obtain high quality spectra from both pressed powder and polymer samples. (See Figs. 8 and 37.)

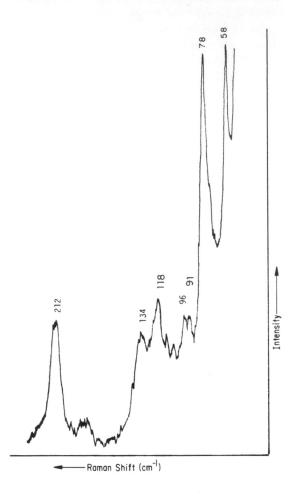

Fig. 37. The spectrum of boric acid powder showing lattice vibrations. The wavenumber is indicated above each band. This spectrum was obtained with a Spex Raman Spectrometer using He-Ne excitation and is reprinted courtesy of Spex Industries.

4. Obtain high quality spectra of gases at one atmosphere pressure without the use of complicated reflection cells. (See Fig. 7.)

5. Obtain high quality spectra from liquid samples of 50 μl or less. (See Fig. 10.)

6. Obtain improved Raman spectra with better polarization data on single crystal samples. (See Figs. 38 and 54.)

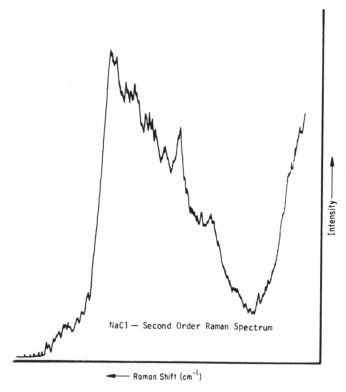

Fig. 38. The second order Raman spectrum of NaCl obtained with the Spex Raman Spectrometer operating in the photon counting mode.

These statements and the associated figures are an attempt to demonstrate the state-of-the-art of modern Raman spectrometers and are probably in the process of being made obsolete as they are written. The optimum performance of a Raman spectrometer still depends upon the ingenuity and patience of the investigator.

A. Applied Physics Corporation (*115*)

The optical schematic of the Cary Model 81 Raman Spectrometer is shown in Fig. 39. This instrument is designed for photoelectric detection and possesses many features desirable for the detection of the weak Raman radiation as excited by mercury arcs. The source is a 3-kW helical, Toronto mercury-arc lamp, which coaxially surrounds the sample. A cooled filter solution circulates around the sample tube. Numerous specialized cells are available for handling small samples (0.2 ml), solid samples, and gas samples.

An elaborate image slicer makes use of the radiation from the entire sample cell and superimposes it on a set of 10-cm high, Shurcliff double slits. The use of a pair of slits gives the light-gathering power of two monochromators working in parallel. Only when working very near the exciting line is it necessary to mask one of these slits in order to decrease the stray radiation.

The double monochromator uses two 1200 lines per mm gratings blazed at 4500 Å in the first order. Both monochromators use the Czerny–Littrow mount in which one mirror serves as both the collimator and telescope mirror. Additional lenses are used to flatten the resultant field. The grating is driven by a cosecant mechanism yielding a recorded output which is linear in wavenumber. The focal length of the collimator is 100 cm and the aperture is 10 cm by 10 cm. The entrance, intermediate, and exit slits are 10 cm high and may be continuously varied from 0 to 1.5 mm, corresponding to a spectral slit width of 0 to 30 cm^{-1}; these slits may be masked at 5 cm and 2.5 cm heights.

The radiation from the monochromator is alternately directed by a semicircular mirror rotating at 30 cps to two matched phototubes (1P-28). Signals of opposite polarity are obtained from these phototubes and are combined and applied to the input of an unbalanced amplifier. This system allows the advantages of ac amplification at the chopping frequency without the normal disadvantage of a 50% loss of energy as in more standard chopping systems. At the same time, nondispersed light from the mercury-arc lamp is chopped by the rotating sector mirror, detected by a reference photomultiplier, amplified, and set through an attenuator to the recorder slide wire. The difference between this signal and the information signal is amplified and synchronously rectified to drive the recorder pen motor.

The original Model 81 has been modified as shown in Fig. 40(a) to make use of Raman excitation by a He–Ne or other laser. A Spectra Physics,

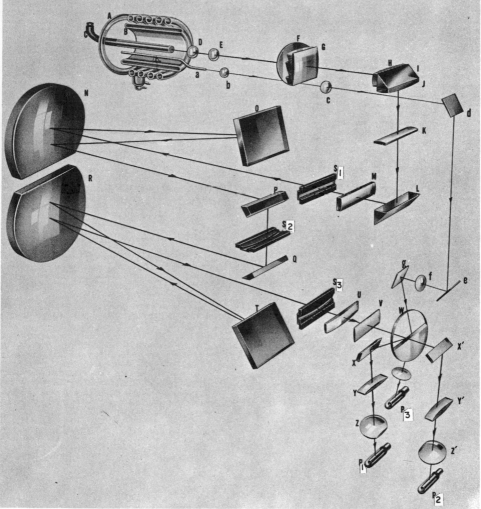

Fig. 39. Cary Model 81 optical diagram. Light from Toronto-type arc lamp A is filtered by fluid in jacket B so that only energy of 4358A wavelength illuminates the sample contained in cell C. Raman light from the end of the sample cell is directed by lenses D and E through collimating lens F to the first image-slicer G. This image-slicer divides the beam into 20 images. These are directed into the 10 sections of the second image-slicer H, each section receiving two images. The second image-slicer, with the aid of lenses J, K, and M, superimposes images of the elements of G into two narrow strips of light in the plane of double entrance slit S_1. Prisms I and L serve only to change the direction of the light. From collimating mirror N the beam is reflected to grating O, then reflected by mirror P through double intermediate slit S_2 to the second mono-chromator. From S_2 it is reflected by mirror Q and the second collimator R to the second grating T, and then directed through double exit slit S_2. Lens U and V direct the beam to rotating mirror W which alternately directs it to phototubes P_1, and P_2 by means of lenses X, Y, Z and X', Y', Z'. The two phototube signals are combined and compared to the reference signal developed by phototube P_3.

Concurrently, part of the filtered lamp radiation is directed by glass light pipe a into an auxiliary optical train (elements b, c, d, e, f, g) to rotating mirror W. It is then directed through lens h to reference phototube P_3 which develops a signal for comparison to the Raman signals from phototubes P_1, P_2. Reprinted courtesy of Cary Instruments.

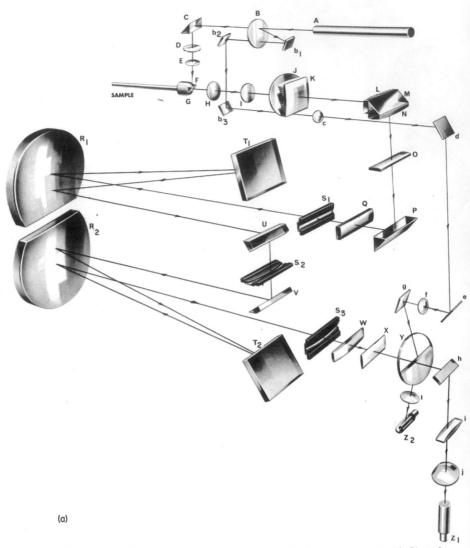

(a)

Fig. 40(a). Cary 81 optical diagram with laser source. Light from laser source A is filtered by isolation filter B which passes energy of 6328 Å wavelength. This energy passes through prism C, half-wave plate D, focusing lens E into very small prism F which directs it into the sample. Raman light from the sample is focused by lens G onto the cell exit lens H which directs it through polarizer I and collimating lens J to the first image-slicer K. This image-slicer divides the beam into 20 images. These are directed onto the 10 sections of the second image-slicer L, each section receiving two images.

The second image-slicer, with the aid of lenses N, O, and Q, superimposes images of the elements of K into two narrow strips of light in the plane of double entrance slit S_1. Prisms M and P serve only to change the direction of the light.

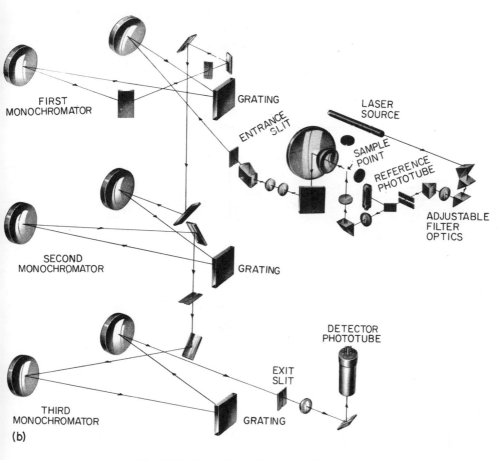

Fig. 40(b). Cary Model 82 optical diagram.

From collimating mirror R_1, the beam is reflected to grating T_1, then reflected by mirror U through double intermediate slit S_3 to the second monochromator. From S_2 it is reflected by mirror V and the second collimator R_2 to the second grating T_2, and then directed through double exit slit S_3.

Lenses W and X direct the beam to rotating mirror Y where it is chopped and directed to phototube Z_1 by means of lenses h, i, and j. The signal from phototube Z_1 is compared to the reference signal developed by phototube Z_3.

Concurrently, part of the laser radiation is reflected by filter B to mirror b_1 which directs it back through filter B into an auxiliary optical train (elements b_2, b_3, c, d, e, f, g) to rotating mirror Y. It is then directed through lens I to reference phototube Z_2 for comparison with Raman signal from phototube Z_1. Courtesy of Cary Instruments.

Model 125, He–Ne laser is mounted on a rigid frame attached to the spectrophotometer. The laser beam passes through a narrow band-pass interference filter and through a half-wave plate which may be used to rotate the plane of polarization. Some of the radiation reflected from the interference filter is sent by an alternate path to the reference phototube. The laser radiation is focused into a sample cell as is shown in Fig. 4f. The radiation from the cell is directed through a polarization analyzer

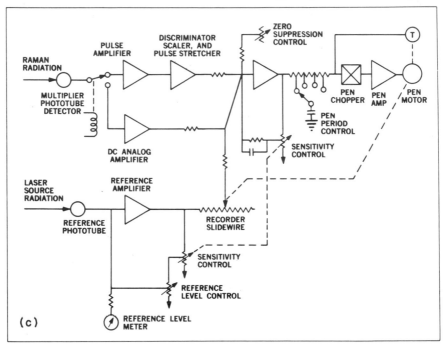

Fig. 40(c). Cary Model 82 electronics block diagram.

into the double monochromator through a pair of Shurcliff slits as described previously.

The phototube compartment has been modified to include a single end window photomultiplier tube (S-20), which replaces the matched 1P-28 phototubes. This single tube may be used with either mercury-arc lamp or laser excitation. The efficiency of this tube is enhanced by making use of multiple reflections (*96,97*) (see Fig. 24). The detection technique is again ac amplification with electronic nulling against the reference signal followed by synchronous rectification.

The Cary Model 81 will scan at any one of 14 speeds ranging from 0.005 cm^{-1}/sec to 10 cm^{-1}/sec, and the chart display may be set at 10, 20, 40, 100, and 200 cm^{-1} per inch. The specifications of the instrument indicate a photometric accuracy and reproducibility of 0.2% and 0.1%, respectively. The wave number accuracy is stated to be 0.5 cm^{-1} over the 0 to 5000 cm^{-1} range with the mercury-arc excitation, and 0.5 cm^{-1} over the 0 to 4000 cm^{-1} range with the laser excitation. The resolution is 1 cm^{-1} and the wavenumber reproducibility is 0.1 cm^{-1}; the stray light is stated to be 1 ppm over the scanning range.

The Cary Model 82 Laser Raman Spectrometer has recently been announced. The Model 82 optical schematic is shown in Fig. 40b and the electronics block diagram is shown in Fig. 40c.

The optical system consists of a triple monochromator using three 1800 line/mm gratings with Chupp-Grantz (*115a*) collimating optics. The Chupp–Grantz off-axis, 530 mm parabolic system yields extremely sharp line images at large slit height to focal length ratios, low *f*-numbers and with sufficiently large enough off-axis angles to eliminate the problems associated with multiple dispersion. The first and second gratings are mounted and driven so as to achieve additive dispersion while the third grating is coupled in a non-dispersive mode to act as a stray radiation filter. The third grating and the Chupp–Grantz mounting allow the stray light to be reduced to less than 10^{-11} at 10 cm^{-1} shifts with a 1 cm^{-1} slitwidth and a fully illuminated 38-mm slit height.

The radiation from the laser source passes through an adjustable optical filter system (*115b*) which may be tuned to pass any laser wavelength and effectively eliminate plasma emission lines. The laser beam intensity is monitored by a reference phototube which senses a small portion of the beam reflected from a glass slide at 45°. The beam is then focused to a diffraction limited spot at the sample point.

The scattered sample radiation is collected by a fast (*f*/1) objective system consisting of an aplanatic lens and an off-axis elliptical mirror. The collected scattered light passes through a system of coupling optics which matches the straight line sample image to the curved entrance slit.

From the entrance slit the radiation is directed into the triple monochromator containing three gratings, six collimating mirrors and two internal slits. All three gratings are mounted on a common drive shaft to maintain tracking accuracy. The radiation leaving the exit slit is focused onto a photomultiplier with a lens system designed to accommodate the specific dimensions of the photocathode.

The four bilateral slits are 38 mm in height and have a range of 0.01

mm to 3 mm in width. The slits may be programmed for either fixed slitwidth or constant spectral bandpass width.

Several low dark-noise photomultiplier tubes may be used with the Model 82 including such tubes as the RCA 31000F with ERMA cathode, the ITT FW 130 with S–20 Cathode or the EMI 6256-S with S–11 cathode. A thermoelectric cooler is available as an option.

Both pulse-rate and dc detection systems are provided. All electronics are solid state. The combination of these two systems provides excellent linearity and a wide dynamic range.

The gratings are driven by a cosecant drive which yields an output linear in wavenumber (cm^{-1}). The scan mechanism and the recorder chart drive are coupled such that the scan speed may be changed during a spectral run without affecting the strip chart recorder scale or position. The scan range extends from 11,800 to 25,000 cm^{-1} and the scan speeds are continuously variable from 0.01 to 100 cm^{-1}/sec. The scan speed may be made $10 \times$ slower by changing the gearing.

B. Applied Research Laboratories (*116*)

The Applied Research Laboratories Raman spectrograph is shown in Fig. 41. The collimator lens has a focal length of 900 mm and a diameter of 100 mm ($f/9$). The dispersion system consists of three extra dense flint 60° prisms having a height of approximately 75 mm and a base of 153 mm. The photographic camera is of the Matsutov type with an effective focal length of 345 mm and an aperture ratio, $f/3.0$. The film holder has a curved film plane and accepts strips of film, 0.313 by 3.92 inches. The height of the spectrum is 5 mm and the total length is 74 mm. The resolution of this instrument is 1.5 cm^{-1} at 4000 Å, 2 cm^{-1} at 4500 Å, and 4 cm^{-1} at 5000 Å. The dispersion is 87 cm^{-1} per mm at 0 cm^{-1} shift, 121 cm^{-1} per mm at 2000 cm^{-1} shift, and 139 cm^{-1} per mm at 3000 cm^{-1} shift.

This instrument is not necessarily supplied with an exciting source, but ARL will supply a Toronto helical mercury-arc system as a separate package.

While the system is basically designed for photographic detection, ARL has adapted the instrument for photoelectric detection. An exit slit scans along the curved focal plane and an attached periscope arrangement transfers the radiation to an externally mounted photomultiplier; the signal is amplified and recorded.

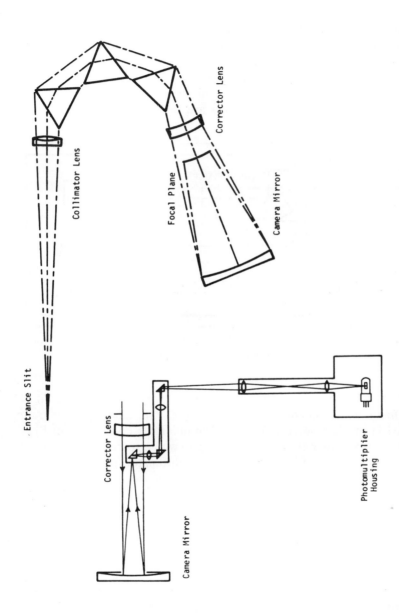

Fig. 41. Optical diagram of the ARL Raman Spectrograph and photoelectric attachment for conversion to a spectrometer.

C. Coderg (*117*)

Two laser Raman spectrometers are manufactured by Coderg in France. Both instruments are designed strictly for photoelectric detection and both feature vertically arranged double monochromators. The curved 30-mm slits are horizontal, which makes it simple to use various types of laser illumination techniques. The scanning speeds range from 1 cm^{-1}/min to 2000 cm^{-1}/min. The instruments are designed to be used with a variety of lasers, illumination systems, and detection system.

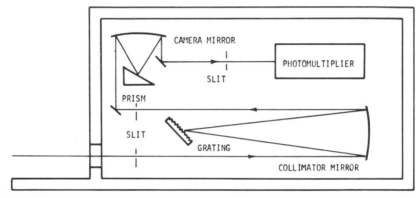

Fig. 42. The optical diagram of the Coderg Chemistry Type Raman Spectrometer The instrument is used in the vertical plane as shown.

The first spectrometer, designated a chemistry type, is shown in Fig. 42. The first monochromator uses a 90 mm by 90 mm, 1200 lines/mm grating blazed in the first order at 7500 Å. The mounting consists of an Ebert–Fastie mirror system (600-mm focal length) with a cosecant drive mechanism. The radiation from the first monochromator passes through an internal slit into a prism monochromator which serves to eliminate stray light and decrease grating ghosts. The second monochromator uses an Ebert–Fastie mirror system with a 300-mm focal length. The radiation passing through the exit slit falls directly on the photomultiplier photocathode. This system permits scanning to within 50 cm^{-1} of the exciting line with a selected resolution of 1, 2, 4, 8, or 16 cm^{-1} at 6328 Å.

The second spectrometer, designated a physics type, is shown in Fig. 43. The system couples together two grating monochromators such as described for the first monochromator in the chemistry instrument. The two gratings are linked together and driven by a cosecant drive mechanism.

This system permits scanning up to the exciting line with a selected resolution of 0.5, 1, 2, 4, 8, 16, 24, 32, 64 cm^{-1} at 4880 Å. The physics type instrument has a provision for mounting the photomultiplier in a vertical position to allow cooling with a dewar system.

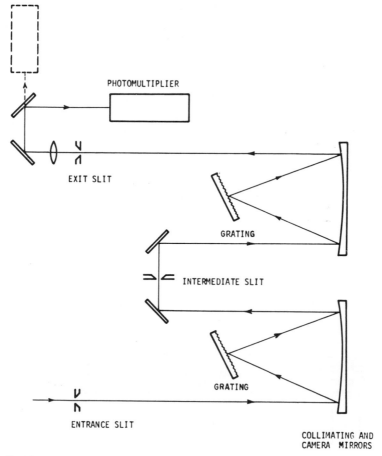

PHOTOMULTIPLIER

EXIT SLIT

GRATING

INTERMEDIATE SLIT

GRATING

ENTRANCE SLIT

COLLIMATING AND CAMERA MIRRORS

Fig. 43. The optical diagram of the Coderg Physics Type Raman Spectrometer. The monochromator is mounted in the vertical plane as shown.

D. Hilger-Watts, Ltd. (*118*)

The Hilger E612 Raman spectrograph consists of a collimator lens with a focal length of 660 mm and a diameter of 86 mm and two glass prisms

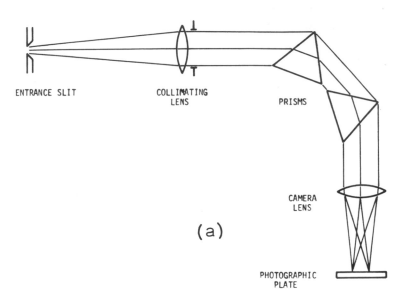

ENTRANCE SLIT   COLLIMATING
                          LENS   PRISMS

(a)

                                        CAMERA
                                        LENS

PHOTOGRAPHIC
PLATE

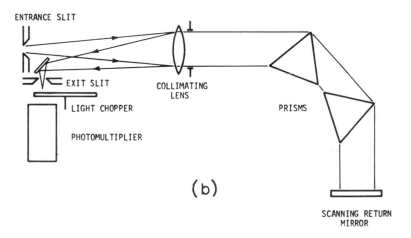

ENTRANCE SLIT

EXIT SLIT   COLLIMATING
                     LENS   PRISMS

LIGHT CHOPPER

PHOTOMULTIPLIER

(b)

SCANNING RETURN
MIRROR

Fig. 44. The Hilger E612 Raman Spectrograph (a) which may be converted to a scanning photoelectric spectrometer (b) in which the prism system is double passed.

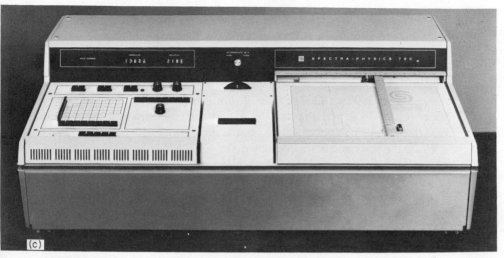

Fig. 44(c). Photograph of the Spectra Physics Model 700 Raman Spectrometer.

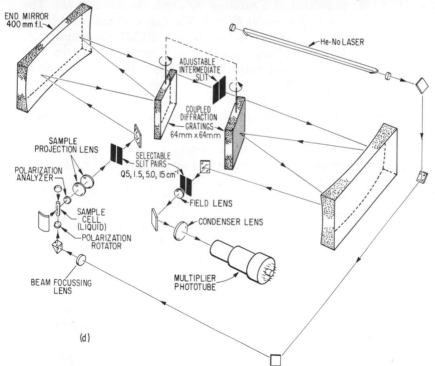

Fig. 44(d). Optical schematic of the Spectra Physics Model 700.

as shown in Fig. 44(a). The instrument may be used in a photographic mode of operation with a $f/5.6$ or a $f/1.5$ camera, or it may be double-passed and used in a photoelectric mode of operation. Both cameras may be mounted on a rotating mount on the spectrograph. The $f/1.5$ camera has a dispersion of 64 Å per mm at 4358 Å and the spectrum is covered from 3900 to 8000 Å in a 29 mm length. The $f/5.7$ camera has a dispersion of 16 Å per mm at 4358 Å and the spectrum is covered from 3900 to 6000 Å in a 86 mm length; both cameras use $4\frac{1}{4}$ by $3\frac{1}{4}$ inch plates.

While the instrument was designed for 4358 Å mercury-arc excitation, realignment jigs are available which allow the prisms to be shifted such that the 6000 to 10,000 Å region is covered, and helium-neon or ruby laser excitation may be used. The dispersion of the instrument is approximately doubled, but the operating conditions are not optimized.

The spectrograph may be converted to photoelectric operation as is shown in Fig. 44(b); a scanning mirror is placed in the camera position and the radiation is double passed through the prisms. An additional curved exit slit is located at a position 90° from the entrance slit. The dispersion is 6.8 cm^{-1} per mm at 4358 Å. The radiation passing through the exit slit is chopped and then is focused on an EMI photomultiplier. The output is ac amplified and synchronously rectified in phase with the chopping frequency, and then displayed on a Brown, high-speed, potentiometric recorder. The exciting source is monitored and the gain of the amplifier is adjusted automatically to compensate for intensity fluctuations. The system allows scanning rates of 15, 30, 60, and 180 cm^{-1} per minute.

The standard source consists of a system of low-pressure mercury discharge lamps mounted coaxially around a sample tube holder.

E. Jarrell-Ash Company (*119*)

Jarrell–Ash have recently announced a Model 25–300 laser Raman system. The instrument uses two one-meter Czerny–Turner mounted grating monochromators to achieve a dual monochromator system as shown in Fig. 17. The gratings are mounted one above the other on a common pivot in order to reduce the tracking problem to a minimum (*91*). The optical path in the second monochromator is reversed from the optical path in the first monochromator and double dispersion is not gained (*88*). The gratings, 102 mm by 102 mm, are ruled 1180 lines per mm and are blazed at 5000 Å in the first order. The stray light at the exit slit is stated to be 2.5×10^{-9} at 12.5 cm^{-1} (5 Å) away from the 6328 Å exciting line. A servomechanism automatically adjusts the width of all the slits in order to maintain a constant spectral slit width while scanning in wavenumber.

The instrument is equipped with a 12-speed cosecant grating scan drive with speeds from 0.01 cm^{-1} to 25 cm^{-1} per min. Digital readout is displayed on two counters reading directly in wavenumbers with an accuracy of ± 1 cm^{-1}. One counter reads absolute wavenumber, and the second counter reads the shift in wavenumbers from the exciting line.

A removable mirror between the first and second monochromators allows the first monochromators to be used with a camera accessory.

Any suitable laser may be mounted below the monochromator and the laser beam is deflected upward into the sample cavity area with Brewster prisms. The sample chamber has an available volume of 66 cm in width, 85 cm in length, and 60 cm in height, and will accommodate a number of illumination systems.

The detection system consists of a thermoelectrically cooled ITT-FW130 (S-20) photomultiplier with a slit-shaped photocathode coupled to a photon counting system. The ratemeter output of the photon counting system is ratioed against the laser intensity and recorded.

F. Spex Industries, Inc. (*120*)

The optical schematic of the Spex Industries Model 1400 double, 3/4-meter Czerny–Turner monochromator is shown in Fig. 16. This optical unit, which may be used as a single or double monochromator in a photoelectric mode of operation or as a single monochromator in a photographic mode of operation, forms the dispersion system of the Spex Laser Raman Spectrometer. The monochromator has a $f/6.8$ aperture ratio and is supplied normally with a matched pair of 1200 lines per mm gratings (102 mm by 102 mm) blazed at 5000 Å. The gratings are driven by a sine-bar arrangement which yields a spectral output with wavelength as a linear function of the drive–screw rotation. An electronic servomechanism coupled to the stripchart recorder yields a trace which is linear in wavenumber. The scanning speeds may be varied between 0.12 and 2300 Å/min. The bilateral, curved slits may use up to a maximum height of 50 mm; resolution is 0.08 Å at 6328 Å. The wavelength counter mechanism is stated to be accurate to 1 Å and to be reproducible to 0.2 Å over a 6000 Å wavelength interval. Light at the exit slit is stated to be 10^{-8} at 10 Å away from the 6328 Å exciting line.

Other gratings are available for the system; a photographic camera may be placed either at the exit slit of the first monochromator or on an additional tower on top of the spectrometer. These features add to the versatility of the instrument. Spex recently has introduced the Model 1401 double monochromator, which uses a cosecant drive mechanism on the coupled gratings to achieve an output which is linear in wavenumber. Digital readout is displayed on two counters reading directly in wavenumbers; one reads absolute wavenumbers, and the second reads the shift in wavenumbers from the exciting line. In all other respects this instrument is similar to the Model 1400 series.

The Spex Raman spectrometer is available as a complete system, tailored to meet the specific needs of the individual investigator. The basic instrument is supplied with a Spectra-Physics, Model 125 He–Ne laser and the compact illumination system shown in Fig. 5. The illumination system includes a half-wave plate for polarization rotation, an interference filter for exciting line isolation, a lens focusing geometry, and a variety of sample mounts (liquid cell, microliter liquid cell, opaque sample holder, and a single crystal goniometer). The Raman radiation is transferred via a lens magnification system (49) through an optional polarization analyzer to a quartz wedge depolarizer into the monochromator. The photomultiplier is an ITT-FW130 which may be cooled to $-25°C$ with a thermoelectric cooler or cooled to $100°K$ with an optional photomultiplier cryostat. Three detection systems are available:

1. ER1: dc-amplification
2. ER2: lock-in amplification
3. ER3: dc amplification and photon counting.

The system has been designed such that any laser or detection scheme may be easily accommodated.

G. Perkin-Elmer Corporation (83)

The first photoelectric Raman instrument produced the Perkin–Elmer Model R, consisted of a helical, Toronto mercury-arc excitation system and a converted infrared spectrometer. The present Perkin–Elmer LR-1 was the first commercial laser Raman spectrometer. The optical schematic of the LR-1 monochromator, a modified Model 99-G double pass monochromator equipped with a 1440 lines per mm grating blazed at 6200 Å in the first order, is shown in Fig. 15. The grating is rotated by a cosecant drive mechanism yielding a spectral output which is linear in wavenumber

(0 to 3800 cm^{-1} shifts). The second-pass radiation appearing at the exit slit is modulated by an internal chopper, while the first pass radiation appears as a dc signal on the exit slit. All reflecting surfaces have multi-layer dielectric coatings to increase the reflectivity (99%). Extensive baffling including a fixed internal slit located at the first pass focus is used to decrease stray light.

The Perkin–Elmer Model 5200 He–Ne laser (2.7 or 6 mw) is mounted in a horizontal position and the output is reflected downward into the illumination region. The illumination schemes favored by Perkin–Elmer are multipass cells, but the focusing technique may be used. An analyzer prism is provided between the sample cell and the spectrometer.

The detection system uses a 14 stage (S-20) photomultiplier tube coupled to the standard Model 107 amplifier, an ac amplifier with synchronous rectification phased with the internal chopper. The output is displayed on a Leeds and Northrup G strip recorder. E. B. Bradley (83a) has reported considerable improvement in the performance of the LR-1 system by replacing the scan motor with a one-sixth rpm motor (Allied Radio Corporation) and replacing the P. E. preamplifier by a Keithley amplifier.

Barrett (49) has used the Perkin–Elmer Model E-1 monochromator, an $f/8$ Ebert-mounted grating instrument, in a single-pass mode of operation with a photon counting system to record Raman spectra of exceedingly small gas samples (see Fig. 7).

H. Spectra Physics

Spectra Physics has produced many of the lasers used with the various monochromators described in this section. Spectra Physics has recently announced the production of a Model 700 Raman spectrometer (120a). The Model 700 is a laboratory bench unit measuring 40 inches long by 23 inches deep (see Fig. 44c). The standard illumination source is the Spectra Physics Model 124A, 15 mW, He–Ne laser utilized in a focused geometry. The system, however, will accept an external input from any laser.

The double monochromator consists of two 40 cm focal length Ebert systems with 1180 1/mm gratings arranged in a back-to-back additive dispersion configuration (see Fig. 44d). An oscillator system provides pulses to a stepping motor which operates the scanning system of the monochromator. The scanning speeds may be varied from 2.5 to 1600

cm^{-1}/min in 14 steps. A set of fixed entrance and exit slits are mounted on a precision indexing slide. These fixed slits allow a choice of spectral band pass of 1, 2, 4, and 8 cm^{-1} as measured at 15,802 cm^{-1}. The intermediate slit is continuously adjustable over the same range as the entrance and exit slits. In addition it has a vertical mask which allows the intermediate slit height to be decreased when a small sample with high Rayleigh scattering is being studied.

The output from the monochromator is focused on the slit-shaped photocathode of an ITT FW-130 photomultiplier tube. A thermoelectric cooler is available as an option. The low level pulse output signal from the tube is amplified with a photon counting system. When the signal level is strong enough to require the gain to be reduced by a factor of 100, a dc detection system is automatically switched in and is used for the remaining levels of amplication. The time constant is automatically set when the slit and scanning speed are selected. Most controls are push button operated.

The amplified output is presented on one axis of an 11 by 17 inches, x–y recorder. The other axis of the recorder is driven by the same pulsing system as the scanning system.

VI. TECHNIQUES OF MEASUREMENT

The intensity of the Stokes-shifted Raman radiation from nonrotating molecules for wavenumber v_j, polarized in a direction ρ, excited by incident radiation of wavenumber v_o and polarized in a direction σ is (121–124)

$$I_{v_j}(\rho) = [2^7\pi^5/135]\frac{(v_o - v_j)^4 \cdot b_j^2}{(1 - e^{-hcv_j/kT})} g_j N(\alpha'_{\sigma\rho})_j^2 I_{v_o}(\sigma) \qquad (15)$$

$$I_{v_j}(\rho) = K(v_j)(\alpha'_{\sigma\rho})_j^2 I_{v_o}(\sigma) \qquad (16)$$

where b_j is the zero-point amplitude, g_j is the degree of degeneracy, N is the number of molecules in the scattering volume, and $(\alpha'_{\sigma\rho})_j$ is the $\sigma\rho$-component of the derivative of the polarizibility tensor with respect to the normal coordinate q_j evaluated at the equilibrium position. The value of $K(v_j)$ may be obtained by comparing the two equations. Measurements may be made to determine (1) the center frequency associated with the Raman band, (2) the degree of polarization of the Raman scattered light with respect to the polarization of the incident light, (3) the band contour, and (4) the relative or the absolute intensity of the scattered radiation (see Fig. 45). Measurements of the wavenumber shifts of the center frequency associated with Raman bands are the most commonly reported data, but information as to the state of the polarization of bands has become common since the advent of photoelectric recording. The measurement of intensities is a difficult experimental problem in the Raman effect since the difference between the incident intensity I_{v_o} and the scattered intensity I_{v_j} can be of the order of 10^6 or greater. Furthermore, the scattering geometry for extended sources poses formidable problems requiring numerous corrections to the raw data (*1,123,125,126*). Only a limited amount of information has been published concerning Raman

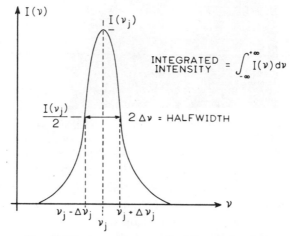

Fig. 45. Contour of a generalized Raman band.

intensities and Raman band contours. The well-defined polarization and scattering geometry of laser excitation can be expected to make a significant contribution to the measurement techniques of Raman intensities.

A. Wavenumber Shifts

An iron arc spectrum is usually photographed adjacent to the Raman spectrum when the excitation wavelength is in a region where there is an abundant number of iron lines, such as for Hg or Ar^+ excitation. The iron arc spectrum is a particularly good comparison spectrum since there are at least 306 iron lines accepted as secondary wavelength standards in the spectral region between 6677 Å and 2447 Å, and 312 iron lines accepted as tertiary standards in the spectral region between 3371 Å and

6750 Å (*80*). The wavelengths of the secondary standards are believed to be correct to 0.002 Å, while the wavelengths of the tertiary standards are correct to at least 0.05 Å. A neon comparison spectrum may be placed on the photographic plate when a He–Ne laser is used for Raman excitation. Numerous neon wavelengths in the region of the 6328 Å He–Ne line also have been adopted as secondary wavelength standards.

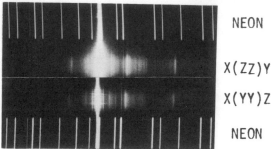

Fig. 46. The Raman spectrum of CdS showing two hour exposures on 103 aF emulsion of the *x(zz)y* and *x(yy)z* geometries. (See page 271 for explanation of the notation.) A comparison neon spectrum is shown above and below the Raman spectra.

The use of a neon comparison spectrum facilitates identifying "leaky" neon lines in the Raman spectrum. Figure 46 shows a Raman spectrum of a CdS crystal with a neon comparison spectrum. The ideal choice for a laboratory wavelength standard is a hollow cathode lamp with an iron cathode and a neon gas fill. This form of lamp yields extremely sharp iron lines and the fill gas provides the neon lines needed in the red spectral region.

The wavelength or wavenumber *in vacuo* of the Raman band may be determined by extrapolating between the known wavelengths or wavenumbers of the lines in the comparison spectrum. The measurements needed for the interpolation may be made directly on the plate with a traveling microscope or comparator, or measurements may be made on a photographic enlargement of the original plate. The interpolation may be linear between two nearby standard lines. If the dispersion curve of the instrument is changing rapidly in the spectral region of interest, it is better to plot an extended dispersion curve and fit the data to a dispersion formula, such as the Hartmann formula

$$\lambda = \lambda_o + \frac{C}{(d_o - d)} \tag{17}$$

where λ_o, C, and d_o are constants. The use of such a dispersion formula with a computer allows rapid calculation of the position of many Raman bands, plus the calculation of the positions of known standard wavelengths to allow checking for accuracy. The wavenumber shift of the Raman band is given by the difference between the wavenumber of the excitation wavelength and the wavenumber of the Raman band.

In high resolution studies, it is possible to measure the relative shifts of rotational Raman lines to at least ± 0.05 cm^{-1}. However, it was common, until recently, for Raman data to be reported with a relative accuracy of 5 cm^{-1}.

Photoelectric recording spectrometers are usually equipped with event markers which place a "pip" on the recording at specified spectral intervals. The scale of such instruments should be checked regularly with a spectral standard, such as a neon lamp or a known Raman spectrum, to insure the calibration of the instrument. Nonlasing lines from a gas laser are often useful for calibration purposes.

B. Polarization and Angular Dependence

The exact details of the technique used to measure the state of the polarization and angular dependence of Raman scattered radiation depends to a large extent upon the state of the scattering medium (gas, liquid, or solid). All techniques which are used may be divided into three categories as follows: (a) the use of natural or unpolarized incident radiation and the analysis of the scattered radiation in terms of its polarization (127), (b) the use of polarized incident light with no analysis of the scattered radiation in terms of polarization (128), and (c) the use of polarized incident radiation and analysis of the scattered radiation in terms of its polarization (124). The analysis of the data will depend on the technique and whether or not the scattering molecules are allowed to assume all possible orientations, such as in a gas, liquid, or randomly oriented crystallites as in a powder.

1. UNORIENTED SAMPLES

Let us first consider the problem of measuring the state of polarization of a Raman band of a nonoriented sample, such as a gas or a liquid. The scattering molecule is free to assume all possible orientations with respect to the laboratory coordinate system, and the expressions for the intensity as a function of the polarization of the Raman scattered radiation must be averaged over all orientations. This amounts to averaging over all projections of the derivative of the polarizability tensor, α', on the laboratory defined axes. The summations which occur in this averaging process are conveniently replaced by functions of the isotropic part, α, and the anisotropic part, γ, of the derivative of the polarizability tensor (129).

$$\alpha = 1/3(\alpha'_{xx}+\alpha'_{yy}+\alpha'_{zz}) \tag{18}$$

$$\gamma^2 = 1/2[(\alpha'_{xx}-\alpha'_{yy})^2+(\alpha'_{yy}-\alpha'_{zz})^2+(\alpha'_{zz}-\alpha'_{xx})^2+6(\alpha'^2_{xy}+\alpha'^2_{yz}+\alpha'^2_{zx})] \tag{19}$$

The most commonly measured quantity for a Raman band is the depolarization ratio, ρ, defined as the ratio of the scattered intensity which is polarized perpendicular to the polarization of the incident radiation, to the scattered intensity which is polarized parallel to the polarization of the incident radiation; all measurements are made in a direction perpendicular to the propagation direction of the incident radiation. For the geometry shown in Fig. 47, the depolarization ratio may be shown to be given by (129)

$$\rho = 3\gamma^2/(45\alpha^2+4\gamma^2) \tag{20}$$

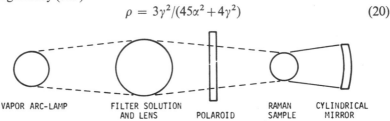

| VAPOR ARC-LAMP | FILTER SOLUTION
AND LENS   POLAROID | RAMAN
SAMPLE | CYLINDRICAL
MIRROR |

Fig. 47. Simple polarization geometry in which the filter solution is used as a liquid lens. Baffles are used usually to restrict the incident radiation to propagation in the plane of the drawing.

A minimum of two measurements are required to determine the depolarization ratio, and Table 4 gives the form of ρ for four possible experimental 90°-geometries. Depolarization values are calculated usually using peak-height ratios, so the values given represent depolarization values at the peak height frequency. The depolarization in the wing of a band may be different from that at the center. The first technique has been the most commonly used with mercury excitation for the determination of depolarization ratios. Using this technique, a completely depolarized Raman band, $\alpha = 0$, will have $\rho = 6/7$, and a completely polarized band arising from a totally symmetric vibration will have $\rho < 6/7$. Figure 48 shows a depolarization illumination system using two Toronto-mercury arcs in cylindrical-elliptical reflectors. One arm of each of the mercury arcs is located at one focus of the elliptical reflector and the Raman sample is located at the second focus. Blackened metal baffles are placed at approximately one-half inch intervals perpendicular to the lamp tubes and Raman sample tube such that radiation incident on the sample is nearly perpendicular to the direction of observation. A liquid filter is usually placed coaxially around the sample tube, and a polaroid sheet with its axis either perpendicular or parallel to the sample tube axis is wrapped around the sample. The data are obtained for both orientations of the polaroid, and the depolarization ratio is calculated as shown by

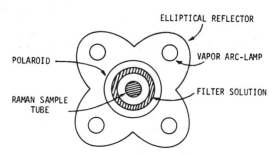

Fig. 48. Polarization geometry using elliptical cylindrical reflectors with a pair of lamps as shown in Fig. 2(a). Baffles are used usually to restrict the incident radiation to propagation in the plane of the drawing.

technique one in Table 4. Since the scattered light is not polarized, no apparatus corrections need to be made. However, the exposures in the case of photographic measurements must be made such that the illumination is constant and the times are equal.

A useful system requiring only one photographic exposure to record all the necessary data for technique three has been devised (*127*). In addition, this system uses a quarter-wave plate prior to the slit to eliminate the apparatus correction.

It is necessary, when using a photographic plate as the detector, to make a plate calibration curve after each set of Raman exposures (*80*). A wide range of relative intensities may be obtained from a continuous unpolarized source by using a sector wheel in conjunction with varying slit widths. The time of exposure of the calibration plate should match, as near as possible, the exposure time of the data plates, and all plates should be developed simultaneously. The plates must be analyzed using a microdensitometer, and the deflection of the calibration plate plotted

TABLE 4

Depolarization Measurement Techniques

Experimental description	Depolarization ratio
No polarization analysis of scattered radiation	$\rho = 6\gamma^2/(45\alpha^2 + 7\gamma^2)$
1. a. Incident light polarized parallel to the observation direction.	
b. Incident light polarized perpendicular to observation direction.	
2. a. Incident light polarized parallel to the observation direction.	$\rho = 6\gamma^2/(45\alpha^2 + 13\gamma^2)$
b. Incident light unpolarized.	
Polarization analysis of scattered radiation	$\rho = 6\gamma^2/(45\alpha^2 + 7\gamma^2)$
3. a. Incident light unpolarized, scattered light observed polarized in a fixed direction.	
b. Incident light unpolarized, scattered light observed polarized perpendicular to the first measurement.	
4. a. Incident light polarized perpendicular to the observation direction, scattered light observed polarized parallel to incident light polarization.	$\rho = 3\gamma^2/(45\alpha^2 + 4\gamma^2)$
b. Incident light polarized as before, scattered light observed polarized perpendicular to incident light polarization.	

versus the log of the relative intensity. See Fig. 20. The intensity, as read from the calibration curve, is given in arbitrary units and depends on the position of the zero of the intensity scale. Since only relative intensities are required for depolarization ratios, the difference of two abscissae from the calibration curve yields $\log(I_1/I_2)$ immediately without any question of the position of the origin. While the photographic technique is quite adequate for the determination of relative intensities and, therefore, depolarization ratios, it is not as well suited for absolute intensity measurements as modern photoelectric techniques.

Photoelectric Raman spectrometers allow the determination of depolarization ratios to be made quite easily. Figure 49 shows the results of a depolarization measurement on potassium ferrocyanide using a

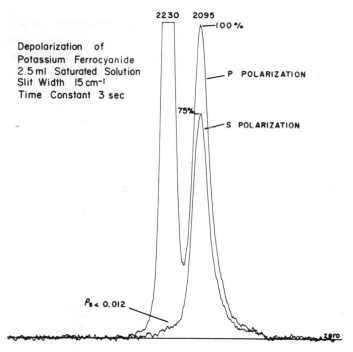

Fig. 49. Polarized spectrum of potassium ferrocyanide as obtained with a PE LR-1 Spectrometer. Reprinted courtesy of Perkin-Elmer Corporation.

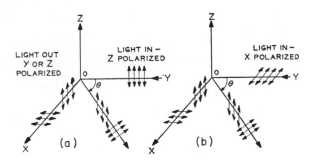

Fig. 50. Geometries used to specify the depolarization ratio and angular dependence of the Raman effect. The sample is at the origin O; the laser is incident in the Y-direction and the scattered light is measured in the XY-plane. At the left (a) the laser light is polarized perpendicular to the XY-plane; at the right (b) the laser is polarized in the the XY-plane. Reprinted from Ref. (*124*), p. 1585, courtesy of *J. Opt. Soc. Am.* and the author.

Perkin–Elmer LR-1 spectrometer. When such measurements are made, care must be taken to correct for or eliminate the difference in the transmission factor of the instrument for different polarizations. In addition, the detection system should be checked to insure that it is linear over the intensity region of interest. This can be accomplished easily with a set of high-speed standard sector wheels. Recently both Classen (*115b*) and Scherer (*129a*) have discussed the problem of measuring depolarization ratios for liquid samples in the highly focused laser sample geometry.

Measurements of the angular dependence of Raman scattering are recent because of the difficulty in obtaining a well collimated Raman source of sufficient intensity. The laser as a Raman source again has solved this problem (*124,130,131*). Considering the experimental situation shown in Fig. 50, Porto (*124*) showed the intensities of the scattered radiation for the two cases to be

$$I^s(\theta) = K(\nu_j)\frac{I_o{}^i[45\alpha^2 + 7\gamma^2]}{45} \tag{21}$$

and

$$I^s_{11}(\theta) = K(\nu_j)\frac{I_o{}^i[6\gamma^2 + (45\alpha^2 + \gamma^2)\cos^2\theta]}{45} \tag{22}$$

where $I^s(\theta)$ is the intensity of the scattered radiation polarized perpendicular to the incident radiation, $I^s_{11}(\theta)$ is the intensity of the scattered radiation polarized parallel to the incident radiation, and $I_o{}^i$ is the intensity of the incident radiation. The angular dependence of a Raman band as a function of its depolarization ratio, when both α^2 and γ^2 are different from zero, is given by

$$I^s(\theta) = K(\nu_j)I_o{}^i\gamma^2[(3 - 4\rho)/\rho], \tag{23}$$

$$I^s_{11}(\theta) = K(\nu_j)I_o{}^i\gamma^2\{6 + [(3 - 3\rho)/\rho]\cos^2\theta\} \tag{24}$$

The measurements may be made by mounting the spectrometer on an arm which rotates about an axis located at the sample position. Figure 51 shows the results of such measurements on benzene and carbon tetrachloride. The bold curve in Fig. 51(a) represents the theoretical curve given by Eq. (22). Very recently measurements of this type on benzene have been made by rotating the laser beam polarization with a half-wave plate and maintaining the sample and spectrometer in fixed positions (*131*). The agreement between theory and experiment is within 2%.

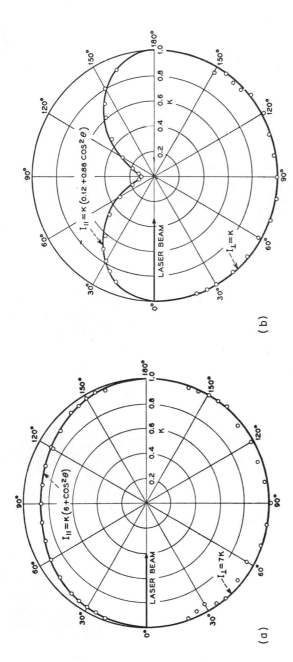

Fig. 51. (a) Angular dependence of the 318 cm^{-1} line of CCl$_4$. The depolarization ratio of this line is 0.75 and the solid curve is the theoretical curve. (b) Angular dependence of the 992 cm^{-1} A$_{1g}$ line of benzene, where the depolarization ratio is 0.065. Reprinted from Ref. (124), pp. 1587–1588, courtesy of *J. Opt. Soc. Am.* and the author.

2. ORIENTED SAMPLES

In the case of liquids, gases, and amorphous solids, the averaging process over all molecular orientations with respect to the incident electric field smears out many of the properties of the polarizability tensor associated with the individual molecules or ions. In the case of a single crystal, where no averaging process is needed, the polarization measurement of a given Raman line yields a direct indication of which of the components of the polarizability tensor change during the vibration, and the angular dependence yields information on the influence of the conservation of momentum of the phonon on the frequency.

Corresponding to each Raman-active mode of a given crystal, there is a polarizability derivative or scattering tensor, α', having a distinctive symmetry. The form of the scattering tensor can be predicted for a vibration of any given symmetry by standard group theoretical methods. Loudon (*132*) has listed the scattering tensors for all 32 crystal point groups and has identified each scattering tensor with the irreducible representations of the Raman-active lattice vibrations by the notation of Wilson, Decius, and Cross (*129*). For example, for the crystal MnF_2 with the rutile structure, D_{4h}, there are four Raman-active modes with symmetries A_{1g}, B_{1g}, B_{2g}, and E_g (see Fig. 52). The associated scattering tensors have the form (*132*)

$$\alpha'(A_{1g}) = \begin{matrix} a & o & o \\ o & a & o \\ o & o & b \end{matrix}$$

$$\alpha'(E_g) = \begin{matrix} o & o & o \\ o & o & d \\ o & d & o \end{matrix}, \quad \begin{matrix} o & o & d \\ o & o & o \\ d & o & o \end{matrix} \tag{25}$$

$$\alpha'(B_{1g}) = \begin{matrix} c & o & o \\ o & c & o \\ o & o & o \end{matrix}, \quad \alpha'(B_{2g}) = \begin{matrix} o & e & o \\ e & o & o \\ o & o & o \end{matrix}$$

The different elements of the matrices, $\alpha_{\rho\delta}$, are the nine components of the tensor obtained by allowing both ρ and σ to take on all values x, y, and z. The values of x, y, and z are the crystal principal axes chosen to be identical with the principal axes defined for the crystal classes by Nye (*133*).

The intensity of the Stokes-shifted Raman radiation in the harmonic oscillator approximation is (*132,133*)

$$I(v_s) = A v_s{}^4 [(n_p + 1)/v_p] (\sum_{\rho\sigma} e_\rho^i \alpha'_{\rho\sigma} e_\sigma^s)^2 \tag{26}$$

where A is a constant, v_s is the Stokes-shifted Raman frequency, v_p is the vibrational frequency of the oscillator, n_p is the occupation number of the initial vibrational state, $e_p{}^i$ is the ρth component of the unit polarization vector of the incident light, $e_\sigma{}^s$ is the σth component of the unit polarization vector of the scattered light, and $\alpha'_{\rho\sigma}$ is the change of

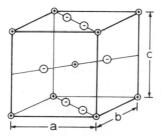

Fig. 52. Tetragonal unit cell for the rutile structure with D_{4h} symmetry. $a = b \neq c$.

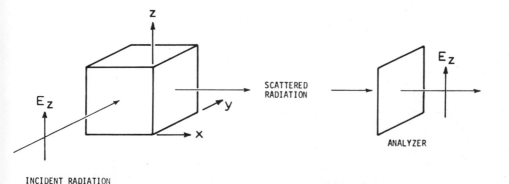

Fig. 53. Geometry for obtaining polarization data on single crystals. The x, y, z axes represent the crystal principal axes, and the geometry of the incident beam and analyzer is set to observe phonons having nonzero values for α'_{zz}.

the polarizability component $\alpha_{\rho\sigma}$ during a vibration having a normal coordinate q_p. A given component of the scattering tensor, $\alpha'_{\rho\sigma}$, may be determined experimentally by arranging the geometry such that the incident light is polarized in the ρ-direction and such that only scattered light polarized in the σ-direction is observed. The geometry in Fig. 53 allows the determination of phonons for which α'_{zz} is nonzero.

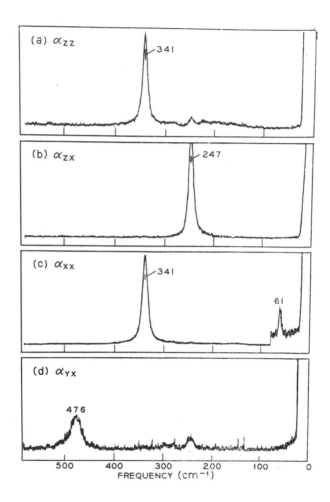

Fig. 54. Raman spectrum of MnF_2; instrumental width $\sim 3\ cm^{-1}$. (a) α_{zz} component showing the A_{1g} phonon at 341 cm^{-1} and a very weak two phonon band. (b) α_{zx} component showing the E_g phonon at 247 cm^{-1}. (c) α_{xx} component showing the A_{1g} and B_{1g} phonons at 341 and 61 cm^{-1}, respectively. The gain is increased by a factor of 10 to show the B_{1g} phonon clearly. (d) α_{yx} component showing the B_{2g} phonon at 476 cm^{-1} and a leakage of much stronger E_g phonon. Reprinted from Ref. (*134*), p. 525, courtesy of the *Phys. Rev.* and the author.

A notation initiated by Porto et al. (55) has proven quite useful in describing polarization data obtained on single crystals. Four symbols, two inside parentheses and two outside, describe the pertinent experimental parameters:

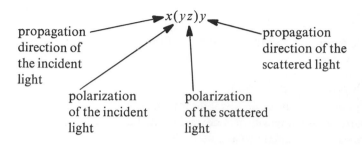

The coordinates within the parentheses indicate the component of the scattering tensor involved. The geometry is always assumed to be 90°-scattering unless otherwise specified.

Care must be taken to insure that the crystal principal axes, as defined by Nye (133), coincide with the laboratory axes. Improper sample orientation complicates the interpretation of the Raman data (132). Porto et al. (134) have demonstrated the variation of the phonon Raman spectrum of TiO_2 with misorientation of the crystal $x–y$ axes and the laboratory $x'–y'$ axes, and have discussed the problems of interpretation of such spectra. Koningstein and Toaning-Ng (134a) have recently made use of an experimental scattering tensor defined in terms of a rotation of the crystal-fixed scattering tensor for cases where it is not possible to properly align the crystal sample.

Figure 54 shows the Raman spectra for different orientations of MnF_2 as obtained by Porto et al. (134) with a Spex Industries Tandem monochromator and a 75 mw, Ar^+-laser (4880 Å) for excitation. The laser was focused into the crystal; the various phonon symmetries are easily observed.

The convergent radiation of the focused laser beam and the necessity of using a finite acceptance angle for collecting the scattered light can cause depolarization effects. Such an effect has been observed in calcite (46). When the intensity of the scattered radiation is sufficient, unfocused, plane-parallel geometry should be used in obtaining polarization data on crystals.

C. Intensities and Band Contours

The measurement of absolute integrated or peak Raman intensities is made experimentally complicated by the large difference between the scattered and incident radiation. The problems associated with such measurements have been discussed at length in the literature (*1,125,126, 135–138*). However, despite the inherent difficulties, the use of photoelectric recording and the persistence of the investigators have resulted in intensity measurements of increasing accuracy. The use of the laser as an exciting source may even make the measurement of intensities relatively straightforward (*131,139,140*).

The measurement of an absolute Raman intensity requires the use of a standard whose intensity is known or can be calculated; several possibilities have been suggested and used.

1. For liquids a standard intensity scale (*125*) has been widely adopted (*136*) which refers to the 458 cm⁻¹ Raman band of carbon tetrachloride taken under the same experimental conditions as the sample. The main difficulty here is the correction to be made for the difference in the index of refraction of carbon tetrachloride and the sample.

2. For gases Yoshino and Bernstein (*126*) have used the measurement of the intensity ratio of Raman to Rayleigh scattered radiation. This method requires the use of an absorption filter to weaken the Rayleigh scattered radiation, and also requires the background of the empty Raman sample tube to be subtracted from the raw data.

3. For gases Golden and Crawford (*137*), proposed using the pure rotational line $J = 1 \rightarrow 3$ of hydrogen (587 cm⁻¹) as a standard. The intensity of the line may be calculated, and the method is independent of the background and needs no absorption filters to decrease the intensity.

4. For a few liquids the Raman cross-section has been measured by direct comparison of the scattered radiation to the incident radiation (*131,139,140*).

The geometry of the illumination system and the large volume of sample (see Fig. 4b) used with mercury arc excitation required a large number of corrections to be made on the raw data. Yoshino and Bernstein (*126*) experimentally determined and made all of the following corrections to their measurements:

1. The theory is based on a uniform, cylindrically symmetrical source of radiation. In practice this cannot be achieved and convergence and nonuniform illumination corrections must be made to account for the lack of cylindrical symmetry.

2. The polarization of the incident radiation is not perfectly defined, due to the Polaroid inefficiency and the reflection and refraction of the light as it passes through the glass sample walls.

3. The multiple-reflection cells required for Raman measurements in gases cause a variation in the intensity enhancement and polarization of the scattered light as a function of wavelength.

4. The spectrometer, including the detector, will have an apparatus transmission function which varies with the polarization and wavelength of the scattered light. Corrections must be made to take into account these transmission and spectral sensitivity factors.

By comparison with theoretical values for hydrogen rotation lines, Yoshino and Bernstein (*126*) showed their corrected intensities were in error by no more than a few percent.

Laser excitation has been used for only a few Raman intensity determinations (*131,139,140*), but these measurements indicate that if the same care is taken as with measurements using mercury-arc excitation, the ease and accuracy of Raman intensity measurements will be considerably enhanced. Laser excitation offers the following advantages in measuring Raman intensities:

1. Only very small volumes of sample are required and multiple-pass cells are not needed even for gases.

2. The illumination of the sample may be made strictly rectilinear, and the cross section of the sample illuminated may be determined accurately.

3. The depolarization of the laser is less than 0.1 %.

4. The power of a laser may be monitored continuously.

The only major corrections needed with the laser illumination scheme are due to the apparatus function of the monochromator.

Skinner and Nilsen (*131*) recently have measured the cross section of the Raman line of benzene occurring at 992 cm^{-1}. The cross section is defined as the power scattered to an angular position (θ, ϕ) per steradian by a single scattering center (e.g., a molecule) in a frequency interval of one cm^{-1} for a given plane of polarization and unit incident intensity.

The cw 130 mw output of an argon ion laser (4880 Å) equipped with a half-wave plate to allow rotation of the plane of the polarization was focused into the sample cell with a 3.2-cm focal length lens. This produced a beam of approximately 50 μ diameter for a length of 1 cm within the sample. The power level of the laser beam was monitored with an EMI 9558 photomultiplier equipped with calibrated optical attenuators to limit the output current to 10^{-6} A and insure that the tube was operating in a linear region of the photocathode. The photomultiplier tube was calibrated with a NBS standard lamp.

The sample cell was a rectangular silica cell in order to simplify the solid-angle correction at the cell to air interfacing. No lenses were used between the sample cell and the spectrometer slits so that the solid angle of collection could be determined directly from the dimensions of the slit.

The spectrometer was a Spex Industries double grating instrument. The resolution with a pair of 12,000-lines/cm gratings used in the second order and 20 μ slit widths was measured to be 0.05 Å. The detector was a cooled EMI 9558 photomultiplier tube, operated such that its dc current never exceeded 10^{-6} A. The detector photomultiplier tube was calibrated against a N.B.S. standard lamp. The dc amplifier was determined to be linear and accurate to within 3 % of full scale reading.

The average value of the Raman peak cross section of the 992 cm^{-1} line of benzene was found to be $d\sigma = 1.05 \times 10^{-29}$ cm^2/molecule, steradian cm^{-1}; the estimated error is about $\pm 8\%$. The linewidth at half peak height was measured to be 2.3 (± 0.5) cm^{-1}. The Raman differential peak cross sections of eight liquids was measured and compared with that of the 992-cm^{-1} line of benzene.

While it is necessary to measure the integrated area (see Fig. 45) of a Raman band in order to determine its integrated intensity, few studies have concentrated upon the determination of band contours. One problem in determining the band contour is the necessary deconvolution or correction of the band shape due to the distortion caused by the apparatus function. If a proper deconvolution of the band shape can be accomplished then it becomes convenient to use the band halfwidth to peak height ratio to measure the intensity of one Raman band relative to another. The laser line provides an ideal source for experimentally determining apparatus functions, and it should be possible to perform the necessary convolution to ascertain true Raman band shapes.

VII. RAPID SCANNING RAMAN SPECTROSCOPY†

The technique of rapid scanning Raman spectroscopy has been developed primarily by Michel Delhaye and his colleagues, M. Bridoux and M. Migeon, at the University of Lille in France. Delhaye reported the initial attempts at rapid scanning Raman spectral studies in 1958 (*141*). The development of this technique by Delhaye et al. (*142–148*) has continued from 1958 when the reported scanning rates were of the order of 6000 to 10,000 cm^{-1} per min over a 350 cm^{-1} spectral region to the present, where information over a 200 cm^{-1} spectral region is recorded in one millisecond. It is Delhaye's goal to reach down to times of the order of 10 nsec. The introduction of giant pulsed lasers and image intensifiers (*148, 149*) to the problem of instantaneously recording Raman data may make this goal feasible. Such Raman data by itself or when combined with rapid scan infrared data should allow the determination of the structures of short-lived molecular species, such as free radicals and electronically excited molecules. Repeated scans using this technique already can provide useful information on the kinetics of chemical reactions (*143*). The perfection of this technique opens many new avenues of research.

The commercial scanning Raman spectrometer usually is capable of scanning at maximum rates of 250 to 1000 cm^{-1} per min. While 1000 cm^{-1} per min is a respectable scanning rate, it is far short of the rate needed to study chemical reactions or excited states of molecules. The first techniques employed by Delhaye (*147*) consisted of rotating a grating (or an equivalent mirror) in a single-pass monochromator, or by moving a prism in the focal plane of a prism monochromator to achieve a double-passing situation. Figures 55 and 56 show simplified sketches representative of two of the many optical configurations used by Delhaye.

The double-passing prism return shown in Fig. 55 is driven in a saw-tooth motion by a cam. The grating shown in Fig. 56 is simply rotated about a vertical axis. The Raman excitation sources may be either continuous or pulsed vapor arcs, primarily mercury arcs. The output from the photomultiplier tube is dc amplified and observed on an oscilloscope whose horizontal sweep is controlled by a potentiometer linked to the

† Much of the information presented in this section was provided to the author most generously by M. Delhaye at the 22nd Symposium on Molecular Structure and Spectroscopy, Ohio State University, Columbus, Ohio, September 1967. Since this chapter was completed, Prof. Delhaye has published an account of his studies (*150*). The author recommends references (*143,146,148*) and (*150*) for those interested in further details of this technique.

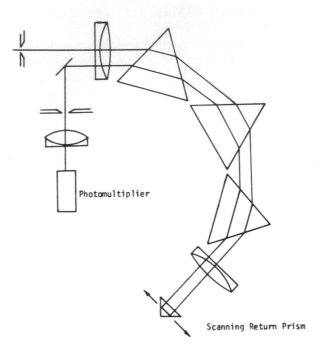

Fig. 55. Rapid scanning prism spectrometer used by M. Delhaye.

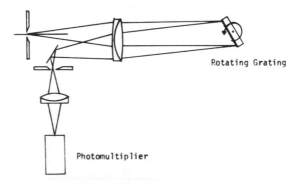

Fig. 56. Rapid scanning rotating grating spectrometer used by M. Delhaye.

optical scanning system. These data may be recorded directly on magnetic tape and at the same time the image on the oscilloscope may be photographed with a movie camera. Figure 57 shows a tracing of a photographic oscillogram of the spectrum of PCl_3 taken at a scanning rate of 20,000 cm^{-1}/min (143). The excitation source was a mercury lamp and

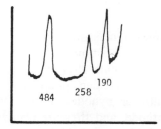

Fig. 57. A tracing of a photographic oscillogram of the spectrum of PCl_3 taken at a scanning rate of 20,000 cm^{-1} per minute obtained by M. Delhaye using Hg-arc excitation.

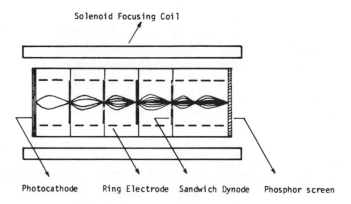

Fig. 58. Schematic of a typical image intensifier.

the spectral slit width was 8 cm^{-1}. Delhaye (143) was able to follow exchange reactions in a mixed solution of $SnCl_4$ and $SnBr_4$ using mercury arcs and rapid scan prism monochromators.

Delhaye (137) recently has studied three different methods which make use of laser excitation. The first method uses a 50 mw argon laser with a high speed grating monochromator manufactured in France by Coderg. The Raman spectrum of PBr_3 covering a spectral region of approximately 300 cm^{-1} may be scanned in 0.1 seconds with a spectral slit width of

4 cm^{-1}. However, the scanning technique in which only information in a given spectral bandwidth (Δv) is presented to the detector in a time interval shorter than the total observation time is less sensitive than the multiplexing technique in which the whole of the spectral information is presented to the detector during the total observation time. As early as 1962, Delhaye began using image intensifiers (149) to construct Raman multiplex spectrometers.

A schematic of a typical image intensifier is shown in Fig. 58. It is essentially an image forming photomultiplier tube. At the front of the tube is a standard photocathode (S11 or S20 response) from which photoelectrons are ejected by incident photons. The dynodes differ from the standard photomultiplier dynodes in that they are placed plane parallel to the photocathode, and they are transmission dynodes. That is, electrons incident on the front of the dynode causes secondary electrons to be ejected from the back side of the dynode. The photoelectrons from the photocathode are accelerated by an electric field toward the first dynode and are focused by an axial magnetic field. The secondary electrons from the first dynode, which possess only a small spread in velocities, are accelerated toward the second dynode and are focused again by the axial magnetic field. This process is continued until sufficient gain has been obtained. The number of dynodes in image intensifiers varies from one to as many as five, and gains up to 10^5 may be obtained. There exists one-to-one mapping of points on the photocathode to points on each successive dynode. At the rear of the tube is a phosphor screen which converts the incident electrons from the last dynode into luminous output. A gain of 10^5 is sufficient to allow a single electron from the photocathode to be observed or photographed as a signal on the phosphor screen.

The dynodes are usually constructed of an alkali halide supported by a conductor, such as aluminum and an Al_2O_3 coating. The thickness of such a dynode sandwich is of the order of 1000 Å, and they may be up to several inches in diameter. Since the dynodes are thin, an appreciable number of the primary or incidcnt electrons can penetrate the dynode and are not well focused by the magnetic field at the next dynode because the associated velocities are quite different from the secondary electrons. These noise electrons cause a general background on the phosphor screen and decrease the contrast. In addition to transmitted primaries, electrons which are stripped from the dynodes by field emission and thermionic emission may contribute to the decrease in the contrast on the phosphor screen. Resolutions of up to 40 line-pairs/mm may be obtained with present image intensifiers.

The image intensifier may be placed in the focal plane of any high quality spectrograph, such as shown in Fig. 59. The image on the phosphor screen may be projected by a fast lens system onto a secondary photodetector, such as a photographic emulsion, a television camera, or a scanning photomultiplier system. The photographic emulsion may be

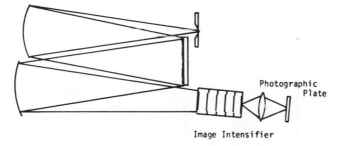

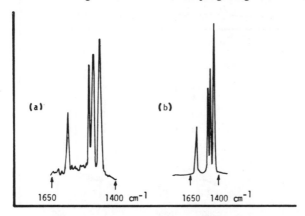

Fig. 59. Use of an image intensifier with a simple grating monochromator.

Fig. 60. (a) The Raman spectrum of azobenzene obtained by M. Delhaye using a single pulse of a SIEMENS ruby laser (0.01 joule) and recorded in one millisecond. (b) The same spectrum obtained using a Coderg Spectrometer scanning at 100 cm^{-1}/ sec with 6328 Å excitation.

placed directly in contact with the phosphor screen of the image intensifier by using a fiber optics field flattener. Delhaye et al., have used the 20th Century IPM 2529 (S11) image intensifier with both mercury lamps and an argon laser to recorded spectra of several liquids, such as CCl_4, in a time span of the order of a millisecond with three to five cm^{-1} resolution. The English Electric Valve P829D (S20) image intensifier has been used with a helium-neon laser to achieve similar results; examples of these results may be seen in Ref. (*148*).

The third technique used by Delhaye and his associates employs both an image intensifier with S1 response as a detector and a pulsed ruby

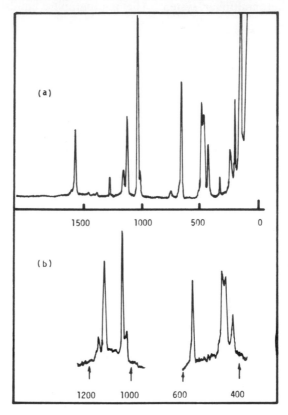

Fig. 61. The Raman spectrum of *o*-dichlorobenzene obtained by M. Delhaye using (a) the Coderg Spectrometer scanning at 100 cm^{-1}/min with 6328 A excitation, and (b) a single pulse of a SIEMENS ruby laser in 1 millisecond using an *S*-20 photocathode image intensifier.

laser. The longer wavelength, 6943 Å, of the ruby laser is ideal for certain photochemical studies in order to prevent photodecomposition and fluorescence. The present laser being used at University of Lille is a Siemens high rate semicontinuous ruby laser, which yields 50 pulses/sec of 2 to 20 millijoules per pulse. A Raman spectrum may be recorded in one millisecond over a 200 cm^{-1} range. Figures 60 and 61 show examples of portions of recent spectra obtained using such a system, as compared to the same spectra obtained with a Coderg Raman Laser (He–Ne) Spectrometer scanning at 100 cm^{-1}/min.

The instrumentation developed by Delhaye and his associates has not yet made its full impact on problems associated with short lifetime events, but it can be expected that in the near future time resolved Raman spectroscopy may be as useful or more useful than rapid scanning infrared spectroscopy.

Acknowledgments

The author wishes to express his thanks and appreciation to all the investigators who willingly supplied reprints and preprints of their papers during the period this manuscript was in preparation. It was not possible, unfortunately, to include or reference all of the work which has been accomplished in Raman instrumentation in the last several years. The author also wishes to extend a thanks to the various manufacturers for supplying information on their Raman instruments, and, in particular, special thanks to A. J. Mitteldorf and D. O. Landon of Spex Industries Inc., and E. H. Eberhardt of ITT Industrial Laboratories for their complete cooperation.

REFERENCES

1. J. Brandmüller and H. Moser, *Einführung in die Raman Spekstroskopie*, Steinkopff, Darmstadt, 1962.
2. B. P. Stoicheff, "High Resolution Raman Spectroscopy," *Advances in Spectroscopy*, Vol. 1, Ed. H. W. Thompson, Wiley-Interscience, New York (1959).
3. B. P. Stoicheff, "Raman Spectroscopy," *Molecular Physics*, Ed. Dudley Williams, Academic, New York (1962).
4. John R. Ferraro, "Advances in Raman Instrumentation and Sampling Techniques," *Raman Spectroscopy*, Ed. H. A. Szymanski, Plenum, New York (1967).
5. C. E. Hathaway and J. Rud Nielsen, *J. Chem. Phys.*, **41**, 2203 (1965).
6. N. S. Ham and A. Walsh, *Spectrochimi. Acta*, **12**, 88 (1958).
7. L. A. Kir'yanova, V. M. Pivovarov, and S. A. Yakovlev, *Opt. Spectrosc.*, **13**, 43 (1962).
8. S. P. S. Porto and D. L. Wood, *J. Opt. Soc. Am.*, **52**, 251 (1962).
9. J. M. Worlock and S. P. S. Porto, *Phys. Rev. Letters*, **15**, 697 (1965).
10. R. C. C. Leite and S. P. S. Porto, *Phys. Rev. Letters*, **17**, 10 (1966).
11. J. Behringer, "Observed Resonance Raman Spectra," *Raman Spectroscopy*, Ed. H. A. Szymanski, Plenum, New York (1967).
12. H. L. Welsh, M. F. Crawford, T. R. Thomas, and G. R. Love, *Can. J. Phys.*, **30**, 577 (1952).

13. C. E. Hathaway and J. Rud Nielsen, *Spectrochimica Acta*, **23A**, 881 (1967).
14. F. Rasetti, Nuovo Cimento, **9**, 72 (1932).
15. F. P. Lossing, D. G. H. Marsden, and J. B. Farmer, *Can. J. Chem.*, **34**, 701 (1956).
16. K. W. F. Kohlrausch, *Der Smekal-Raman-Effekt*, Springer, Berlin (1938).
17. H. Stammreich, *Spectrochim. Acta*, **8**, 41 (1956).
18. N. Ham and A. Walsh, *Spectrochim. Acta*, **12**, 88 (1958).
19. T. H. Maiman, *Nature*, **107**, 493 (1960).
20. A. Javan, W. R. Bennett, and D. R. Herriott, *Phys. Rev. Letters*, **6**, 106 (1961).
21. A. J. Bevols and W. A. Barker, *Appl. Opt.*, **4**, 531 (1965).
22. H. Kogelnik and S. P. S. Porto, *J. Opt. Soc. Am.*, **53**, 1446 (1963).
23. R. C. C. Leite and S. P. S. Porto, *J. Opt. Soc. Am.*, **54**, 981 (1964).
24. A. Weber and S. P. S. Porto, *J. Opt. Soc. Am.*, **55**, 1033 (1965).
25. P. A. Fleury, S. P. S. Porto, L. E. Cheesman, and H. J. Guggenheim, *Phys. Rev. Letters*, **17**, 84 (1966).
26. A. Weber, S. P. S. Porto, L. E. Cheesman, and J. J. Barrett, *J. Opt. Soc. Am.*, **57**, 19 (1967).
27. J. A. Koningstein and R. G. Smith, *J. Opt. Soc. Am.*, **54**, 1061 (1964).
28. J. Brandmüller, *Naturwissensch.*, **54**, 293 (1967).
29. A. Mooradian and G. B. Wright, *Phys. Rev. Letters*, **16**, 999 (1966).
30. B. Tell and R. J. Martin, *Phys. Rev.*, **167**, 381 (1968).
31. J. E. Geustic, H. J. Levinstein, J. J. Rubin, S. Singh, and L. G. Van Uitert, *Appl. Phys. Letters*, **11**, 269 (1967).
32. *Laser Focus*, **4**, 16 (1968).
33. J. Brandmüller, Z. Angew, *Physik*, **5**, 95 (1953).
34. M. C. Tobin, *J. Opt. Soc. Am.*, **49**, 850 (1959).
35. H. Moser and D. Stieler, and Z. Angew, *Physik*, **12**, 280 (1960).
36. B. Schrader, F. Nerdel, and G. Kresze, *Z. Anal. Chem.*, **170**, 43 (1959).
37. R. H. Partridge, *J. Chem. Phys.*, **45**, 1679 (1966).
38. J. Rud Nielsen, *J. Opt. Soc. Am.*, **20**, 701 (1930); **37**, 494 (1947).
39. J. H. Callomon and B. P. Stoicheff, *Can. J. Phys.*, **35**, 373 (1957).
40. H. L. Welsh, E. J. Stansbury, J. Ramanko, and T. Feldman, *J. Opt. Soc. Am.*, **45**, 338 (1955).
41. J. U. White, N. L. Alpert, and A. G. DeBell, *J. Opt. Soc. Am.*, **45**, 154 (1955).
42. A. C. Menzies and J. Skinner, *J. Sci. Instrum.*, **26**, 299 (1949).
43. H. L. Welsh, C. Cumming and E. J. Stansbury, *J. Opt. Soc. Am.*, **41**, 712 (1951).
44. B. Schrader, *Z. analyt. Chem.*, **197**, 295 (1963).
45. L. Couture, *Ann. Phys.* (*Paris*), **2**, 5 (1947).
46. S. P. S. Porto, J. A. Giordmaine, and T. C. Damen, *Phys. Rev.*, **147**, 608 (1966).
47. R. F. Schaufele, *J. Opt. Soc. Am.*, **57**, 105 (1967).
48. J. Brandmüller, K. Burchardi, H. Hacher, and H. W. Schrötter, *Z. Angew. Phys.*, **22**, 177 (1967).
49. J. J. Barrett and N. I. Adams, III, *J. Opt. Soc. Am.*, **58**, 311 (1968).
50. A. Weber, The Spex Speaker, **11**, December 1966.
51. W. F. Murphy, M. V. Evans, and P. Bender, *J. Chem. Phys.*, **47**, 1836 (1967).
52. J. G. Atwood, *J. Opt. Soc. Am.*, **53**, 1343 (1963).
53. G. B. Benedek and K. Fritsch, *Phys. Rev.*, **149**, 647 (1966).
54. J. J. Barrett and J. D. Rigden, 9th European Congress on Molecular Spectroscopy, Madrid, Spain, Sept. 1967.

55. T. C. Damen, S. P. S. Porto, and B. Tell, *Phys. Rev.*, **142**, 570 (1960); *Phys. Rev.*, **144,** 771 (1966).
56. I. Richman, *J. Opt. Soc. Am.*, **56,** 1589 (1966).
57. J. A. Koningstein, *J. Chem. Phys.*, **46,** 2811 (1967).
58. R. F. Schaufele, *J. Opt. Soc. Am.*, **57,** 105 (1967).
59. R. F. Schaufele and T. Shimanouchi, *J. Chem. Phys.*, **47,** 3605 (1967).
60. R. F. Schaufele, *Macromolecular Reviews*, Vol. 3 (to be published).
61. G. F. Bailey, S. Kint, and J. R. Scherer, *Anal. Chem.*, **39,** 1040 (1967).
62. W. F. Murphy and H. J. Bernstein, 22nd Symposium on Molecular Structure and Spectroscopy, Columbus, Ohio, Sept. 1967.
63. G. B. B. M. Sutherland, *Proc. Roy. Soc.* (*London*), **A141,** 535 (1933).
64. W. J. Taylor, A. Lee Smith, and H. L. Johnston, *J. Opt. Soc. Am.*, **41,** 91 (1951).
65. E. J. Allin, T. Feldman, and H. L. Welsh, *J. Chem. Phys.*, **24,** 1116 (1956).
66. J. R. Ferraro, J. S. Ziomek, and K. Puckett, *Rev. Sci. Instr.*, **35,** 754 (1964).
67. J. E. Griffiths, R. P. Carter, and R. R. Holmes, *J. Chem. Phys.*, **41,** 3863 (1964).
68. N. Craig and J. Overend, *Spectrochim. Acta*, **20,** 1561 (1964).
69. R. Savoie and A. Anderson, *J. Opt. Soc. Am.*, **55,** 133 (1965).
70. James I. Bryant, *Spectrochim. Acta*, **24A,** 9 (1968).
71. B. Schrader, F. Nerdel, and G. Kresze, *Z. Physik. Chem.*, **12,** 132 (1957).
72. G. E. Walrafen, *J. Chem. Phys.*, **43,** 479 (1965).
73. R. A. Bailey and G. J. Janz, "Experimental Techniques in the Study of Fused Salts," *Chemistry of Non-Aqueous Solvents*, Ed. J. J. Lagowski, Academic, New York (1965).
74. W. Bues, *Z. anorg. allg. Chem.*, **279,** 104 (1955).
75. G. E. Walrafen, to be published.
76. L. J. Schoen, L. E. Kuentzel, and H. P. Broida, *Rev. Sci. Instr.*, **29,** 633 (1958).
77. J. H. R. Clarke, C. Solomons, and K. Balasubrahmanyam, *Rev. Sci. Instr.*, **38,** 655 (1967).
78. L. Whatley, E. Lippincott, A. Van Valkenburg and C. Weir, *Science*, **144,** 968 (1964).
78a. J. W. Brasch, A. J. Melveger, and E. R. Lippincott, *Chem. Phys. Letters*, **2,** 99 (1968).
78b. O. Brafman, S. S. Mitra, R. K. Crawford, W. B. Daniels, C. Postmus, and J. R. Ferraro, *Sol. State Comm.* **7,** 449 (1969).
78c. S. S. Mitra, O. Brafman, W. B. Daniels, and R. K. Crawford, *Phys. Rev.* **186,** 942 (1969).
79. D. H. Rank, R. J. Pfister, and P. D. Coleman, *J. Opt. Soc. Am.*, **32,** 390 (1942).
80. R. A. Sawyer, *Experimental Spectroscopy*, Dover, New York, (1963).
81. J. Rud Nielsen, *J. Opt. Soc. Am.*, **20,** 701 (1930).
82. John Strong, *Concepts of Classical Optics*, Freeman, San Francisco (1958).
83. Perkin-Elmer, Instrument Division, Norwalk, Conn., LR-1 Instruction Manual (1968).
83a. E. B. Bradley, University of Kentucky, private communication.
84. George R. Harrison, Richard C. Lord, and John R. Loofbourow, *Practical Spectroscopy*, Prentice-Hall, Englewood Cliffs, New Jersey (1948).
85. W. G. Fastie, *J. Opt. Soc. Am.*, **42,** 641 (1952); **43,** 1174 (1953).
86. M. Czerny and A. F. Turner, *Z. Physik*, **61,** 792 (1930).
87. G. W. Stroke and H. H. Stroke, *J. Opt. Soc. Am.*, **53,** 333 (1963).

88. R. L. Christensen and R. J. Potter, *Appl. Opt.*, **2**, 1049 (1963).

89. P. H. van Cittert, *Rev. Opt.*, **5**, 393 (1926).

90. D. Landon and S. P. S. Porto, *Appl.* **4**, 762 (1965).

91. H. I. Mandelberg, *Appl. Opt.*, **5**, 674 (1966); **6**, 347 (1967).

92. D. O. Landon, *Appl. Opt.*, **6**, 346 (1967).

93. *Kodak Plates and Films for Science and Industry*, Eastman Kodak Company (1962).

94. J. D. Fernie, *Astron. Soc. Pacific*, **74**, 238 (1962).

95. ITT Industrial Laboratories, Fort Wayne, Indiana, Applications Notes E2, E3, E4 and E5 and Multiplier Phototube Data.

96. T. Hirschfeld, *Appl. Opt.*, **7**, 443 (1968).

97. J. B. Oke and R. E. Schild, *Appl. Opt.*, **7**, 617 (1968).

98. E. H. Eberhardt, *IEEE Tr. Nucl. Sci.*, **NS-14**, 7 (1967).

99. E. H. Eberhardt, *Appl. Opt.* **6**, 251, 359 (1967).

100. G. Y. Farkas and P. Varga, *J. Sci. Intrum.*, **41**, 704 (1964).

101. Products for Research, Inc., Danvers, Mass., "Photomultiplier Operating Tube Environment."

101a. J. K. Nakamura and S. E. Schwarz, *Appl. Opt.*, **7**, 1073 (1968).

102. R. H. Dicke, *Rev. Sci. Instr.*, **17**, 268 (1947).

103. Technical Bulletin 109, Princeton Applied Research, Princeton, New Jersey.

104. Y.-H. Pao, R. N. Zitter, and J. E. Griffiths, *J. Opt. Soc. Am.*, **56**, 1133 (1966).

105. Y.-H. Pao and J. E. Griffiths, *J. Chem. Phys.*, **46**, 1671 (1967).

106. J. E. Griffiths and Y.-H. Pao, *J. Chem. Phys.*, **46**, 1679 (1967).

107. S. O. Rice, *Bell System Tech. J.*, **23**, 282 (1944); **24**, 46 (1945).

108. R. H. Wilcox, *Rev. Sci. Instr.*, **30**, 1009 (1959).

109. R. R. Alfano and N. Ockman, *J. Opt. Soc. Am.*, **58**, 90 (1968).

109a. R. J. Anderson and J. E. Cleary, private communication.

109b. J. E. Cleary, *J. Opt. Soc. Am.*, **57**, 841 (1967).

110. G. M. Morton, *Appl. Opt.*, **7**, 1 (1968).

111. E. H. Eberhardt, *Appl. Opt.*, **6**, 251 (1967).

112. E. H. Eberhardt, *IEEE Tr. Nucl. Sci.*, **NS11**, 48 (1964).

113. F. T. Arecchi, E. Gatti, and A. Sona, *Rev. Sci. Instr.*, **37**, 942 (1966).

113a. R. Fisher, *Appl. Opt.*, **7**, 1079 (1968).

114. W. A. Baum, *Astronomical Techniques, Vol. II*, Ed. W. A. Hiltner, Univ. of Chicago Press (1962), p. 26.

114a. Solid State Radiation Inc., 2261 South Carmelina Avenue, Los Angeles, California 90064.

114b. Miller, S. A., *Rev. Sci. Instr.*, **39**, 1923 (1969).

115. Applied Physics Corporation, 2724 S. Peck Road, Monrovia, California.

115a. V. L. Chupp and P. C. Grantz, *Appl. Opt.*, **8**, 925 (1969).

115b. H. H. Claassen, H. Selig, and J. Shamir, *Apply. Spectry.* **23**, 8 (1969).

116. Applied Research Laboratories, Inc., P. O. Box 1710, Glendale, California.

117. Coderg, 15, Impasse Barbier, 92-Clichy, France.

118. Hilger and Watts, Ltd., St. Pancras Way, Camden Road, London NW1, England.

119. Jarrell-Ash Company, 590 Lincoln Street, Waltham, Massachusetts, Preliminary Bulletin No. 34A.

120. Spex Industries, Inc., P. O. Box 798, Metuchen, New Jersey. The Spex Speaker *XII*, April, December, 1966; XII, June, December, 1967.

121. G. Placzek, *Marx's Handbuch Radiol.*, **6**, 209 (1934).

122. L. A. Woodward and D. A. Long, *Trans. Faraday Soc.*, **45,** 1131 (1949).
123. H. W. Schrötter and H. J. Bernstein, *J. Mol. Spec.*, **12,** 1 (1964).
124. S. P. S. Porto, *J. Opt. Soc. Am.*, **56,** 1585 (1966).
125. H. J. Bernstein and G. Allen, *J. Opt. Soc. Am.*, **45,** 154, 237 (1955)
126. T. Yoshino and H. J. Bernstein, *J. Mol. Spec.*, **2,** 213, 241 (1958).
127. P. Bender and P. A. Lyons, *J. Chem. Phys.*, **18,** 438 (1950).
128. J. T. Edsall and E. B. Wilson, *J. Chem. Phys.*, **6,** 124 (1938).
129. E. B. Wilson, Jr., J. C. Decius, and P. C. Cross, *Molecular Vibrations*, McGraw-Hill, New York (1955).
129a. J. R. Scherer and G. F. Bailey *Appl. Spectry.*, **24,** 259 (1970).
130. T. C. Damen, R. C. C. Leite, and S. P. S. Porto, *Phys. Rev. Letters*, **14,** 9 (1965).
131. J. G. Skinner and W. G. Nilsen, *J. Opt. Soc. Am.*, **58,** 113 (1968).
132. R. Loudon, *Advan. Phys.*, **13,** 423 (1964).
133. J. F. Nye, *Physical Properties of Crystals*, Oxford, Clarendon (1957).
134. S. P. S. Porto, P. A. Fleury, and T. C. Damen, *Phys. Rev.*, **154,** 522 (1967).
134a. J. A. Koningstein and Toaning-Ng, *J. Opt. Soc. Am.*, **58,** 1462 (1968).
135. R. E. Hester, "Raman Intensities and the Nature of the Chemical Bond," *Raman Spectroscopy*, Ed. H. A. Szymanski, Plenum Press, New York (1967).
136. H. W. Schrötter and H. J. Bernstein, *J. Mol. Spec.*, **12,** 1 (1964).
137. D. M. Golden and B. Crawford, Jr., *J. Chem. Phys.*, **36,** 1654 (1962).
138. D. G. Rea, *J. Opt. Soc. Am.*, **49,** 90 (1959).
138a. W. F. Murphy, W. Holzer and H. J. Bernstein, *Apply. Spectry.* **23,** 211 (1969).
139. F. J. McClung and D. Weiner, *J. Opt. Soc. Am.*, **54,** 641 (1964).
140. D. Weiner, S. E. Schwarz, and F. J. McClung, *J. Appl. Phys.*, **36,** 2395 (1965).
141. M. Delhaye, Colloquium on Raman Spectroscopy, Stuttgart, March 13–14, 1958.
142. M. Delhaye, and M. B. Delhaye-Buisset, VII Colloquium Spectroscopicum Internationale, May 1959.
143. M. Delhaye, Thesis, Lille, France, 1960.
144. M. Delhaye, *Bul. Soc. Chim.*, 683, 1962.
145. M. Delhaye, and M. Bridoux, C. R. Acad. Sc. (Paris), **261,** 2079, 2613 (1965).
146. M. Bridoux, Mme Crunelle-Cras, M. Delhaye, M. Migeon, F. Wallart, and J. Wrobel, *Publ. GAMS*, 26, June 1965.
147. M. Delhaye, M. Bridoux, and M. Migeon, 22nd Symposium on Molecular Structure and Spectroscopy, Columbus, Ohio, 1967.
148. M. Bridoux, *Rev, Opt.* to be published.
149. W. A. Hiltner, *Astronomical Techniques*, Chap. 16, Univ. of Chicago Press, 1962.
150. M. Delhaye, *Appl. Opt.*, **7,** 2195 (1968).

CHAPTER 5

The Stimulated Raman Effect

P. LALLEMAND

ÉCOLE NORMALE SUPÉRIEURE
UNIVERSITY OF PARIS
PARIS, FRANCE

I. INTRODUCTION

Inelastic light scattering by matter has been discussed in preceding chapters. It was assumed that the intensity of the light scattered per unit solid angle and per unit frequency bandwidth is proportional to the intensity of the incident light beam. One could then define a scattering cross section. We are going to show that this is not always true, and

287

describe cases where the scattered intensity increases nonlinearly as the input intensity becomes very large, in such a manner that the ratio scattered intensity per input intensity may vary from the typical 10^{-10} to almost unity.

We shall discuss the origin and characteristics of this nonlinear scattering, which is called stimulated Raman scattering when the frequency change between input and output frequencies corresponds to an optical phonon or a molecular vibration or rotation of the scattering medium. Then applications of this effect will be discussed.

Let us consider the scattering process between 2 photons and the medium, that we represent schematically in Fig. 1(a). An input photon L at frequency v_L and wave vector $\mathbf{k}_L$ interacts with the medium which is initially in state $| v_a, \mathbf{k}_a \rangle$. After interaction, the medium is in state $| v_b, \mathbf{k}_b \rangle$, and we have a new photon S at frequency $v_S = v_L - (v_b - v_a)$ and wave vector $\mathbf{k}_S = \mathbf{k}_L - (\mathbf{k}_b - \mathbf{k}_a)$. If v_S is smaller than v_L, the scattered wave is called the Stokes component, and if larger the anti-Stokes. Their intensities will be called $\mathscr{I}_S$ and $\mathscr{I}_{aS}$, respectively; $\mathscr{I}_L$ is the laser intensity.

The probability P for the creation of one photon S can be calculated using harmonic oscillator-like wave functions for the electromagnetic modes:

$$P = AN_L(1 + N_S) \tag{1}$$

where N_L and N_S are the occupation numbers of the electromagnetic modes $(v_L, \mathbf{k}_L)$ and $(v_S, \mathbf{k}_S)$, and A is an expression depending upon the scattering medium, the frequencies and the polarizations of the photons. In the usual spontaneous Raman scattering, the quantity N_S is negligibly small, and as a result the scattered intensity is proportional to the input intensity.

The term AN_LN_S which is schematically represented in Fig. 1(b) corresponds to an amplification of the scattered beam at frequency v_S, as we have:

$$\frac{dN_S}{dt} = AN_LN_S + AN_L \tag{2}$$

$$N_S = N_{S_0} e^{AN_Lt} + AN_Lt \tag{3}$$

When the laser beam is single-mode, we can calculate

$$N_L = \frac{I_L}{hv_L} \frac{n_L}{c},$$

where c/n_L is the phase velocity of the laser beam in the medium. The intensity per mode I is to be distinguished from the total beam intensity $\mathscr{I}$.

In most cases $AN_L t \ll 1$, and N_S is proportional to N_L, but when I_L is large enough ($\gtrsim 10^6$ W/cm^2) one obtains an exponential growth with time of the scattered intensity. This is the stimulated scattering of light.

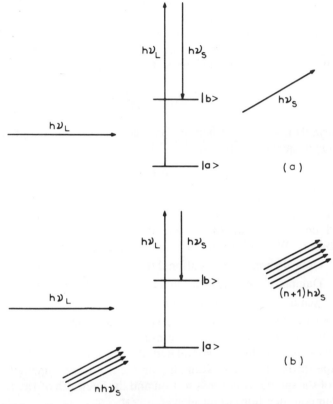

Fig. 1. (a) Schematic description of spontaneous scattering; (b) schematic description of stimulated scattering, the beam v_S is amplified by addition of one photon.

We can as well consider the propagation of a travelling wave S at frequency v_S and wave vector $\mathbf{k}_S$ in a medium where I_L is constant. The intensity per mode will be:

$$I_S(z) = \frac{h v_S c}{n_S} \left(e^{N_L A(n_s/c)z} - 1\right) + I_S(o)\, e^{N_L A(n_s/c)z}$$

$$= \frac{h v_S c}{n_S} \left(e^{g I_L z} - 1\right) + I_S(o)\, e^{g I_L z} \tag{4}$$

where n_S is the refractive index at frequency v_S and $I_S(o)$ the input intensity. The first term represents the usual spontaneous scattering for

$$\frac{n_S}{c} A N_L z \ll 1.$$

We see that the scattered intensity varies exponentially with the length z due to the stimulated scattering process at a rate proportional to the laser intensity. We can define a gain constant for the Stokes intensity:

$$g = \frac{n_S}{c} \frac{A}{I_L} N_L = \frac{n_S n_L}{c^2} A \frac{1}{h v_L} \tag{5}$$

This formula is still valid when the laser beam is multimode, provided the following inequality is satisfied:

$$\frac{1}{A} \left(\frac{\partial A}{\partial v_L} \Gamma_L + \frac{\partial A}{\partial k_L} \delta k_L \right) \ll 1$$

where Γ_L is the laser linewidth and $\delta k_L / k_L$ is its angular aperture.

Until now the nature of the transition $\mid v_a, \mathbf{k}_a \rangle \to \mid v_b, \mathbf{k}_b \rangle$ has been left arbitrary. We shall consider the following cases:

1. Optical phonon or vibrational transition: Raman effect.
2. Damped molecular rotational transition: Rayleigh wing scattering.
3. Acoustical phonon: Brillouin effect.

These cases have been studied by spontaneous or thermal† scattering, and all give rise to a corresponding stimulated scattering.

Let us first consider the stimulated Raman effect. We shall calculate the value of the stimulated Raman gain from the experimentally known values of the spontaneous cross section and the linewidth of the transition, using our considerations of the gain.

When $g \mathscr{I}_L z \ll 1$, the Stokes intensity per mode is

$$I_S = \frac{h v_S c}{n_S} g \mathscr{I}_L z$$

The Stokes intensity in a solid angle $\delta\Omega$ and frequency interval δv is:

$$\mathscr{I}_S = \frac{h v_S c}{n_S} g \mathscr{I}_L z \times (2\pi)^{-3} k_S^2 \, \delta k_S \, \delta\Omega$$

† The distinction between spontaneous and thermal scattering corresponds to the conditions $[h(v_b - v_a)/kT] > 1$ or < 1. This must be taken into account when one calculates the stimulated gain from the true spontaneous scattering cross section.

where

$$k_S = 2\pi n_s \frac{v_S}{c}$$

$(2\pi)^{-3}k_S^2 \, \delta k_S \delta\Omega$ is the number of Stokes modes in $\delta v \, \delta\Omega$.

By definition of the differential scattering cross section $\partial^2\sigma/\partial v \, \partial\Omega$ we have:

$$\mathscr{I}_S = \frac{v_S}{v_L} N \frac{\partial^2\sigma}{\partial v \, \partial\Omega} z\mathscr{I}_L \, \delta\Omega \, \delta v$$

where N is the number of molecules per unit volume. Therefore equating these two expressions for $\mathscr{I}_S$ we get

$$g = \frac{c^2}{n_s^2 h v_S^2 v_L} N \frac{\partial^2\sigma}{\partial\Omega \, \partial v} \tag{6}$$

Assuming a Lorentzian line shape for $\partial^2\sigma/\partial\Omega \, \partial v$ of full width at half intensity Δv_{vib} we have

$$\left(\frac{\partial^2\sigma}{\partial\Omega \, \partial v}\right)_{\mathrm{max}} = \frac{\partial\sigma}{\partial\Omega} \frac{1}{\pi\Delta v_{\mathrm{vib}}} \tag{7}$$

We then deduce

$$g_{\mathrm{max}} = \frac{c^2 N}{\varepsilon_s h v_S^2 v_L \pi\Delta v_{\mathrm{vib}}} \left(\frac{\partial\sigma}{\partial\Omega}\right) \tag{8}$$

for the gain constant at the center of the line.

In the case of the $Q_{01}(1)$ vibrational transition in hydrogen gas at high pressure, it is known (1–5) that $\partial\sigma/\partial\Omega = 0.7 \times 10^{-30}$ cm^2 and $\Delta v_{\mathrm{vib}} = 5.7 \times 10^7$ Hz per amagat or that $g = 1.5 \times 10^{-3}$ cm^{-1} (MW/cm^2)$^{-1}$.

We see that large laser intensities are required to observe the stimulated Raman gain. This is why this effect had not been observed experimentally (6,7) until 1962 when Q-switch giant pulse lasers (8,9) became available.

Starting from a simplified description of the Raman scattering process in terms of photons, we have shown the essential difference between the spontaneous and the stimulated Raman scattering. In the first case, the scattered intensity is proportional to the laser intensity, whereas in the second case the Stokes beam is amplified exponentially at a rate $g\mathscr{I}_L z$ also proportional to the laser intensity. In the next section of this chapter we shall give a brief review of the theoretical work performed to calculate the Raman gain, and in order to calculate the total Stokes gain $\exp g\int_0^l \mathscr{I}_L(z) \, dz$, we shall investigate the propagation of intense light beams in matter where self-trapping and self-focusing may take place due to nonlinear index of refraction changes. The associated stimulated Rayleigh wing scattering will also be discussed. The results of these calculations will be compared with experimental studies of the stimulated Raman effect in the third section, and some applications will be described in the fourth section. Finally, we shall briefly describe the stimulated Brillouin effect.

II. THEORETICAL ANALYSIS OF THE STIMULATED RAMAN EFFECT

Two distinct problems must be solved in order to give a complete description of a stimulated Raman effect experiment. First, one must calculate the gain constant g for given laser and Stokes fields at a given position in the active medium. Second, one must study the propagation of the beams in the medium to be able to calculate the total gain.

A. Gain Constant Calculation

In the introduction, an expression for the gain constant g was derived from the spontaneous Raman cross section and the linewidth of the scattered light. A first principle calculation of g requires the calculation of $\partial\sigma/\partial\Omega$ and Γ. The Kramers–Heisenberg (10) formula can be used to determine $\partial\sigma/\partial\Omega$ if all energy levels and transition matrix elements are known. This is discussed elsewhere in this book. In the case of Γ, the problem is even more difficult, because the broadening mechanisms of the vibrational levels are not well known. Some cases have been treated (for example in diatomic gases by Van Kranendonk) (11), but usually the experimental values of Γ are used.

We shall consider here the problem in the following way. We wish to know the polarization induced in the medium by two classical fields

$$\mathbf{E}_L = \varepsilon_L\, e^{i(\omega_L t - k_L z)} + cc \qquad \text{and} \qquad \mathbf{E}_S = \varepsilon_S\, e^{i(\omega_S t - k_S z)} + cc$$

This can be done by introducing phenomenological nonlinear susceptibilities as is done in nonlinear optics (12), or by consideration of polarizability changes with molecular motions.

1. INTRODUCTION OF NONLINEAR SUSCEPTIBILITIES

Usually the response of a medium to an electromagnetic field is written as

$$\mathbf{P}(\mathbf{r}, \omega) = \chi(\omega) : \mathbf{E}_L(\mathbf{r}, \omega) \tag{9}$$

where χ is the susceptibility. This linear relation between $\mathbf{P}$ and $\mathbf{E}_L$ is valid when $| \mathbf{E}_L |$ is very small compared to the internal electric fields of molecules as is the case in ordinary optics, but when $| \mathbf{E}_L |$ is large, one can use a power series expansion of $\mathbf{P}$

$$\mathbf{P} = \chi_1 : \mathbf{E} + \chi_2 : \mathbf{E} \cdot \mathbf{E} + \chi_3 : \mathbf{E} \cdot \mathbf{E} \cdot \mathbf{E} + \dots \tag{10}$$

The coefficients χ_n are tensors of rank $n+1$. They are called nonlinear susceptibilities.

If several input fields are present, $\mathbf{P}$ will be expressed as a power series expansion of the electric fields. The coefficients χ are functions of the frequencies of the various fields. For instance, when E_L and E_S are present, some of the third order terms are:

$$\mathbf{P}_{(3)}(3\omega_L) = \chi_{(3)}(3\omega_L, \omega_L, \omega_L, \omega_L) : \mathbf{E}(\omega_L) . \mathbf{E}(\omega_L) . \mathbf{E}(\omega_L) \tag{11}$$

$$\mathbf{P}_{(3)}(\omega_S) = \chi_{(3)}(\omega_S, \omega_L, -\omega_L, \omega_S) : \mathbf{E}(\omega_L) . \mathbf{E}(\omega_L)^* . \mathbf{E}(\omega_S) \tag{12}$$

$$\mathbf{P}_{(3)}(\omega_L) = \chi_{(3)}(\omega_L, \omega_L, -\omega_L, \omega_L) : \mathbf{E}(\omega_L) . \mathbf{E}(\omega_L)^* . \mathbf{E}(\omega_L) \tag{13}$$

$$\mathbf{P}_{(3)}(2\omega_L - \omega_S) = \chi_{(3)}(2\omega_L - \omega_S, \omega_L, \omega_L, -\omega_S) : \mathbf{E}(\omega_L) . \mathbf{E}(\omega_L) . \mathbf{E}(\omega_S)^* \tag{14}$$

in which the frequency of the corresponding nonlinear polarization is specified. The usual term, $\chi_{(1)}$, leads to the index of refraction; the terms, $\chi_{(2)}$, which vanish in nonpiezoelectric materials, lead to second harmonic generation. Equation 11 leads to third harmonic generation. We shall see that Eqs. 12 and 14 give rise to the stimulated Raman effect, and that Eq. 13 leads to nonlinear index changes. A classification of the various effects corresponding to the different nonlinear susceptibilities has been given by Franken and Ward (*13*).

Quantum mechanical expressions for the nonlinear susceptibilities have been derived (*14*), but they involve so many unknown matrix elements that they are not used to derive stimulated Raman effect gain coefficients. An actual calculation has been performed only for $\chi_{(2)}$ (*15,16*).

2. CLASSICAL CALCULATION (*17–19*)

We turn now to a more physical description of the Raman effect. Let us consider the polarizability α of the system. It is a function of the positions

Q of the nuclei in the case of the Raman effect, or of some other degree of freedom for other types of scattering. In the presence of the two fields E_L and E_S, the Lagrangian density due to the coupling between the light beams and the medium is:

$$L = (E_L + E_S)\alpha(Q)(E_L + E_S)^* \tag{15}$$

We keep only secular terms of the type

$$L = E_L E_S^* \int_0^\infty e^{i(\omega_L - \omega_S)t}\alpha[Q(t)]\, dt \tag{16}$$

According to Placzek's approximation (20), we write:

$$\alpha(Q) = \alpha(Q_0) + \frac{\partial\alpha}{\partial Q}Q \tag{17}$$

where Q_0 is the equilibrium value of Q, which is assumed to satisfy a dispersionless damped harmonic oscillator equation. We keep the terms

$$L = E_L E_S^* \frac{\partial\alpha}{\partial Q}Q^* \tag{18}$$

We can then write down the equations of motion for Q and the fields E_L, E_S and E_{aS}

$$\Delta E_S - \frac{1}{c^2}\frac{\partial^2}{\partial t^2}E_S = \frac{4\pi}{c^2}\frac{\partial^2}{\partial t^2}\chi_S E_S + \frac{4\pi}{c^2}\frac{\partial^2}{\partial t^2}\left(\frac{\partial\alpha}{\partial Q}\right)Q^* E_L \tag{19}$$

$$\Delta E_L - \frac{1}{c^2}\frac{\partial^2}{\partial t^2}E_L = \frac{4\pi}{c^2}\frac{\partial^2}{\partial t^2}\chi_L E_L + \frac{4\pi}{c^2}\frac{\partial^2}{\partial t^2}\left(\frac{\partial\alpha}{\partial Q}\right)(E_S Q + E_{aS}Q^*) \tag{20}$$

$$\Delta E_{aS} - \frac{1}{c^2}\frac{\partial^2}{\partial t^2}E_{aS} = \frac{4\pi}{c^2}\frac{\partial^2}{\partial t^2}\chi_{aS}E_{aS} + \frac{4\pi}{c^2}\frac{\partial^2}{\partial t^2}\left(\frac{\partial\alpha}{\partial Q}\right)E_L Q \tag{21}$$

$$\frac{\partial^2 Q}{\partial t^2} + \Gamma\frac{\partial Q}{\partial t} + \omega_0{}^2 Q = \frac{\partial\alpha}{\partial Q}(E_L E_S^* + E_L^* E_{aS}) \tag{22}$$

where the χ's are linear susceptibilities, and ω_0 and Γ the frequency and damping of the vibration.

One has to normalize α properly for 1 or N molecules per unit volume. This system of 4 coupled nonlinear differential wave equations (21) will be studied in a few particular cases.

Equation 22 describes a damped harmonic oscillator driven by two electromagnetic fields.

Equations 19 to 21 are the normal wave equations in matter, with an additional driving term due to the nonlinearity of the medium.

We shall always assume ε_L constant so that Eq. 20 can be neglected. This is called the parametric approximation.

a. Neglect of anti-Stokes field

If E_{aS} is neglected, we have two coupled oscillators, Q and E_S. We use as a trial solution

$$E_S = \varepsilon_S\, e^{i(\omega_S t - \mathbf{k}_S \mathbf{r})}$$

$$Q = q\, e^{i(\omega_0 t - \mathbf{k}_0 \mathbf{r})}$$

where

$$\omega_L = \omega_S + \omega_0 \quad \text{and} \quad \mathbf{k}_L = \mathbf{k}_S + \mathbf{k}_0$$

If we assume that the coupling term is small compared to the phonon damping, we can eliminate q between Eqs. 19 and 22. We thus obtain:

$$-k_S^2 \varepsilon_S + n_S^2 \frac{\omega_S^2}{c^2} \varepsilon_S = \frac{4\pi\omega_S^2}{c^2}\left(\frac{\partial\alpha}{\partial Q}\right)^2 \frac{|\varepsilon_L|^2 \varepsilon_S}{(\omega_L - \omega_S)^2 - \omega_0^2 + i\omega_0\Gamma} \tag{23}$$

so that we can write

$$-k_S^2 \varepsilon_S + n_S^2 \frac{\omega_S^2}{c^2} \varepsilon_S = \frac{4\pi}{c^2}\omega_S^2 P(\omega_S) \tag{24}$$

with

$$P(\omega_S) = \chi_{(3)}(\omega_S, \omega_L, -\omega_L, +\omega_S)\,|\varepsilon_L|^2 \varepsilon_S \tag{25}$$

$$= \left(\frac{\partial\alpha}{\partial Q}\right)^2 \frac{|\varepsilon_L|^2 \varepsilon_S}{(\omega_L - \omega_S)^2 - \omega_0^2 + 2i\omega_0\Gamma} \tag{26}$$

So we have obtained an expression for one of the nonlinear susceptibilities defined in Eq. 12, normally $\chi_{(3)}(\omega_S, \omega_L, -\omega_L, \omega_S)$. From Eq. 23, we get

$$k_S = k_{S_0} + \frac{4\pi\omega_S^2}{2k_{S_0}c^2}\left(\frac{\partial\alpha}{\partial Q}\right)^2 \frac{|\varepsilon_L|^2}{(\omega_L - \omega_S)^2 - \omega_0^2 + 2i\omega_0\Gamma} \tag{27}$$

$$= k_{S_0} + \frac{4\pi\omega_S^2}{2k_{S_0}c^2}\chi_{(3)}|\varepsilon_L|^2 \tag{28}$$

We find that the imaginary part of $\chi_{(3)}$ corresponds to a gain constant at the Stokes frequency:

$$g = \frac{8\pi^2}{n_S\lambda_S}\frac{1}{\mathscr{I}_L} Im\chi_{(3)}|\varepsilon_L|^2 \tag{29}$$

and that the real part of $\chi_{(3)}$ corresponds to an index change

$$\delta n = \frac{2\pi}{n} \, Re \, \chi_{(3)} | \, \varepsilon_L \, |^2 \tag{30}$$

Had we considered $\varepsilon_S = 0$ instead, we would have found that $\chi_{(3)}(\omega_{aS}, \omega_L, -\omega_L, +\omega_{aS}) = \chi_{(3)}{}^*(\omega_S, \omega_L, -\omega_L, +\omega_S)$, neglecting dispersion. As a result $Im \, \chi_{(3)}(\omega_{aS})$ is positive at resonance, and there is attenuation of the anti-Stokes beam. If we assume that the phonon damping is small compared to the coupling, we have two strongly coupled systems, and the resonance frequency is modified by interaction with the electromagnetic fields. However, the coupling constants remain small even for large laser fields, and the effect has not been observed to date.

b. *Coupling of Stokes and anti-Stokes waves with the laser beam*

We consider the parametric approximation in the case of strong phonon damping, so that we can use nonlinear susceptibilities. We therefore have two equations:

$$\Delta E_{aS} - \frac{\varepsilon_{aS}}{c^2} \frac{\partial^2 E_{aS}}{\partial t^2} = \frac{4\pi}{c^2} \frac{\partial^2}{\partial t^2} [\chi E_L{}^2 E_S{}^* + \chi_{aS} \, | \, E_L \, |^2 E_{aS}] \tag{31}$$

$$\Delta E_S - \frac{\varepsilon_S}{c^2} \frac{\partial^2 E_S}{\partial t^2} = \frac{4\pi}{c^2} \frac{\partial^2}{\partial t^2} [\chi E_L{}^2 E_{aS}^* + \chi_S \, | \, E_L \, |^2 E_S] \tag{32}$$

The nonlinear susceptibility χ can be shown (13) to be

$$\chi = (\chi_S \chi_{aS}^*)^{\frac{1}{2}} + \chi_{N \cdot R}$$

$\chi_{N \cdot R}$ is a non-resonant third order nonlinear susceptibility, which is due to the nonlinear response of the electrons driven by the electromagnetic fields.

We shall first consider only the term

$$\frac{4\pi}{c^2} \frac{\partial^2}{\partial t^2} \, \chi E_L{}^2 E_S{}^*$$

in Eq. 31. This is a source term at frequency $2\omega_L - \omega_S = \omega_L + \omega_0 = \omega_{aS}$ for the anti-Stokes field, but its wave vector $2k_L - k_S$ is not always equal to k_{aS} because of color dispersion in the medium as $k = n\omega/c$. We then get for the intensity of the anti-Stokes beam

$$\mathscr{I}_{aS} = | \, \chi \, |^2 \left(\frac{\sin \, (2\mathbf{k}_L - \mathbf{k}_S - \mathbf{k}_{aS}) \cdot r}{| \, 2\mathbf{k}_L - \mathbf{k}_S - \mathbf{k}_{aS} \, |} \right)^2 \left(\frac{4\pi}{c} \right)^4 \frac{n_L{}^2 n_S}{n_{aS}^3} \omega_{aS}^2 | \, \chi \, |^2 \mathscr{I}_L{}^2 \mathscr{I}_S \tag{33}$$

A coherence length for the anti-Stokes generation is defined as $l_{aS} = \pi/|\,2\mathbf{k}_L - \mathbf{k}_S - \mathbf{k}_{aS}\,|$. The periodic variation of $\mathscr{I}_{aS}$ is due to the fact that the polarization $P(\omega_{aS})$ at frequency ω_{aS} at $z = l_{aS}$ is just out of phase with the electromagnetic wave at $z = l_{aS}$ generated by $P(\omega_{aS})$ at $z = 0$. We should remark that the anti-Stokes intensity depends upon the square of the modulus of χ, whereas the Stokes gain depends upon its imaginary part. Such processes are called parametric processes. It is usually possible to find directions of the Stokes and anti-Stokes wave vectors for which the momentum mismatch $2\mathbf{k}_L - \mathbf{k}_S - \mathbf{k}_{aS}$ vanishes. This is shown in Fig. 2 for normal dispersion. We call θ_{aS}° the angle between $\mathbf{k}_L$ and $\mathbf{k}_{aS}$. The situation would be more involved in anisotropic or optically active materials where the index of refraction depends upon the state of polarization of the beam.

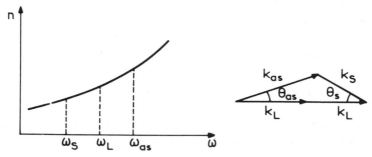

Fig. 2. Frequency variation of the index of refraction and phase-matching condition for anti-Stokes generation.

The directions for which $\Delta\mathbf{k} = 0$ are called phase-matching directions. The anti-Stokes intensity will grow indefinitely, at least as long as $\mathscr{I}_{aS} \ll \mathscr{I}_S$ and $\mathscr{I}_L$. The phase-matched angle θ_{aS}° outside the medium is given by the expression:

$$\theta_{aS}^{\circ 2} = n\left(1 - \frac{\omega_0}{\omega_L}\right)\left\{(n_{aS} - n_L) - (n_L - n_S)\left(\frac{\omega_L - \omega_0}{\omega_L + \omega_0}\right)\right\} \tag{34}$$

This means that if we send in the medium a collimated laser beam and an uncollimated Stokes beam, the angular aperture of which being larger than $\theta_S^\circ = (k_{aS}/k_S)\theta_{aS}^\circ$, anti-Stokes light will be emitted along a cone (22) of angular aperture θ_{aS}°. At the same time there is attenuation of the Stokes beam at θ_S°.

Actually in usual experiments the Stokes and anti-Stokes beams grow together. Thus we must consider both equations at the same time. This has been studied by Bloembergen and Shen (23). The essential result is that there is no gain at the angles θ_s° and θ_{aS}° for the Stokes and anti-Stokes waves respectively. The anti-Stokes emission takes place at an angle $\theta_{aS} \neq \theta_{aS}^\circ$ and for a frequency $\omega_{aS} \neq \omega_L + \omega_0$; we again find a frequency shift due to the coupling of the waves. Theoretical results are quite complicated because there are two parameters $\theta_{aS} - \theta_{aS}^\circ$ and $\omega_{aS} - (\omega_L + \omega_0)$. However, it turns out that the angle $\theta_{aS} - \theta_{aS}^\circ$ is quite small compared to the usual laser beam divergence and has not been observed.

We have thus shown that the Stokes wave propagates with a gain constant $g\mathscr{I}_L$ that can be calculated from experimental data on the spontaneous scattering or from theoretical expressions. This applies only for $|E_S| \ll |E_L|$ when saturation does not take place. For large Stokes conversion, saturation effects take place due to attenuation of the laser beam, saturation of the molecular transition or creation of higher order Stokes and anti-Stokes waves at frequencies $\omega_L \pm m\omega_0$ where m is an integer. We now turn to the study of beam propagation in media where the index of refraction is intensity-dependent.

B. Beam Propagation, Self-trapping and Self-focusing

We have seen that when $\chi_{(3)}(\omega, \omega_L, -\omega_L, +\omega)$ has a nonzero real part, the Stokes beam propagates with an index

$$n = n_0 + \frac{2\pi}{n} Re \, \chi_{(3)} |E_L|^2 = n_0 + n_1 |E_L|^2$$

We are going to discuss the consequences of this index change for the propagation of a laser beam of finite aperture.

If $n_1 > 0$, the index at the center of the beam is larger than at the edges, so we get the equivalent of a converging lens and focusing action.

1. SELF-TRAPPING (24)

Let us first consider the case where this focusing is just enough to balance diffraction. Then the beam propagates with a constant radius. This is called self-trapping. Maxwell's equations have been used (24,25) to study this problem, but we shall only give a simple argument due to Chiao, Garmire and Townes (24).

Consider a beam with radial intensity distribution $I = I_0$ for $r \leq R$ and $I = 0$ for $r > R$. The index increase δn creates a light pipe represented in Fig. 3(a). The beam will be considered as stable if $\theta_{lim} = \theta_{diffraction}$

$$\theta_{\text{lim}} = \sqrt{\left(\frac{2\delta n}{n}\right)} = \frac{1.22\lambda}{2R} \tag{35}$$

The total power of the beam is then

$$P_{st} = \frac{c(1.22)^2\lambda^2}{16n_1} \tag{36}$$

Maxwell's equations yield

$$P_{st} = \frac{5.763\lambda^2 c}{16\pi^3 n_1}$$

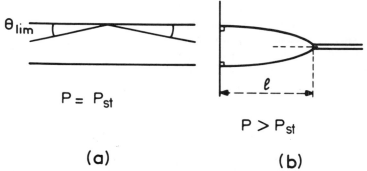

$$\theta_{\text{lim}}$$

$$P = P_{st}$$

$$\ell$$

$$P > P_{st}$$

(a)   (b)

Fig. 3. (a) Self-trapping of light beams occurs when $\theta_{\text{limit}} = \theta_{\text{diffraction}}$; (b) Self-focusing of an intense light beam in a length l and beginning of filament after the focus.

Typical values of P_{st} are of the order of 10 to 100 kW for ruby laser light at 6943 Å in liquids.

To determine (26,27) the radius of the self-trapped filament it is necessary to add higher order terms in the development

$$n = n_0 + n_1 \mid E_L \mid^2 + n_2 \mid E_L \mid^4 +$$

2. SELF-FOCUSING (25,28)

If $P > P_{st}$ focusing action overcomes diffraction and the beam radius will shrink with distance. Analytical and numerical studies of this problem yield a self-focusing length,

$$l = \frac{R}{2}(n_0 n_1)^{\frac{1}{2}}(E_m - E_{cr})^{-1} \tag{37}$$

where

$$E_{cr} = \frac{1.22\lambda}{8R}\left(\frac{n_0}{n_1}\right)^{\frac{1}{2}} \tag{38}$$

R is the input beam radius, and E_m the maximum of the input electric field. Figure 3(b) schematically shows focusing to a very small diameter in a length l. There is a corresponding very large increase of intensity which has drastic consequences for the stimulated Raman effect which depends exponentially upon $\mathscr{I}_L$.

After the focus, it is experimentally found (29) that a stable small diameter filament develops. Many studies have been devoted to these filaments, but it is fair to say that one cannot derive with accuracy the expression $\int \mathscr{I}_L \, dz$ along a filament. Furthermore, the intensities are so large ($> 10^9$ W/cm^2) that saturation takes place together with uncertain higher order effects. As a result, we cannot calculate the total Stokes gain in cases where self-focusing takes place, and thus fail to reach our initial goal. This very fascinating problem is, as will be shown later, a very serious drawback for the stimulated Raman effect. However, well chosen situations where self-focusing is eliminated can be found, to make possible an experimental study of the stimulated Raman effect.

C. Generalization to Stimulated Scattering by Other Excitations

As indicated in the introduction, any spontaneous scattering process is accompanied by a stimulated analog. Assuming that x is the coordinate of the excitation which gives rise to the scattering through the term $\partial \alpha / \partial x$, we shall write a system of coupled equations, with source terms: $(\partial \alpha / \partial x)E_L x^*$ and $(\partial \alpha / \partial x)E_L E_S^*$ for the Stokes field and the excitation respectively. The calculation will be detailed for two cases:

1. Rayleigh wing scattering

2. Brillouin scattering

1. RAYLEIGH WING SCATTERING (30)

Let us consider (31) a liquid or gas composed of optically anisotropic molecules with a polarizability tensor:

$$\begin{pmatrix} \alpha_\| & 0 & 0 \\ 0 & \alpha_\| & 0 \\ 0 & 0 & \alpha_\perp \end{pmatrix}$$

In the absence of any field, the angular distribution of the molecular axes is isotropic: $dN = (1/4\pi) \, d\Omega = f_0 \, d\Omega$.

In the presence of an optical field E_L, there is partial alignment and the distribution function f becomes

$$f = f_0 + \frac{f_0}{16kT}(\alpha_{\parallel} - \alpha_{\perp}) \mid E_L \mid^2 (\cos^2 \theta - \tfrac{1}{3}) \tag{39}$$

This is analogous to alignment by a dc electric field in the Kerr effect, the only difference coming from the absence of terms proportional to the permanent electric dipole moment of the molecules, because the time average,

$$(1/\theta) \int_0^\theta \mathbf{P} \cdot \mathbf{E} \, dt = 0 \text{ for } \theta \gg \omega_L^{-1}$$

This effect is called the optical Kerr effect (32).

If collisions are very frequent, the orientation of molecules satisfies a diffusion equation, and according to Debye (33) we get for two applied fields with parallel polarization

$$x + \tau \frac{\partial x}{\partial t} = \frac{\alpha_{\parallel} - \alpha_{\perp}}{16kT} E_L \cdot E_S{}^* \tag{40}$$

where

$$f - f_0 = x(\cos^2 \theta - \tfrac{1}{3}) f_0 \tag{41}$$

$$\tau = \tfrac{1}{3}\tau_{\text{Debye}} = 8\pi a^3 \eta / 6kT \tag{42}$$

for molecules of radius a in a medium of viscosity η. In addition we have

$$\nabla^2 E_S{}^* - \frac{\partial^2 \varepsilon_S}{\partial t^2} E_S{}^* = \frac{N4\pi}{c^2} \frac{\partial^2}{\partial t^2} \left[\frac{16}{45} (\alpha_{\parallel} - \alpha_{\perp}) E_L{}^* x \right] \tag{43}$$

From Eqs. 40 and 43 we get a nonlinear susceptibility,

$$\chi(\omega_S, \omega_L, -\omega_L, +\omega_S) = \frac{N(\alpha_{\parallel} - \alpha_{\perp})^2}{45kT} \frac{1}{1 + i(\omega_L - \omega_S)\tau} \tag{44}$$

The imaginary part is minimum for $\omega_S = \omega_L - (1/\tau)$, at which frequency there is maximum gain for the stimulated Rayleigh wing scattering.

The real part is maximum for $\omega_S = \omega_L$, and there is maximum index change,

$$dn = \frac{2\pi}{n} \frac{N(\alpha_{\parallel} - \alpha_{\perp})^2 \mid \varepsilon_L \mid^2}{45kT} \tag{45}$$

In reality, this model is valid only for dilute gases. For dense media, one must consider the difference between applied and effective fields, and take into account the effect of molecular interactions. Kielich (34) has considered this problem. It turns out that this $\chi_{(3)\text{Rayleigh}}$ can be related (35) to the dc Kerr effect or to the depolarization ratio of the scattered light.

This optical Kerr effect produces a birefringence of the medium, which can be measured directly as was done by Gires and Mayer (32) and later by Paillette (36). Other experimental techniques to measure δn have been used by several authors (37).

In addition to molecular reorientation, other effects, such as electrostriction (35), and the electronic Kerr effect (37–41) can cause index changes. The optical Kerr effect is thought to be the dominant effect in liquids with anisotropic molecules, but only a careful study (40) of the temperature variation of the index change can help to distinguish these various mechanisms.

2. Brillouin Scattering (18,41)

In this case the index of refraction is modulated by sound waves which are coupled to the light by electrostriction. The frequency shift between laser and Stokes waves is the same as for spontaneous Brillouin scattering:

$$\Delta v = v_L 2n \frac{v_S}{c} \sin \frac{\theta}{2} \tag{46}$$

in an isotropic medium where θ is the scattering angle, n the index of refraction and v_S the velocity of sound.

We can write down the two coupled wave equations in which the additional driving term is provided by electrostriction:

$$\frac{\partial^2 E_S}{\partial t^2} - \frac{c^2}{\varepsilon_0} \nabla^2 E_S = -\frac{\gamma'}{\rho_0 \varepsilon_0} \frac{\partial^2}{\partial t^2} (\rho^* E_L)$$

$$\frac{\partial^2 \rho}{dt^2} + \alpha_S \frac{\partial \rho}{\partial t} - v_S^2 \nabla \rho^2 = -\frac{\gamma'}{8\pi} \nabla^2 E_L E_S^*$$

where ρ is the density variation, ρ_0 the average density, and $\gamma' = \gamma K$, where γ is the electrostrictive constant and K the bulk modulus.

$$v_S = \left(\frac{K}{\rho_0}\right)^{\frac{1}{2}}$$

is the sound velocity. At resonance, for highly damped sound waves and steady state, we obtain

$$Im \, \chi_{\text{Brillouin}} = -\frac{\gamma'^2}{32\pi^2 \rho_0} \frac{\omega_{\text{sound}}}{\alpha_S v_S^2}$$

III. EXPERIMENTAL STUDY OF THE STIMULATED RAMAN EFFECT

A. Gain Measurements

As discussed previously, the essential feature of stimulated scattering is the existence of a gain $G = \exp g \mathscr{I}_L z$ at the Stokes frequency. We are now going to describe experimental studies for measuring this gain. There are two methods to do this. We can consider either an oscillator or an amplifier at the Stokes frequency.

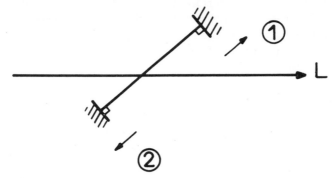

Fig. 4. Raman oscillator pumped by the laser beam L.

1. OSCILLATORS

a. *With mirrors*

The active medium is placed in between two mirrors as indicated in Fig. 4; these mirrors have reflectivities R_1 and R_2 at v_S and $R_1' = R_2' = 0$ at v_L. If G_1 is the gain for a Stokes beam propagating in direction (1) and G_2 the gain for direction (2), and if we neglect diffraction and absorption losses at frequency v_S, we get at threshold:

$$G_1 G_2 R_1 R_2 = 1$$

This true oscillation threshold must be distinguished from an observational threshold of the stimulated Raman effect. We note that this notion is often loosely defined, as many experimentalists consider an observational threshold which may vary considerably with the detector's sensitivity (from 10^{-4} to $> 10^6$ W).

Such experiments have been performed by several authors (6,42–47), most of them using a resonator placed perpendicular (44,46) to the laser beam. But, as it is fairly difficult to measure $\mathscr{I}_L$, R_1, R_2 and the filling factor of the cavity when the laser beam is not uniform over the Stokes resonator modes, this technique has been used to compare thresholds in various liquids and for several Raman transitions using selective mirrors (48). In the case of high pressure hydrogen gas (46), results are in good agreement with the predictions.

The spatial properties of the emitted Stokes beam ought to correspond to the spatial modes of the resonator. This is the case for H_2 gas (46) and some liquids (49), but for other liquids with large optical Kerr constant, nonlinear index changes distort the modes and the spatial properties of the output. In addition the quality factor Q of the cavity is reduced.

The modes of the cavity of length L must be taken into account, and their frequency spacing $c/2nL$ compared to the frequency width δv_R of the Raman resonance. If $(c/2nL) > \delta v_R$, proper tuning of the cavity is necessary, and pulling effects can take place. If $(c/2nL) < \delta v_R$, several Stokes modes will be generated, separated by

$$\delta v = \frac{c}{2nL}\left(1 - \frac{\delta v_c}{\delta v_R}\right),$$

where δv_c is the linewidth of the resonator modes.

Studies of this effect have been performed by Tannenwald (50). This might conceivably lead to a method of measuring δv_R.

In any case, a detailed analysis of the experimental situation will be required when such a Raman oscillator is used to generate Stokes light for frequency measurements, in order to eliminate errors due to mode pulling.

b. *Without mirrors*

Instead of using a resonator to fold the beam and obtain a large total Stokes gain, one can as well increase the length z of the medium. If we assume $|E_L|^2 = $ Const. the total Stokes gain is $G = \exp g\mathscr{I}_L z$. Thus one Stokes photon at the entrance of the medium gives rise to a very intense beam at the end, if G is of the order of e^{30}; this corresponds to super-radiant emission. The initial photon can either be produced by spontaneous Raman scattering, or come from electromagnetic field fluctuations. This method of generating Stokes light is obviously simpler than the preceding one. It is usually advantageous to increase the gain by focusing the laser beam.

When a collimated (unfocused) laser beam is used, geometrical considerations show that the Stokes emission will be concentrated forward and backward, when the beam diameter $2R$ is small compared to the distance necessary to achieve large amplification. Usually the Stokes beam is polarized parallel to the input laser beam polarization. Some studies of Stokes polarizations for various laser polarization have been performed by McClung et al. (51). When the beam is focused these conclusions still apply, unless one uses a cylindrical lens which focuses the beam along a line perpendicular to the direction of the beam as was done by Emmett and Schawlow (52). In that case, emission takes place at right angles to the direction of the beam. Interesting studies of the polarization of the scattering can be performed this way.

In the case of a superradiant oscillator we take $\mathscr{I}_S(0) = 0$, in Eq. (4) to calculate the Stokes intensity; we see that the threshold is not well defined.

Measurements of Stokes power in such conditions have been performed by several authors (53–55). Results are very seldom in agreement with Eq. 4. Usually one gets an $\mathscr{I}_S$ versus $\mathscr{I}_L$ curve of the type indicated in Fig. 5. The change in slope corresponds to the appearance of gains much larger than expected for superradiant emission. These results show a first discrepancy between experiment and theory (56). As we shall discuss later, it corresponds to the appearance of high intensity filaments.

In order to apply Eq. (4) to experimental results in such a way that it is valid for true superradiant emission, care must be taken to avoid spurious reflections which need not be large in view of the large gains available ($\sim e^{10}$ or more per pass). This would give rise to output Stokes power versus laser intensity in qualitative agreement with Fig. 5. Also indicated in Fig. 5 is the second Stokes emission at $\omega_L - 2\omega_0$.

When the Stokes power becomes large, saturation effects take place due to mechanisms that are not well known. As a result the laser beam suffers structure changes and is attenuated. In liquids the gains forward and backward are expected to be equal since as was shown by Porto and Leite (57) the scattering cross section is the same, for a totally symmetric Raman transition, and the linewidth should not depend upon direction.†
As a result the forward and backward Stokes emissions in a true superradiant situation ought to be equal. Experimentally, this is not found to be the case, at least when the total Stokes powers are compared; we shall describe this in more detail in Section IV.

† This is not true in a low pressure gas where the Doppler width depends upon the scattering angle.

2. AMPLIFIERS

The preceding considerations on oscillators with or without mirrors show that it would be more profitable to study low gain amplifiers with a well controlled input, instead of relying upon ill-defined spontaneous scattering or electromagnetic field fluctuations as is done in an oscillator. One can use a setup, shown in Fig. 6, in which Stokes light generated in the oscillator cell is amplified by the laser in the amplifier cell (58–60).

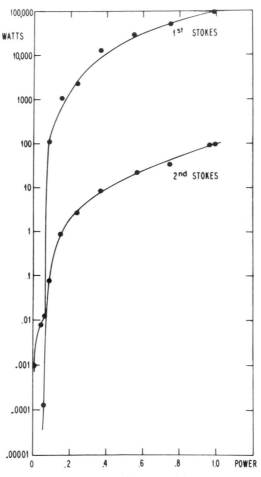

Fig. 5. Power output of a superradiant Raman oscillator vs input laser power. The input power is expressed in arbitrary units. Note the sharp break of the first Stokes curves. [After Ref. (60).]

Proper attenuation and decoupling is provided by filter F; the input and output Stokes intensities are measured with detectors M and S. The gain is defined as

$$G = \mathscr{I}_S \text{(out)}/\mathscr{I}_S \text{(in)}$$

If necessary, a birefringent plate Q is used to change the polarization of E_S compared to that of E_L. This setup has been used in many cases, but it

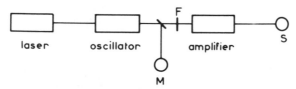

Fig. 6. Experimental setup for Raman amplification of the Stokes beam generated in the oscillator. The Stokes power is measured before and after amplification by the detectors M and S. The filter F is used to attenuate the Stokes beam.

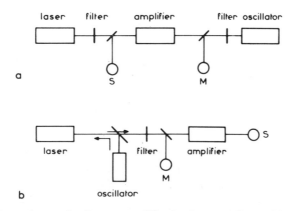

Fig. 7. Experimental setup for Raman amplification by an undistorted laser beam (a) for backward amplification; (b) for forward amplification.

has a great flaw, as the amplifying laser beam may be and usually is very much distorted in the oscillator. It is therefore more appropriate to use one of the two schemes described in Fig. 7, in which an undisturbed laser beam is used. In case (b), the backward Stokes beam is reflected by the laser mirror before going into the amplifier. Care must be taken to avoid time delays comparable to the pulse duration.

a. *In nonself-focusing media: gases and solids*

Results (*46*) obtained when the Raman active transition was the $Q_{01}(1)$ transition in H_2 gas are described below. This gas was chosen because it has a very small Kerr constant so that no self-trapping takes place. Starting from a ruby laser at 14,400 cm^{-1}, the Stokes frequency is around 10,250 cm^{-1}. In Fig. 8 we present results of forward gain measurements

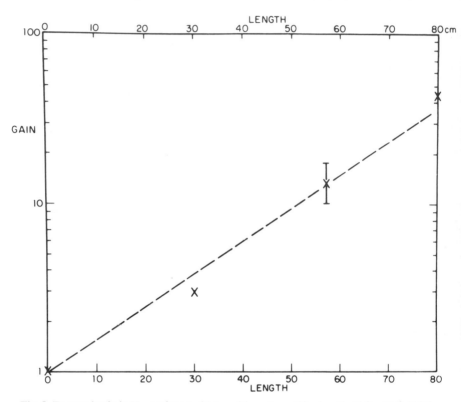

Fig. 8. Forward gain in H_2 gas for $Q_{01}(1)$ transition vs amplifier length. [After Ref. (*46*).]

with amplifier length l. We find that G varies exponentially with l. Furthermore the slope of $\log G$ vs l is within experimental errors equal to the predicted slope $g = 1.5 \times 10^{-3}$ $cm^{-1}/MW/cm^2$. Uncertainties in the comparison come from inaccuracy of the measurement of the laser intensity about which more will be said later.

We can also measure the gain as a function of χ_R'' which we can vary by pressure changes or by frequency detuning around the center of the

Stokes gain profile. In Fig. 9 we show the backward gain vs pressure when the oscillator and the amplifier are at the same frequency. The theoretical solid curve has been deduced from linewidth measurements and was adjusted to fit the measured gain at high pressure where both $d\sigma/d\Omega$ and δv_R vary linearly with the density ρ. In the case of forward gain

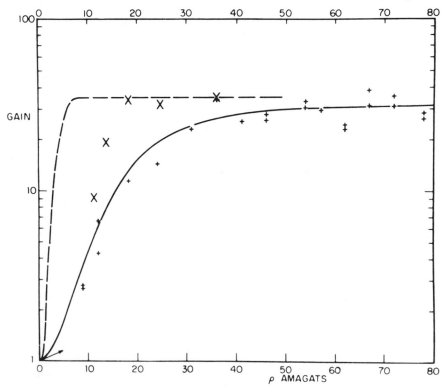

Fig. 9. Backward ($+$) and forward ($\times$) gain in H_2 gas vs amplifier density. The solid and dashed curves are theoretical curves which fit the data at high pressure.

measurements the agreement with the calculated gain is not good at low pressure, because the Stokes gain linewidth becomes comparable to the laser linewidth. Furthermore the time delay between the Stokes and laser pulses can produce troubles.

In Fig. 10 we show the gain as a function of frequency detuning; as we expect,

$$g = g_0 \Bigg/ \left[1 + \left(\frac{2\delta v}{\delta v_R} \right)^2 \right].$$

The detuning was obtained by varying the pressure of the oscillator, as it is known (61) that the Raman vibrational frequency shifts with density.

In the case of a solid like $CaCO_3$, nonlinear index changes will be small, and the measured gain ought to be equal to the calculated one. This has been shown to be the case by Mayer and Bisson (62) for the 1088 cm^{-1} vibration of $CaCO_3$, provided the inhomogeneities of the input laser beam distribution are properly taken into account.

We can conclude this discussion of the Raman gain in a medium where nonlinear index changes are expected not to be large enough to produce self-focusing by saying that there is good agreement between experimental and theoretical studies.

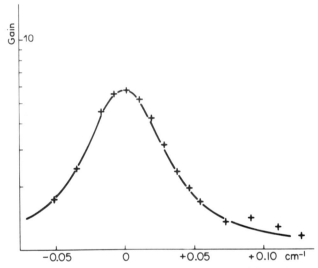

Fig. 10. Gain in H_2 gas vs frequency detuning expressed in cm^{-1} from the center of the gain profile (density in the amplifier: 49 amagats).

b. *In self-focusing media*

Let us use the amplifying setup depicted in Fig. 6 with a liquid such as benzene. There is Stokes emission corresponding to the totally symmetric vibration at 992 cm^{-1}. We measure the gain as a function of amplifier length; a typical result (59) is shown in Fig. 11. The gain G can be represented as

$$G = a\, e^{\alpha z} + b\, e^{\beta z}$$

where $\beta/\alpha \sim 10^{2\pm1}$. Studies show that one has a true linear amplifier as the gain does not depend upon the input Stokes power at least when $\mathscr{I}_S \ll \mathscr{I}_L$. The gain coefficient α is about equal to the value calculated from the input laser power and the Raman susceptibility. But for z large enough, the second term dominates: it has been called anomalous gain, and constitutes the most striking difference between experiment and theories that neglect beam distortion by the medium.

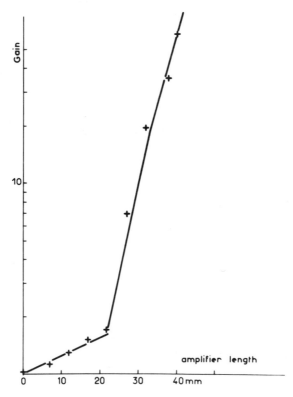

Fig. 11. Gain in benzene vs amplifier length, showing the appearance of anomalous gain.

This anomalous gain, that we already encountered in the case of superradiant oscillators is due to self-focusing of the laser beam in the amplifier cell (*63*). The amplifier length corresponding to $a\,e^{\alpha z} \sim b\,e^{\beta z}$ is about equal to the self-focusing length l.

These conclusions were reached from the following observations.

The length l depends critically upon the beam structure at the input of the amplifier. In particular it increases with the distance between amplifier and oscillator, because the hot spots or filaments diffract very rapidly after leaving the oscillator cell due to their small diameter (10 to 50 μ).

The beam intensity profile locally assumes very large increases in some areas after traversing a length l in the medium. These hot spots can be photographed (63), or can be detected by a nonlinear process such as second harmonic generation in a quartz crystal (64) or by drastic lowering of the Raman emission threshold in another liquid situated immediately after the first cell (63,65).

From these results on the apparently simple amplifier measurements, one sees that a detailed study of self-focusing and subsequent filaments is required before any information can be learned about χ_R'' from gain measurements in experiments where self-focusing takes place. We shall give some details about filaments, and then compare the e-folding length, l_R, for the Raman gain if self-focusing did not occur, defined as $l_R = 1/g\mathscr{I}_L$, and the self-focusing length.

B. Self-focusing

In Section II, we have defined self-trapping and self-focusing and given the expression for the self-focusing length. A nonlinear optical process will be very sensitive to intensity increases. As a result, the stimulated Raman effect is a very good tool to study self-focusing if one assumes that the theory for the Raman gain is always valid.

The most obvious manifestation of self-focusing is the very sharp threshold for Stokes emission in a superradiant oscillator as shown in Fig. 5. The Raman threshold length has been measured as a function of laser power by Wang (66). His results shown in Fig. 12 are in good agreement with theory because the laser beam used was very uniform.

If the laser beam is very inhomogeneous, we can, in a simplified manner, consider it as the sum of many spots of different size. The radius of the first spot to be focused depends upon P_L and n_1. As a result the threshold length for the stimulated Raman effect is not proportional to $(P_L^{\frac{1}{2}} - P_{cr}^{\frac{1}{2}})^{-1}$ as expected from Eq. 37. This ought to be kept in mind when stimulated Raman effect threshold measurements are used to derive the value of the nonlinear index coefficient,

$$n_1 = \frac{dn}{d|E_L|^2}.$$

Photographic studies by Garmire, Chiao, and Townes (29) have shown that after the focus there is formation of a filament of more or less constant radius around 10 to 15 μ. If the input beam is well enough prepared, this so-called large scale filament is fairly reproducible from shot to shot, but a finer study shows that it contains small scale filaments (27) of small diameter (typically several μ) lasting a very short time and located at random. The nature of these small scale filaments is not very well understood. There is considerable interest in them and many theoretical studies

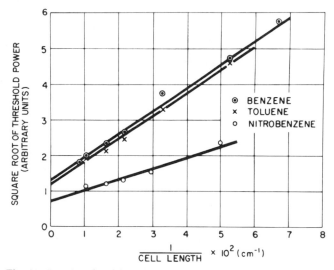

Fig. 12. Results of self-focusing length measurements by Wang (66).

are being made to account for their empirically found characteristics, especially their diameter. It is then necessary to add higher order terms to the index change. It is hoped that some insight may be obtained about higher order nonlinear optical processes in matter from these studies on filaments. But this leads quite far from our topic of the stimulated Raman effect as a tool to study Raman transitions. It is fair to say that the intensity distribution is not well enough known in the filaments to calculate the total gain constant $\int g \mathscr{I}_L \, dz$. Therefore experiments in which self-focusing takes place are, at least for the moment, unsuitable for deducing Raman susceptibilities.

To avoid this problem, experimental situations should be considered in which self-focusing does not or hardly does take place. To decide which amplifier characteristics to choose, one ought to compare the self-focusing length $l_{s.f.}$ and e-folding Raman gain length l_R. We have seen that

$$l_{s.f.} = \frac{R}{2}(n_0 n_1)^{\frac{1}{2}}[E_m - E_{cr}]^{-1} \quad \text{and} \quad l_R = 1/g\mathscr{I}_L.$$

For materials like H_2 gas, $l_R \ll l_{s.f.}$ so that amplifier experiments are "safe," but in a medium like CS_2, $l_R > l_{s.f.}$ in typical experimental situations, and one must use very short cells with small gains which may be hard to measure due to large fluctuations in the ratio $\mathscr{I}_{(S)}/\mathscr{I}_{(M)}$ of the intensities (measured with detectors S and M in Fig. 6) from shot to shot. In practice, gains between 1.00 and 1.05 to 1.10 will be too small to be measured as one cannot take averages over many laser shots due to the fairly slow repetition rate of Q-switched lasers.

In addition to self-focusing, difficulties arise from the usually multimode character of the input laser beam. As we shall discuss in Section IV, lasers can be made to operate at a single frequency, but the spatial structure of the beam is multimode. The number of modes is equal to the "étendue" of the beam $A(d\Omega/\lambda^2)$ where A is the cross section and $d\Omega$ the solid angle of the beam.

Several studies have been devoted to the influence of multimoding in nonlinear optical experiments. In the case of second harmonic generation Ducuing and Bloembergen (67) have performed theoretical and experimental studies, and the situation is well understood. In the case of the stimulated Raman effect, the problem is more complicated as self-focusing depends upon the beam structure, and the gain varies exponentially with intensity. Bloembergen and Shen (19) have shown theoretically that N laser modes give rise to a gain constant log N times larger. To date, no thorough experimental study of this problem has been performed.

We conclude these two paragraphs on the Raman gain and self-focusing by again emphasizing the problems which arise when deducing Raman susceptibilities from gain measurements. Before discussing applications of the stimulated Raman effect, we shall describe experimental results on the anti-Stokes emission, and the linewidth of the Stokes emission.

C. Anti-Stokes Emission

We have calculated in Section II, A, 2, b the angle of the anti-Stokes emission, θ_{aS}°, as given by Eq. 34. Refractive indices are known with good accuracy, and it is possible to calculate θ_{aS}°. It is found experimentally that the anti-Stokes emission takes place along cones with angular aperture θ in isotropic media. A detailed analysis by Garmire (68) shows that in fact there exist two cones with different θ. Table 1 gives some experimental values of the angular aperture of the two cones together with the predicted values. We see that one type of cone is the predicted

TABLE 1

First Anti-Stokes Cone Angles
in 10^{-2} Radians[a]

Substance	θ_{th}	θ_{exp}	
Benzene	2.57	2.58	3.25
Toluene	2.58	2.5	3.0
Carbon disulfide	2.35	2.2	3.3
Nitrobenzene	4.3	4.17	5.8
Acetone	4.0	3.6	5.7
Cyclohexane	4.3	4.0	5.2

[a] The θ_{th} is calculated from known refraction indexes; θ_{exp} are experimentally measured values by Garmire (68).

Fig. 13. Phase matching condition for anti-Stokes generation when the laser beam has a large angular aperture, as is the case in a filament.

one, but that angular apertures for the second kind are larger. We again find an anomaly in the stimulated Raman effect usually referred to as the anti-Stokes angle anomaly. Again this is due to self-trapping and filaments in which there is a large angular distribution of $\mathbf{k}_L$ directions. A qualitative explanation (19) of this anomaly is presented in Fig. 13, in which are considered 2 laser photons with different $\mathbf{k}_L$, and a $\mathbf{k}_S$ closer to the axis; the resulting angle between k_{aS} and the axis is larger than in Fig. 2.

D. Spectrum of Stokes Emission

The gain profile is the same as the spontaneous scattering line shape. As a result one can estimate the stimulated Raman linewidth from the total gain at the center of the line in a superradiant oscillator

$$\delta v_{\text{stim}} = \delta v_{\text{spont}} \left(\frac{\log 2}{\log \frac{G_{\text{max}}}{2}} \right)^{\frac{1}{2}}$$

whereas in an oscillator one has

$$\delta v_{\text{stim}} = \frac{2\pi h v (\delta v_c)^2}{P_{\text{output}}}$$

where δv_c is the resonator mode linewidth as defined previously.

These values are lower limits because of the finite pulse duration and saturation effects. In any case δv_{stim} is expected to be smaller than δv_{spont}.

Experimental values of the stimulated linewidth are found to be anything from 10^{-2} to 10^3 or more cm^{-1}. These unexpectedly very broad lines constitute the third stimulated Raman effect anomaly.

In gases and solids, linewidths are usually less than $\delta v_L + \delta v_R$ where δv_L and δv_R are laser and Raman transition linewidths respectively. To obtain line narrowing in order to make precise frequency measurements it is necessary to use a superradiant oscillator or a small resonator with mode spacing larger than $\delta v_L + \delta v_R$, but in that case there are large pulling effects.

What is the situation in liquids? Stoicheff (69) who first studied this question found that if the input laser light is monochromatic (single longitudinal mode), the stimulated Raman line is very narrow, but that it is very broad if the laser light is not monochromatic (composed of several longitudinal modes). These observations apply in all cases, provided one takes into account possible creation of side bands of the laser light in the active medium such as Brillouin or stimulated Rayleigh wing Stokes components. We again find that we must know the exact laser beam structure inside the medium where the Stokes line is created, and that this structure need not be the same as that of the input both in space and time.

We have discussed previously the spatial deformation of the beam and the creation due to nonlinear index changes. We now discuss temporal changes due to time varying index changes, in terms of a very simplified model which will give only qualitative results.

In Section II, C, 1 we discussed the influence of two fields E_L and E_L' with frequencies v_L and $v_L + \delta v$ on the orientation of optically anisotropic molecules. As a result, we get an index modulation at frequency δv proportional to:

$$\frac{(\alpha_\parallel - \alpha_\perp)^2}{kT} \mid E_L \mid \mid E_L' \mid \frac{1}{\mid 1 + i\delta v\tau \mid}$$

If another wave at frequency v propagates in the index modulated medium, there will be creation of side bands at frequencies $v + m\delta v$ where m is an integer. If we neglect the influence on the molecular orientation of the test field and its side bands, the test field $\varepsilon_0 \exp(-i(\omega t + kz))$ becomes after a length z:

$$\begin{aligned}
E &= \varepsilon_0 \exp\left(i(n + \delta n \sin \Delta\omega t)\frac{\omega}{c} z - i\omega t \right) \\
&= \varepsilon_0 \exp\left(in \frac{\omega}{c} z - i\omega t \right)\left[J_0\left(\delta n \frac{\omega z}{c} \right) + 2iJ_1\left(\delta n \frac{\omega z}{c} \right) \sin \delta\omega t \right. \\
&\quad \left. + 2J_2\left(\delta n \frac{\omega z}{c} \right) \cos 2\delta wt + \ldots \right]
\end{aligned}$$

We can easily deduce the amplitude ε_m of the side band at frequency $v + m\delta v$ from that expression.

To estimate the number of side bands after a length z, the product $\mid E_L E_L' \mid z$ is required. We can deduce its value from the Raman gain; then we know the argument of the Bessel functions

$$\delta n \frac{\omega z}{c} = \frac{1}{2} \frac{\chi_{\text{Rayleigh}}(\text{max})}{Im \chi_{\text{Raman}}} gz \frac{1}{\mid 1 - i\delta\omega\tau \mid}$$

We see that the extent of the broadening is directly related to the nonlinear index of refraction change $dn/d\mid E_L \mid^2$, which is also proportional to χ_{Rayleigh}. This simple description gives a fair estimate of the extent of the broadening and shows a periodic variation of ε_m for a given product $\mid E_L E_L' \mid z$ as observed by Shimizu (70), but it does not explain the asymmetry of the broadening. The more complete theory of De Martini et al. (71) well describes the experimental results.

We now present some experiments on the line broadening in which some parameters are varied.

The output of a rotating prism Q-switched laser giving 2 modes 1.6 cm^{-1} apart is used to generate Stokes light at 8858 Å in cyclohexane.

As the Kerr constant of cyclohexane is very small, the Stokes spectrum consists of 2 modes only. We then let this Stokes light interact with the laser beam in CS_2 and record in Fig. 14 the spectra as a function of interaction length. We see a fast increase in the linewidth, but the line is very asymmetric.

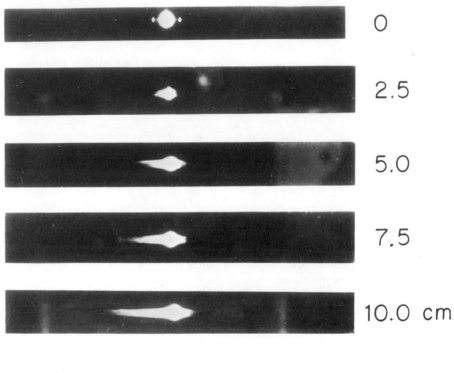

0

2.5

5.0

7.5

10.0 cm

100 Å

Fig. 14. Broadening of the cyclohexane Stokes line in increasing lengths of carbon disulfide when the input beam is multimode.

We can vary the size of the index change by the term $|1 - i\delta\omega\tau|^{-1}$, as τ is a function of the temperature. Experimental results have been obtained on benzaldehyde (72).

If the input laser is single-mode, then due to the finite duration of the pulse τ_p, there are Fourier components over $1/\tau_p$, and associated time varying modulation of the index of refraction. Hence, broadening can be observed from a single-mode laser (71,73), but it should be of much smaller extent than for 2 widely separated modes, as discussed before.

From a single-mode laser, nonlinear optical effects can create light close to the laser frequency, and afterwards these two frequencies can beat and produce line broadening. We shall discuss here experimental results on the stimulated Rayleigh wing scattering, which we introduced theoretically in Section II, C, 1.

We have seen that if molecular reorientation occurs in a time τ, there is gain at frequency $\omega_L - (1/\tau)$ (we neglect here the Stokes–anti-Stokes coupling that was considered by Kelley et al. (74–76)). Experiments by Fabelinskii et al. (30,77) and by Rank et al. (78) have demonstrated the existence of stimulated emission at this new frequency. Figure 15 from

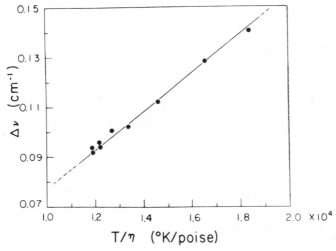

Fig. 15. Stimulated Rayleigh wing scattering shifts vs T/η, obtained by Rank et al. (78).

Rank's (78) paper shows the frequency shift in nitrobenzene vs relaxation time τ deduced from viscosity measurements, as $\tau = 8\pi a^3\eta/6kT$. These results are in good agreement with theory.

Once this light is created, it can beat with the laser and give rise to very broad spectra as observed by Fabelinskii (77).

Another way to generate Stokes light close to the laser light is by means of the stimulated Brillouin effect. Backward scattered Brillouin light is reflected by the laser mirrors into the cell if proper optical isolation is not provided. The two beams then modulate the index as was demonstrated by Rank et al. (79).

This Section (III) has described the three anomalies found in the experimental studies of the stimulated Raman effect. They are:

1. Anomaly of the gain
2. Anomaly of the anti-Stokes cone angle
3. Anomaly of the linewidth.

We have shown that they are all related to static or time varying nonlinear index changes. As a result, in the absence of a detailed description of the filaments, one cannot use stimulated Raman gain measurements to determine χ_R''. In addition, frequency measurements will not be accurate when line broadening takes place. To avoid these problems, one will use a single mode laser to get sharp lines and low gain amplifiers to avoid self-focusing.

IV. APPLICATIONS

We shall discuss here some applications of the stimulated Raman effect, and try to put forward some advantages over spontaneous Raman scattering. But first we should give some details about the input light source.

A. Laser

As was seen above, the laser must produce a beam of great power, > 1 MW, with a fairly small linewidth (comparable to the Raman line widths), and be well collimated. It is therefore necessary to use a Q-switch laser.

The most commonly used laser is the ruby laser that gives large enough output powers. Without special care, the output linewidth will be of the order of 1 cm^{-1}, but this width can be reduced easily if a selective mirror (80) is used as one of the laser mirrors, and if the Q-switching is made by a saturable absorber (81) (organic dye or nonlinear glass).

Usual ruby lasers will produce beams with fairly large "étendue," and increasing the brightness by reducing the "étendue" without losing power is a difficult problem. To increase the brightness, a first step is to use a ruby crystal as good as can be found and to design a flash lamp arrangement producing a very uniform pumping of the ruby. Then it may prove necessary to add a small aperture inside the laser cavity to select only part of the ruby.

Tests of the beam quality can be performed as follows:

The spectral structure can be studied with a high resolution Fabry–Perot interferometer. In the best case where only 1 longitudinal mode of the laser is observed, the linewidth is usually found to be larger than that expected from the duration of the pulse. This discrepancy comes from a shift (82) of the laser frequency as a function of time due to a time variation of the optical length of the cavity. The sharpest laser lines observed are of the order of $\Delta v \simeq 200$ MHz. A simpler way to test the spectral structure is to send the beam on the photocathode of a fast photodetector followed by a fast oscilloscope. If several modes are present with frequency differences in the band pass of the detection system, modulation of the photocurrent will be observed. In fact, one must select a small part of the beam to obtain maximum modulation, because if different areas of the beam are incoherent with one another, the modulation effect may average out.

The spatial distribution may be studied from a measurement of the "étendue" $A \cdot d\Omega / \lambda^2$ of the beam, A being the cross section and $d\Omega$ its solid angle. One can further study the coherence of different parts of the beam from the contrast of interference patterns. A detailed photometric study of photographs of the near and far field patterns of the beam is somewhat unreliable, because one needs to know the instantaneous distribution of intensity and not its average value over the whole laser pulse.

Similar studies will have to be performed for the other lasers that may be employed. To date the following lasers have been used:

1. Nd^{3+}, $CaWO_4$ giving a narrow line at 1.06μ
2. Nd^{3+}, glass which will produce very broad lines unless precautions are taken.

This may be an advantage if one can lock the phases of all the modes in such a way as to give as output a periodic train of very intense pulses of duration of the order of 10^{-12} sec (83). Such a mode-locked laser was recently used by Giordmaine et al. (84) to study the stimulated Raman effect in liquids and self-focusing. In media where

$$\tau_{pulse} < \tau_{molecular\ alignment} < \tau_{repetition\ rate\ of\ pulse}$$

the Kerr effect will hardly take place, and the stimulated Raman effect threshold will be very high.

On the other hand, if careful mode selection is used, the Nd^{3+} glass laser will produce very sharp lines, and brighter beams than from the ruby laser can be obtained, due to the superior optical quality of Nd^{3+} glass compared to that of ruby.

From these two lasers, new frequencies are obtained by nonlinear optical effects:

1. Second harmonic in piezoelectric crystals like KDP or $LiNbO_3$ (from a good Nd^{3+}, glass laser, conversion efficiency into $0.53\ \mu$ can be as good as 40%).

2. Stimulated Raman effect in liquids.

B. Detectors

As the Stokes intensity can easily be 1% or more of the input laser intensity, there is no detection problem. Even at threshold, where intensities are of the order of the spontaneous intensity, due to the very short duration of the pulse, one can get rid of the photomultiplier dark current noise through suitable gating.

TABLE 2

List of Some Materials That Exhibit
Stimulated Raman Effect

Substance	$\nu_{vib}(cm^{-1})$
Carbon tetrachloride	460
Carbon disulfide	655
Chloroform	663
Calcium tungstate	911
Deuterated benzene	944
Benzene	990; 3064
Aniline	997
Styrene	999; 1631; 3056
Benzonitrile	1002; 2229
Toluene	1004
Calcite	1086
Diamond	1332
Nitrobenzene	1344
Oxygen	1552
Nitrogen	2327
Cyclohexane	2852
Acetone	2921
Hydrogen	4155

C. Materials

The stimulated Raman effect has been observed in many cases: liquids, solids, gases, and powders (85). In general, the emission takes place only for at most 3 Raman transitions at the same time. This can be easily understood in the following manner: when the laser intensity grows, as soon as the largest Raman gain reaches about e^{30}, saturation begins to occur associated with depletion of the laser beam. As a result the Raman gain for weaker lines cannot reach large values, and these lines are not observed. A very serious limitation of the stimulated Raman effect comes from this competition that is won by 1 or 2 of the strongest lines. Even with selective mirrors in a resonator (47), one rarely gets more lines.

Table 2 gives a partial list of materials that have been studied. One finds that most materials are organic liquids with optically anisotropic molecules (86).

D. Spectroscopic Applications

Two types of measurements can be performed with the stimulated Raman effect: first, Raman frequency measurements; second, gain measurements with an oscillator, or an amplifier. The results should be identical to those of the spontaneous Raman effect.

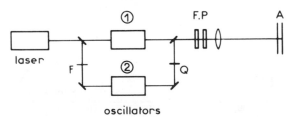

oscillators

Fig. 16. Experimental setup for frequency shift measurement. The substance under study is in oscillator (1). Oscillator (2) is used as a reference. Filter F is used to decouple the oscillators, Q is a half-wave plate at the Stokes frequency, FP is a Fabry–Perot etalon, A is made of two crossed analyzers placed side by side.

1. Frequency Measurements with Oscillators

We shall try to take advantage of the gain narrowing which may be considerable when a resonator is used. Moreover, the stimulated Stokes beams are intense and well collimated so that one can use a dispersive spectrometer and, in particular, a Fabry–Perot interferometer. Figure 16 describes a setup that was used to measure variations of the frequency of the vibrational $Q_{01}(1)$ transition in hydrogen gas as a function of pressure (87,88). It was necessary to monitor the laser frequency with a second hydrogen Raman oscillator in parallel with the first one. Figure 17 shows typical results that can be obtained with the stimulated Raman effect.

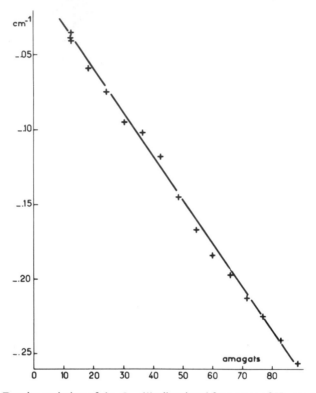

Fig. 17. Density variation of the Q_{01} (1) vibrational frequency of H_2 gas at 300°K.

Each point corresponds to one photograph of a Fabry–Perot ring pattern obtained with one 20 MW laser shot that could be repeated every 5 secs. This would take more time with conventional spontaneous Raman scattering. But a real drawback of this method is its limitation to only one $Q_{01}(J)$ line. Experimental situations exist (89) in which another line $Q_{01}(J)$, with $J \neq 1$, will dominate, but have not been studied; this technique could be extended to other gases.

Tannenwald (*90*) has measured the frequency shift of the 466 cm^{-1} line of quartz as a function of temperature; results are shown in Fig. 18.

In liquid mixtures, it was observed that the frequency varies with concentration. For instance, the 656 cm^{-1} Raman line of pure liquid CS_2 was found to be shifted by about $+1$ cm^{-1} in an 80 cc CCl_4, 10 cc CS_2 mixture. But in such a situation with a liquid of large Kerr effect, line broadening and even line shifting can take place; thus these data are not very reliable.

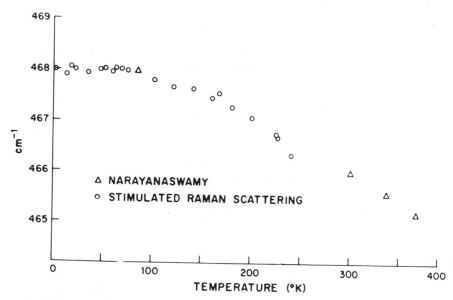

TEMPERATURE DEPENDENCE OF 466-cm^{-1} VIBRATION IN QUARTZ

Fig. 18. Temperature dependence of the 466 cm^{-1} vibration in quartz, from Tannenwald (*90*).

In the case of potassium vapor, the stimulated Raman effect corresponding to the transition between the $^2P_{1/2}$ and $^2P_{3/2}$ states has been observed (*91,92*). In this case, the exciting line was the nitrobenzene Stokes line at 14,400–1345 cm^{-1} in near resonance with the $^2S_{1/2} - {}^2P_{3/2}$ transition. It populates the $^2P_{3/2}$ state, and then produces stimulated Raman scattering from that state.

2. Frequency Measurements with Amplifiers

If a large enough gain cannot be achieved to get sizable output in an oscillator, one can study a small amplification of an input test beam at the Stokes frequency. One can as well study a small anti-Stokes absorption. One can start either from a spectrally broad or a sharp test beam.

If a spectrally broad test beam is used, one will search for changes in the spectrum after interaction with the laser beam in the medium. The difficulty is to generate a test beam coincident in space and time with the laser beam in the medium under study, that is intense enough to photograph spectra in one or a few laser shots. A few techniques to generate such a test beam are indicated below:

1. Focus the laser beam in a high pressure gas cell where a spark will take place (93). But the light is emitted isotropically and consequently is not very bright.

2. Use a laser pumped dye laser (94). These devices produce broad (~ 100 cm^{-1}) spectra that can be centered over a considerable span of wave lengths by suitable choice of dye and concentration. In some cases it may be possible to stimulate some Raman transitions if a suitable dye is dissolved in the liquid under study (95). Then at some frequency the product of the Raman gain by the dye gain will be larger than the gain of the dominant Raman line of the liquid under consideration.

3. As was shown above, the stimulated Raman effect produces very broad lines in some liquids when the input laser light is multimode. This provides a very good test source for Raman amplification in another liquid. This technique was used in the case of anti-Stokes absorption by Jones and Stoicheff (96); Fig. 19 shows some of their spectra. The broad emission is produced by toluene in one cell immediately followed by another cell filled with benzene (Fig. 19c) or nitromethane (Fig. 19d). Absorption is clearly seen on these spectra that can be used to measure Raman frequencies. No such experiment has been performed for Stokes amplification, but we can mention one experiment where this effect takes place (31). Consider a mixture of carbon disulfide and cyclohexane in proportions such that only the line of cyclohexane at 2850 cm^{-1} is excited. If the laser is multimode, carbon disulfide, which self-focuses the beam, produces side bands due to index modulation. Some of these side bands will be amplified by the 2920 and 2935 cm^{-1} lines of C_6H_{12}. This is clearly shown on the spectrum in Fig. 20.

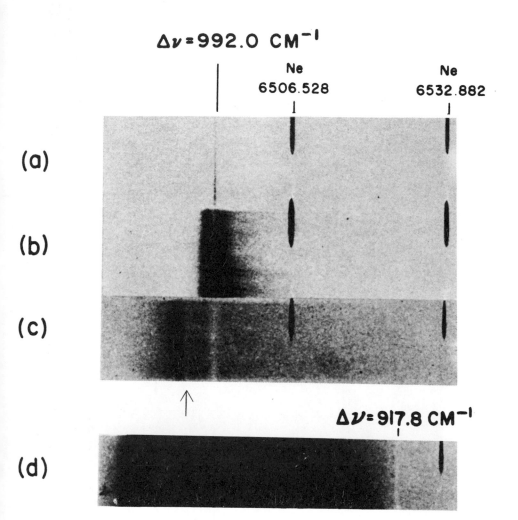

Fig. 19. The anti-Stokes line of liquid benzene at $\nu_0 + 992.0$ cm^{-1}. (a) Sharp and (b) broad stimulated Raman emission lines of benzene obtained when laser radiation is emitted in one or two lines, respectively; (b) also shows the sharp absorption line from benzene. (c) Inverse Raman spectrum, obtained with a single laser pulse using as a background continuum the broad emission whose center is indicated by the arrow. (d) Inverse Raman line of nitromethane at $\nu_0 + 917.8$ cm^{-1}. From Jones and Stoicheff (96).

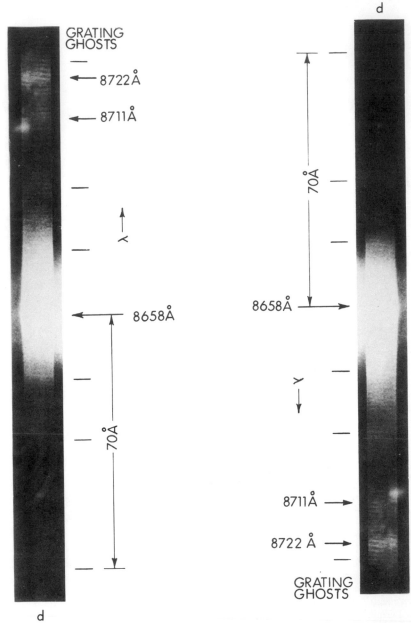

Fig. 20. Broad linewidth of the Stokes emission of a mixture 85cc cyclohexane, 15 cc CS₂ pumped by a multimode laser. Note the amplification at 8711 and 8722 Å.

If a spectrally sharp test beam is used, it will be interesting to measure the Raman gain vs frequency, in order to determine gain profiles. We described such gain experiments previously in Section III, A, 2 for the $Q_{01}(1)$ line of H_2 in a backward amplifier, where frequency tuning is obtained by changing the pressure. Results of such an experiment (87) are shown in Fig. 21. It is found that the linewidth is smaller than the

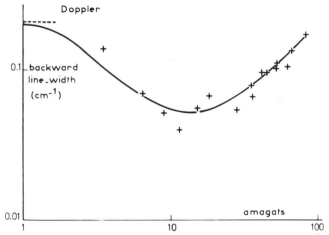

Fig. 21. Linewidth of the $Q_{01}(1)$ transition of hydrogen gas vs density in amagat units. [After Ref. (87).]

Doppler linewidth for backward scattering:

$$\Delta v = (v_L + v_S)\left(\frac{8kT\log 2}{mc^2}\right)^{\frac{1}{2}}$$

This is due to collisional narrowing discussed by Dicke (97). These results have also been obtained by spontaneous Raman scattering (98), but it was necessary to use a single-mode argon-ion laser because of the very small scattering efficiency. But here again the stimulated Raman effect is limited to the $Q_{01}(J = 1)$ transition.

Instead of measuring Stokes gains, one can measure parametric generation of anti-Stokes light, from a laser and a Stokes beam. We discussed this parametric process in Section II, A, 2, b. This technique was used by Maker and Terhune (37) in the case of liquids. Figure 22 shows the anti-Stokes power output vs interaction length. It varies as $\sin^2 (z/L)$ where L is the coherence length. The value of L deduced from these data is in good agreement with the value calculated from indices of refraction.

From the maxima of anti-Stokes intensity, the value of χ can be deduced. Figure 23 shows the frequency variation of χ for 3 liquids. We should note again that the coupling constant χ, which is measured here, is the modulus of χ_{Raman}, whereas the Stokes amplification depends only upon, the imaginary part of χ_{Raman}.

In practice this technique is more sensitive than that of Stokes amplification, because noise and fluctuations affect it much less than gain measurements, which must be larger than:

$$\exp(\delta) = \frac{\left[\overline{\left(\frac{S}{M} - \frac{\overline{S}}{M}\right)}\right]^{\frac{1}{2}}}{\dfrac{\overline{S}}{M}}$$

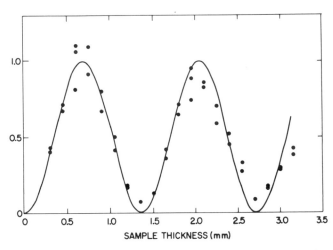

Fig. 22. Variation of the anti-Stokes intensity parametrically generated *vs* sample length in nonphase-matched conditions. [From Maker and Terhune (*37*).]

where S/M is the ratio of amplifier output over input for one laser shot, and the averages are taken over the limited and often small number of laser shots. In effect, fluctuations in this ratio are found to be large without self-focusing, and make measurements very unreliable with self-focusing. Ordinarily δ is seldom less than 10%. No such minimum conversion is required in anti-Stokes parametric generation provided a good enough filter at ν_{aS} is used, and anti-Stokes creation in cell windows is kept at a minimum. In Stokes amplification, fluctuations due to the multimode character of the laser beam would be reduced if a nonlinear monitoring were used, as in the case of second harmonic generation (99); this has so far not been done.

These examples of spectroscopic applications show that accurate frequency and linewidth measurements can be performed in some cases, due to the high intensity and narrow linewidth of the stimulated Raman emission.

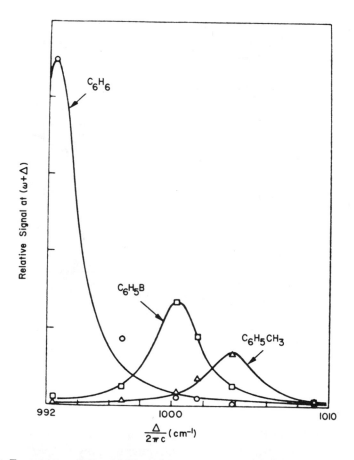

Fig. 23. Frequency variation of the anti-Stokes intensity maxima in benzene, bromo-benzene, and toluene; $\omega + \Delta = \omega_{as}$. [After Ref. (37).]

E. Application of the Stimulated Raman Effect as Light Source

In oscillators, one can convert up to 20% or sometimes more of the laser light into Stokes light. This provides a pulsed light source, the frequency of which can be chosen from a rather long list (*86*). The characteristics of the output beam will depend on those of the initial laser beam, as we considered previously.

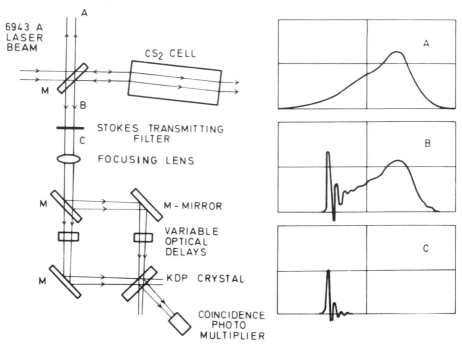

Fig. 24. Right: (A) Incident laser pulse; (B) reflected Raman Stokes plus Brillouin light; filters in front of the photodiode favor the Raman Stokes light by a factor of 3; (C) reflected Raman Stokes light only (20 nsec per division). Left: Schematic of the experimental arrangement to measure the length of the Raman spikes. [From Maier, Kaiser and Giordmaine (*101*).]

We shall discuss now the temporal properties of the emission. Usually, when $\mathscr{I}_L$ is much more than the threshold intensity, the forward Stokes pulse duration is of the same order as the laser duration, unless there is strong competition with the Brillouin scattering. Any temporal inhomogeneity of the input laser beam, due to multimoding, will give rise to a much more pronounced inhomogeneity of the Stokes beam, due to the exponential character of the gain (*100*). But one can find conditions where the backward Stokes is emitted in very short and intense pulses (*101,102*). Consider the following geometry: a long cell filled with H_2 gas or a non self-focusing medium. Near the end is placed a lens which focuses the laser beam inside the medium. The laser intensity is chosen in such a manner that the Raman gain from the entrance window to the lens is below threshold. The Stokes beam is thus generated around the focus. As the backward wave interacts with the incoming laser beam, it depletes the laser front, and a sharper and sharper Stokes pulse is generated. This has been observed in H_2 gas and in CS_2 by Maier, Kaiser and Giordmaine (*101*), where self-focusing near the end of the cell acts as a lens. Figure 24 shows the intensity as a function of time of the input laser [Fig. 24(A)], total backward output (Raman and Brillouin [Fig. 24(B)], and backward Raman Stokes [Fig. 24(C)]. The Stokes pulse is very short and a nonlinear technique as shown on the left of Fig. 24 is required to measure pulse durations around 3×10^{-11} sec. This technique provides fast pulses that may be used for other stimulated Raman studies described below.

F. Excitation of Molecular Vibrations

In Section II, A, 2, a, we calculated the Raman gain from the set of Eqs. 19–22. If we have two light beams E_L and E_S, they create the vibrational excitation Q.

If E_L and E_S are very large, it is possible that the corresponding vibrational transition $v = 0$ to $v = 1$ will be saturated. In such a case, the Raman gain will decrease, and there will occur gain corresponding to the $v = 1$ to $v = 2$ transition. This problem has not been studied in detail, for the required intensities are such that other nonlinear phenomena may occur at the same time.

One may study the lifetime of the excitation Q; this has been done by De Martini and Ducuing (*103*), in the case of the Q_{01} transition of H_2. At $t = 0$ the stimulated Raman effect populates the $v = 1$ state of hydrogen molecules. Afterwards this population is deduced from anti-Stokes intensity measurements. (The experimental set up is shown in Fig. 25.) The Q-switched laser a generates stimulated Raman emission, and the relaxed laser b is used for the anti-Stokes measurements.

Figure 26 presents the variation of population with time. Figure 27 shows the variation of relaxation time with pressure. This type of measurements is superior to the usual sound relaxation or shock tube measurements, because it allows the study of a selected vibration, and can be used in a temperature range where $\hbar\omega_{\text{vib}}/kT \gg 1$.

This technique, or others derived from those used in usual resonance experiments, could be extended to short relaxation times (down to 10^{-10} sec) using the fast pulses that were described in Section IV, E.

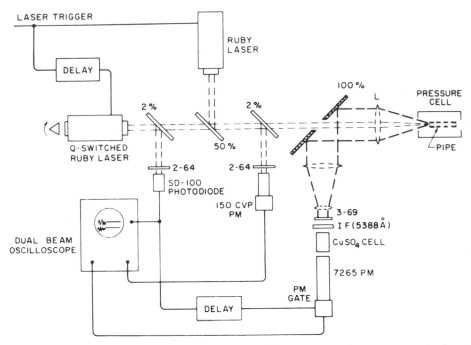

Fig. 25. Schematic diagram of the experimental arrangement for measurement of vibrational lifetimes in H_2 gas. From De Martini and Ducuing (*103*). Optical filtering is done with Corning glasses 2-64 or 3-69.

In addition, if the vibrational transition is both Raman and infrared active, there will be infrared emission. This has been observed by Mayer (*104*) in the case of the $Q_{01}(1)$ transition of H_2, when a dc electric field is applied to induce a dipole moment, as was done for infrared absorption measurements (*3,4*). Furthermore the coupling between electromagnetic waves and nuclear motion gives rise to a dispersion of the vibrational frequency for transverse optical phonons. The coupled excitation is called a polariton and was studied in spontaneous Raman scattering by

Henry and Hopfield (*105*) and by Porto et al. (*106*). If one could stimulate such transitions, one would have a tunable Raman and infrared source by changing the angle of emission (*107*). Transitions of this type that have been observed in stimulated Raman emission are the 127 cm^{-1} transition in quartz studied by Tannenwald (*90*) and 628 cm^{-1} A_1TO phonon in LiNbO$_3$ studied by Kurtz and Giordmaine (*108*).

Infrared emission corresponding to the 127 cm^{-1} Raman line in quartz has been observed (*109*).

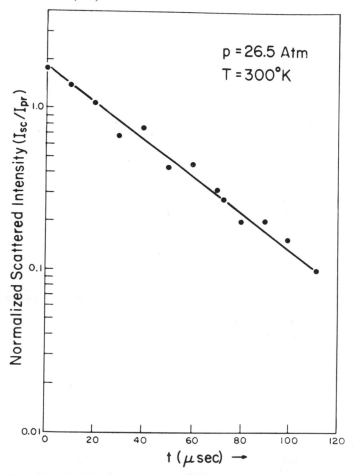

Fig. 26. Time dependence of the ratio of the intensity I_{sc} of anti-Stokes scattering from the excited medium to that of the probing beam I_{pr}. Excitation by stimulated scattering occurs at $t = 0$. [From De Martini and Ducuing (*103*).]

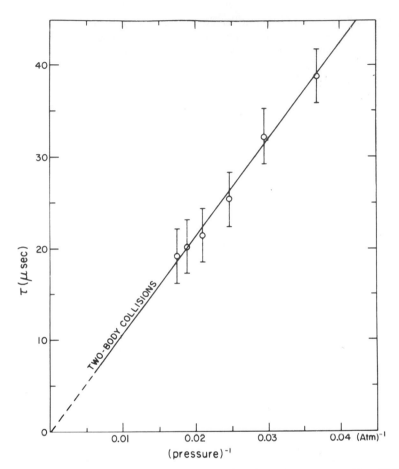

Fig. 27. The vibrational lifetime $t_{H2\cdot H2}$ as a function of pressure at $T = 300°K$. Experimental points are shown with their associated error flags. [From De Martini and Ducuing (*103*).]

The possibility of exciting coherent molecular vibrations is probably the only feature that is unique to the stimulated Raman effect.

Instead of using the stimulated Raman effect itself to excite optical phonons, one can use two light sources at frequencies ω_1 and ω_2 such that $\omega_1 - \omega_2 = \omega_{vib}$. The optical phonon excitation will in turn be detected by its influence on another test light source or on one of the exciting beams. Such experiments have been performed in quartz for a transition at 207 cm^{-1} (*110*) which has not been observed in stimulated Raman experiments, and for the polariton in GaP (*111*).

Before describing the stimulated Brillouin effect, we shall give a brief description of 3-quanta spectroscopy, as a part of high intensity laser applications, although to date this has been studied only in the spontaneous regime.

G. Three-quanta Spectroscopy (*112*)

Starting from a laser at frequency v_L, we can obtain emission of light at frequency $hv_S = 2hv_L \pm hv_{vib}$. This process is schematically represented on Fig. 28. This process has been studied theoretically by Kielich (*113*) and

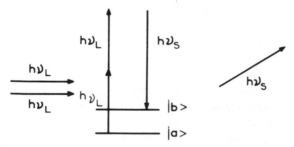

Fig. 28. Schematic description of 3-quanta inelastic nonlinear light scattering.

others. First experiments were performed by Maker, Terhune, and Savage (*112*). The scattering efficiency is extremely small; thus, only the spontaneous scattering has been observed. This process corresponds to different selection rules than 1 or 2 photon spectroscopy. The levels $|a>$ and $|b>$ must have the same parity. In the case where $|b>$ and $|a>$ are the same, the process gives information about molecular association (both through the intensity of the scattering, and the linewidth of the scattering), and about the order–disorder parameter near a phase transition as studied by Freund (*114*) for NH_4Cl.

We have shown in this Section (IV) that the stimulated Raman effect can be used to get spectroscopic information with some advantages (intensity, speed) and many disadvantages (limited use, self-focusing, and broadening) compared to the spontaneous Raman effect. Its main applications lie in the field of light sources and vibrational excitation.

V. STIMULATED BRILLOUIN EFFECT

We shall give only a very brief description of this subject as it is not the main topic of this book.

In Section II, C, 2, we calculated the Brillouin gain in the steady state situation. Experiments have been performed to check these predictions. With an amplifier setup, Bret and Denariez (*115*) measured a Brillouin gain in good agreement with the calculated value for the gain, provided self-focusing does not take place. They verified that the steady state regime applied when δv_L was less than δv_B (where δv_L is the laser linewidth and δv_B the Brillouin component linewidth) and did not apply when $\delta v_L > \delta v_B$. Their results, together with results of other authors on oscillators, show that the stimulated Brillouin effect is a valuable tool to measure sound frequencies (*77*), provided mode pulling (*116*) effects in cavities are eliminated (the most troublesome being the laser resonator itself in which the backward Brillouin light is amplified). This can be done with an optical isolator, or by putting the cell at a distance $L > c\tau_p$ from the laser, τ_p being the pulse duration.

Table 3 gives some results obtained by this technique. In addition to speed of sound measurements, it may be possible to use stimulated Brillouin experiments in amplifiers to determine Brillouin linewidth (*117*) and thus sound attenuation. In addition, the equivalent of vibrational excitation experiments can be performed with appropriate changes, as was done by Tang (*118*) and Heinicke et al. (*119*).

TABLE 3

Brillouin Shift and High Frequency Speed of Sound[a]

Material	Shift (cm^{-1})	$T(°C)$	v_S (GHz)	v_s (m/sec)
Carbon disulfide	0.194	26.0	5.82	1256
Carbon tetrachloride	0.146	26.0	4.38	1049
Glycerol	0.386	26.0	11.6	2734
Benzene	0.211	27.3	6.33	1473
Cyclohexane	0.224	26.0	6.72	1522
BSC-2 glass	0.866	28.0	26.0	5960
DF-3 glass	0.638	28.0	19.1	4120

[a] Brillouin shift and high frequency speed of sound v_s in a few materials obtained by stimulated Brillouin scattering experiments (*79*).

VI. CONCLUSION

In this chapter on the stimulated Raman effect, we have introduced the concept of gain due to stimulated emission at optical frequencies corresponding to each spontaneous scattering process. Then, we have described the experimental work that was performed to check the predictions of the theory, which must include a description of the propagation of intense light beams in matter due to self-trapping and self-focusing. Finally the main applications of the stimulated Raman effect are described. They include:

1. Generation of intense light beams by frequency shifting of laser light

2. Excitation of molecular vibrations

3. Possibility of collecting spectroscopic data accurately and quickly when all complications due to self-focusing are eliminated.

REFERENCES

1. E. Ishiguro, T. Arai, M. Mizushima, and M. Kotani, *Proc. Phys. Soc.*, A65, 178 (1952).
2. E. J. Stansbury, M. F. Crawford, and M. L. Welsh, *Can. J. Phys.*, 31, 954 (1953).
3. M. F. Crawford and R. C. McDonald, *Can. J. Phys.*, 36, 1022 (1958).
4. R. W. Terhune and C. W. Peters, *J. Mol. Spectry*, 3, 138 (1959).
5. G. G. Bret and M. M. Denariez, *Phys. Letters*, 22, 583 (1966).
6. E. J. Woodbury and W. K. Ng, *Proc. IRE.*, 50, 2367 (1962).
7. G. Eckhardt, R. W. Hellwarth, F. J. McClung, S. E. Schwarz, D. Weiner, and E. J. Woodbury, *Phys. Rev. Letters*, 9, 455 (1962).
8. R. W. Hellwarth, *Advances in Quantum Electronics*, Ed. J. R. Singer, Columbia Univ. Press, 334, (1961).
9. F. J. McClung and R. W. Hellwarth, *Proc. IEEE*, 51, 46 (1963).
10. H. A. Kramers and W. Heisenberg, *Z. Phys.*, 31, 681 (1925).
11. J. Van Kranendonk, *Can. J. Phys.*, 41, 433 (1963).
12. N. Bloembergen, *Nonlinear Optics*, Benjamin, New York (1965).
13. P. A. Franken and J. F. Ward, *Rev. Mod. Physics*, 35, 23 (1963).
14. N. Bloembergen and Y. R. Shen, *Phys. Rev.*, 133, A37 (1964) and Y. R. Shen and N. Bloembergen, *Phys. Rev.*, 137, A1787 (1965).
15. F. N. H. Robinson, *B.S.T.J.*, 46, 913 (1967).
16. C. Flytzanis and J. Ducuing, *Phys. Letters*, 26A, 315 (1968).
17. E. Garmire, F. Pandarese, and C. H. Townes, *Phys. Rev. Letters*, 11, 160 (1963).
18. R. Y. Chaio, E. Garmire, and C. H. Townes, *Proc. Int. School Phys. "Enrico Fermi" Course XXXI*, Academic, New York, p. 326 (1964).
19. N. Bloembergen and Y. R. Shen, *Phys. Rev. Letters*, 12, 504 (1964).

20. G. Placzek, *Marx Handbuch der Radiologie*, 2nd ed., Vol. VI, Academische Verlagsgesellschaft, Leipzig, pp. 206–374 (1934).
21. R. W. Terhune, *Solid State Design*, **4**, 38 (1963).
22. J. A. Armstrong, N. Bloembergen, J. Ducuing, and P. S. Pershan, *Phys. Rev.*, **127**, 1918 (1962).
23. Y. R. Shen and N. Bloembergen, *Phys. Rev.*, **137**, A1787 (1965).
24. R. Y. Chiao, E. Garmire, and C. H. Townes, *Phys. Rev. Letters*, **13**, 479 (1964).
25. V. I. Talanov, *Izv. VU Z'ov Radio Fizika*, **7**, 564 (1964).
26. A. Piekara, *I.E.E.E. J. of Quantum Electronics*, **2**, 249 (1966).
27. R. G. Brewer, J. R. Lifsitz, E. Garmire, R. Y. Chiao, and C. H. Townes, *Phys. Rev.*, **166**, 326 (1968).
28. P. L. Kelley, *Phys. Rev. Letters*, **15**, 1005 (1965).
29. E. Garmire, R. Y. Chiao, and C. H. Townes, *Phys. Rev. Letters*, **16**, 347 (1966).
30. D. I. Mash, V. V. Morozov, V. S. Starunov, and I. L. Fabelinskii, *JETP Letters*, **2**, 25 (1965).
31. N. Bloembergen and P. Lallemand, *Phys. Rev. Letters*, **16**, 81 (1966).
32. F. Gires and G. Mayer, *Compt. Rend. Acad. Sci. (Paris)*, **258**, 2039 (1961).
33. P. Debye, *Polar Molecules*, Dover, N.Y., chapter 3, 1945.
34. S. Kielich, *Phys. Letters*, **24A**, 383 (1967).
35. Y. R. Shen, *Phys. Letters*, **20**, 378 (1966).
36. M. Paillette, *Compt. Rend. Acad. Sci. (Paris)*, **262**, 264 (1966).
37. P. D. Maker and R. W. Terhune, *Phys. Rev.*, **137A**, 801 (1965).
38. A. P. Veduta, *J.E.T.P. Letters*, **5**, 124 (1967).
39. P. Lallemand, *Bull. Am. Phys. Soc.*, **11**, 113 (1966).
40. Y. R. Shen and Y. J. Shaham, *Phys. Rev.*, **163**, 224 (1967).
41. R. Y. Chiao, C. H. Townes, and B. P. Stoicheff, *Phys. Rev. Letters*, **12**, 592 (1964).
42. R. W. Hellwarth, *Appl. Opt.* **2**, 847 (1963).
43. H. Takuma and D. A. Jennings, *Appl. Phys. Letters*, **4**, 185 (1964).
44. J. H. Dennis and P. E. Tannenwald, *Appl. Phys. Letters*, **5**, 58 (1964).
45. E. B. Aleksandrov, A. M. Bonch-Bruevich, N. N. Kostin, and V. A. Khodovoi, *Sov. Phys. JETP*, **22**, 986 (1966).
46. N. Bloembergen, G. G. Bret, P. Lallemand, A. S. Pine, and P. Simova, *I.E.E.E. J. Quantum Electronics*, **3**, 197 (1967).
47. P. V. Avizonis, A. H. Guenther, T. A. Wiggins, R. V. Wick, and D. H. Rank, *Appl. Phys. Letters*, **9**, 309 (1966).
48. S. E. Schwarz and A. S. Pine, *App. Phys. Letters*, **9**, 49 (1966).
49. A. S. Pine, *Phys. Rev.*, **149**, 113 (1966).
50. P. E. Tannenwald, *Bull. Am. Phys. Soc.*, **12**, 662 (1965).
51. D. H. Close, C. R. Giuliano, R. W. Hellwarth, L. D. Hess, F. J. McClung, and W. G. Wagner, *I.E.E.E. J. Quantum Electronics*, **2**, 553 (1966).
52. J. L. Emmett and A. L. Schawlow, *Bull. Am. Phys. Soc.*, **12**, 686 (1967).
53. G. Bret, *Compt. Rend. Acad. Sci. (Paris)*, **259**, 2991 (1964).
54. P. Lallemand and N. Bloembergen, *Appl Phys. Letters*, **6**, 210 (1965).
55. C. C. Wang, *J.A.P.*, **37**, 1943 (1966).
56. F. J. McClung, W. G. Wagner, and D. Weiner, *Phys. Rev. Letters*, **15**, 96 (1965).
   G. Bret and G. Mayer, *Physics of Quantum Electronics*, Ed. P. L. Kelley, B. Lax, and P. E. Tannenwald, McGraw-Hill, New York, p. 180, 1966.
57. R. C. C. Leite and S. P. S. Porto, *Phys. Rev. Letters*, **17**, 10 (1966).

58. G. Bret and G. Mayer, *Compt. Rend. Acad. Sci.* (*Paris*), **258**, 3265 (1964).

59. P. Lallemand and N. Bloembergen, *Appl. Phys. Letters*, **6**, 212 (1965).

60. N. Bloembergen and P. Lallemand, *Physics of Quantum Electronics*, Ed. P. L. Kelley, B. Lax, and P. E. Tannenwald, McGraw-Hill, New York, p. 137, 1966.

61. A. D. May, V. Degen, J. C. Stryland, and H. L. Welsh, *Can. J. Phys.*, **39**, 1769 (1961).

62. G. Bisson and G. Mayer, *Compt. Rend. Acad. Sci.* (*Paris*), **265**, 397 (1967), *J. Phys.*, **29**, 97 (1968).

63. P. Lallemand and N. Bloembergen, *Phys. Rev. Letters*, **15**, 1010 (1965).

64. G. Hauchecorne and G. Mayer, *Compt. Rend. Acad. Sci.* (*Paris*), **261**, 4014 (1965).

65. Y. R. Shen and Y. J. Shaham, *Phys. Rev. Letters*, **15**, 1008 (1965).

66. C. C. Wang, *Phys. Rev. Letters*, **16**, 344 (1966).

67. J. Ducuing and N. Bloembergen, *Phys. Rev.* **133**, 1493 (1964).

68. E. Garmire, *Physics of Quantum Electronics*, Ed. P. L. Kelley, B. Lax, and P. E. Tannenwald, McGraw-Hill, New York, p. 167, 1966.

69. B. P. Stoicheff, *Phys. Letters*, **7**, **186** (1963).

70. F. Shimizu, *Phys. Rev. Letters*, **19**, 1526 (1967).

71. F. De Martini, C. H. Townes, T. K. Gustafson, and P. L. Kelley, *Phys. Rev.*, **164**, 312 (1967).

72. P. Lallemand, *App. Phys. Letters*, **8**, 276 (1966).

73. R. J. Joenk and R. W. Landauer, *Phys. Letters*, **24A**, 228 (1967).

74. R. Y. Chiao, P. L. Kelley, and E. Garmire, *Phys. Rev. Letters*, **17**, 1158 (1966).

75. R. L. Carman, R. Y. Chiao, and P. L. Kelley, *Phys. Rev. Letters*, **17**, 1281 (1966).

76. V. I. Bespalov and V. I. Talanov, *J.E.T.P. Letters*, **3**, 307 (1966).

77. I. L. Fabelinskii, *Molecular Scattering of Light*, Plenum, N.Y., Chapter X, 1968.

78. C. W. Cho, N. D. Foltz, D. H. Rank and T. A. Wiggins, *Phys. Rev. Letters*, **18**, 107 (1967).

79. T. A. Wiggins, R. V. Wick, N. D. Foltz, C. W. Cho, and D. H. Rank, *J. Opt. Soc. Am.*, **57**, 661 (1967).
     R. V. Wick, D. H. Rank and T. A. Wiggins, *Phys. Rev. Letters*, **17**, 466 (1966).

80. D. A. Kleinman and P. P. Kisliuk, *B.S.T.J.*, **41**, 453 (1962).
     F. J. McClung and D. Weiner, *I.E.E.E. J. Quantum Electronics*, **1**, 94 (1965).

81. W. R. Sooy, *App. Phys. Letters*, **7**, 36 (1965).
     M. Herscher, *App. Phys. Letters*, **7**, 39 (1965).

82. D. Pohl, *Phys. Letters*, **26A**, 357 (1968).

83. A. J. De Maria, C. H. Ferrer, and G. E. Danielson, Jr., *App. Phys. Letters*, **7**, 22 (1966).
     A. J. De Maria, D. A. Stotser, and H. Heynau, *App. Phys. Letters*, **7**, 174 (1966).
     J. A. Armstrong, *App. Phys. Letters*, **10**, 16 (1967).

84. S. L. Shapiro, J. A. Giordmaine, and K. W. Wecht, *Phys. Rev. Letters*, **19**, 1093 (1967).

85. V. A. Zubov, G. V. Peregudov, M. M. Sushchinskii, V. A. Chirkov, and I. K. Shuvalov, *J.E.T.P. Letters*, **5**, 150 (1967).

86. G. Eckhardt, *I.E.E.E. J. Quantum Electronics*, **2**, 1 (1966).

87. P. Lallemand, P. Simova, and G. Bret, *Phys. Rev. Letters*, **17**, 1239 (1966).

88. P. Lallemand and P. Simova, *J. Mol. Spectry.*, **26**, 262 (1968).

89. R. W. Minck, E. E. Hagenlocker, and W. G. Rado, *Phys. Rev. Letters*, **17**, 229 (1966).

90. P. E. Tannenwald, to be published in Proceedings of the Siberian Academy of Sciences.
91. N. S. Shiren, P. P. Sorokin, J. R. Lankard, T. G. Kazyaka, and E. C. Hammond, *Bull. Am. Phys. Soc.*, **12**, 112 (1967).
92. M. E. Movsesyan, N. N. Badalyan, and V. A. Iradyan, *J.E.T.P. Letters*, **6**, 127 (1967).
93. S. Dumartin, B. Oksengorn, and B. Vodar, *Compt. Rend. Acad. Sci.* (*Paris*), **261**, 3767 (1965).
94. P. P. Sorokin, J. R. Lankard, E. C. Hammond, and V. L. Moruzzi, *IBM J. Res. and Develop.*, **11**, 130 (1967).
95. Y. S. Bobovich and A. V. Bortkevich, *Optics and Spectry.*, **23**, 475 (1967).
96. W. J. Jones and B. P. Stoicheff, *Phys. Rev. Letters*, **13**, 657 (1964).
97. R. H. Dicke, *Phys. Rev.*, **122**, 1218 (1961).
98. J. Murray, and A. Javan, *Bull. Am. Phys. Soc.*, **12**, 113 (1967).
99. N. Bloembergen, R. K. Chang, J. Ducuing, and P. Lallemand, Proceedings of Seventh International Conference on Semi Conductors, p. 121, Dunod, Paris (1964).
100. R. W. Hellwarth, *Physics of Quantum Electronics*, Ed. P. L. Kelley, B. Lax and P. E. Tannenwald, p. 159, McGraw-Hill, New York (1966).
101. M. Maier, W. Kaiser, and J. A. Giordmaine, *Phys. Rev. Letters*, **17**, 1275 (1966).
102. W. Culver, *Bull. Am. Phys. Soc.*, **12**, 479 (1967).
103. F. De Martini and J. Ducuing, *Phys. Rev. Letters*, **17**, 117 (1966).
104. G. Mayer, *Compt. Rend. Acad. Sci.* (*Paris*), **266**, (1968).
105. C. H. Henry and J. J. Hopfield, *Phys. Rev. Letters*, **15**, 964 (1965).
106. S. P. S. Porto, B. Tell, and T. C. Damen, *Phys. Rev. Letters*, **16**, 450 (1966).
107. F. De Martini, *J. App. Phys.*, **37**, 4503 (1966).
108. S. K. Kurtz and J. A. Giordmaine, *Phys. Rev. Letters*, **22**, 192 (1969).
109. J. M. Arefev, S. V. Krivokhizha, Yu. I. Kyzylasov, V. S. Starunov, and I. L. Fabelinskii, *J.E.T.P. Letters*, **8**, 84 (1968).
110. G. Chartier and S. Biraud, *Phys. Rev. Letters*, **21**, 1641 (1968).
111. J. P. Coffinet and F. De Martini, *Phys. Rev. Letters*, **22**, 60 (1969).
112. R. W. Terhune, P. P. Maker, and C. M. Savage, *Phys. Rev. Letters*, **14**, 681 (1965).
113. S. Kielich, *Bull. Acad. Polon, Sci.*, **12**, 53 (1964).
114. I. Freund, *Phys. Rev. Letters*, **19**, 1278 (1967).
115. G. G. Bret, M. M. Denariez, *Compt. Rend. Acad. Sci.* (*Paris*), **264B**, 1815 and **265B**, 144 (1967).
116. R. G. Brewer, *App. Phys. Letters*, **9**, 51 (1966).
117. D. Pohl, M. Maier, and W. Kaiser, *Phys. Rev. Letters*, **20**, 366 (1968).
118. J. Walder, and C. L. Tang, *Phys. Rev. Letters*, **19**, 623 (1967).
119. W. Heinicke, G. Winterling, and K. Dransfeld, *Phys. Rev. Letters*, **22**, 170 (1969).

CHAPTER 6

Brillouin Scattering

R. S. KRISHNAN

INDIAN INSTITUTE OF SCIENCE
BANGALORE 12, INDIA

I. INTRODUCTION

It is well known that the molecules of a gas are constantly in a state of motion, and though collisions occur frequently between different molecules, their movements in the interval between such collisions are more or less independent of each other. When a beam of monochromatic light passes through such a gas and is scattered by it, the translatory movements of the molecules should give rise to a change of frequency or Doppler effect in the scattered light. When we pass from the case of a gas to a liquid, complications will arise from the fact that the positions and velocities of the molecules are no longer chaotically distributed, and it is therefore no longer possible to regard the molecules as an assembly of completely independent scattering centers. The nature of the Doppler effect in light scattering to be expected in the case of a liquid would evidently require very careful consideration. An insight into the phenomenon to be expected in such a case is furnished by the theory of light scattering originally put forward by Einstein (1). In this theory, the molecular structure of the medium is completely ignored, and fluctuations of density are regarded as arising in it from the presence of sound waves of various wave lengths associated with the thermal energy of the medium. These sound waves produce periodic stratifications in the optical density of the medium, which reflect light according to the ordinary laws of geometrical optics, but the reflection is of sensible intensity only for a particular wave length, depending on the length of the sound waves which reflect the light and the angle of reflection, in the manner given by the well known Bragg formula. This view was first pointed out by Brillouin (2), who regarded the thermal scattering of light as a "coherent reflection" of light waves by the sound waves of thermal origin traversing the medium. It was further shown that the reflection should be accompanied by shifts of frequency in the nature of a Doppler effect, which vary with the direction of observation of the scattered light and with the frequency of the incident light. The frequency shifts are identical with the frequency of sound waves which are effective in the scattering along the particular direction of observation. The frequency shifts are given by the formula

$$\Delta v = \pm \frac{2 v_i v_e n}{c} \sin \theta/2 \qquad (1)$$

where v_e is the velocity of sound in the medium, c is the velocity of light, n is the refractive index of the medium, v_i is the frequency of the incident radiation and θ is the angle of scattering.

It is hardly to be expected, however, that the Brillouin formula would completely describe the Doppler effect observed in the light scattered by an actual liquid, since the theory ignores the molecular structure of the medium and is therefore an idealization. Only in the case of a crystalline solid is there reason to expect the observed phenomena to agree most closely with the Brillouin theory. The phenomena to be expected in liquids should evidently be intermediate between those characteristic of a crystal and a gas. At very low temperatures the resemblance between the effects observed in a liquid and a crystal should be greatest, while at high temperatures the phenomena in the liquid and gas should approximate to each other.

As the change of wavelength to be expected from Eq. (1) is of the order of 0.05 Å, i.e., very much smaller than those associated with the infrared vibrations, high resolving power instruments have to be used to detect this change and the feebleness of the scattered light makes it more difficult. It was therefore not surprising to find that experimental confirmation of Brillouin's predictions followed, rather than preceded, the discovery of the Raman effect in 1928. The very first confirmation came when attempts were made to observe Raman lines of very small shifts close to the exciting line. Gross (3) reported for the first time the existence of the Brillouin effect or Doppler shifted components in the light scattered by liquids. He and later Meyer and Ramm (4), Ramm (5), and Birus (6) confirmed these observations, using an echelon grating, while Rafalowski (7) used the Lummer Gehrcke plate as the interferometer with similar results. Although, in general, all of them reported the observation of a triplet, Gross claimed to have observed in liquids a central line in the position of the incident radiation bordered on either side by a whole series of components. As no photograph of the effect was reproduced by any of these workers, the subject remained in an unsatisfactory state. Using a specially designed low density cathode cooled mercury vapour lamp and a Fabry–Perot etalon, Rao (8) obtained for the first time the most satisfactory patterns of the Doppler shifted Brillouin components in liquids (see Fig. 1). The investigations with liquids were further extended by Venkateswaran (9) and Sunanda Bai (10) using not only a Fabry–Perot etalon, but also a Lummer Gehrcke plate and the 4680 Å of the zinc arc as the source of radiation. The main results that emerged from these investigations were that every liquid exhibits two Brillouin lines and a line in the position of the unmodified radiation bordered on either side with a feeble continuous background arising from the anisotropy of the scattering molecule.

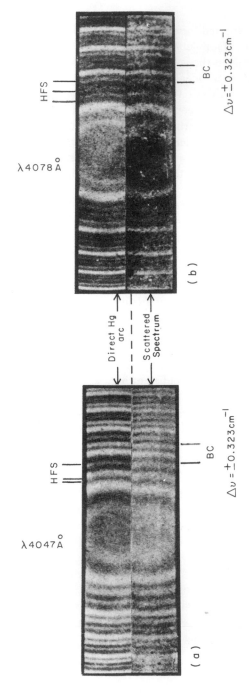

Fig. 1. Fabry-Perot interference pattern of Brillouin scattering taken by Rao (8) using mercury radiation as exciter. (a) λ 4047 Å excitation (b) λ 4078 Å excitation. The interferometer spacing was 5 mm. The hyperfine structure components (HFS) are marked on the top side and the Brillouin components (BC) with frequency shifts are indicated on the bottom side of each picture.

The fine structure of the scattered radiation predicted by the Brillouin theory was first observed in a solid like quartz by Gross (*11*), later by Raman and Venkateswaran (*12*) in gypsum, and by Sibaiya (*13*) in Rochelle salt. They employed the same technique which was used for studying liquids. Using the 2537 Å radiation of a quartz mercury arc in conjunction with an ordinary high dispersion spectrograph, the author (*14*) photographed the Brillouin components in a series of crystals including diamond, sodium chloride, quartz, etc. The observation of the Brillouin components in crystals furnishes one of the best examples of the dualism between the classical and quantum points of view between the concept of waves and particles. The observed frequency shift is in accordance with Eq. (1) which was derived on the basis of the wave-nature of light. On the quantum mechanical picture, the observed shifted components can be considered as a sort of Raman effect arising from the interaction of the incident photon and the acoustic phonons in the crystal.

Using the ultraviolet technique, Brillouin components were also recorded by the author (*15*) in the scattering by amorphous substances such as fused quartz. Investigations of the intensity and polarization of Brillouin spectra of liquids were carried out by Rank et al. (*16*)

Several investigators considered the theory of the thermal scattering of light in crystals as proposed by Brillouin, and came to the conclusion that in a crystal only three pairs of Doppler components occur in the scattered light due respectively to the three types of elastic waves which are propagated with different velocities in any given direction in the crystal. The symmetry of the crystal was not taken into consideration, and the influence of birefringence on the Brillouin components was neglected. Chandrasekharan (*17*) showed that if the birefringence was taken into consideration, there should in general be twelve Doppler components which can appear in the case of a birefringent crystal. He derived the following most general expression for the birefringent crystal:

$$\Delta v = \pm v_i \frac{v_e}{c} \sqrt{(n_i{}^2 + n_s{}^2 - 2n_i n_s \cos \theta)} \tag{2}$$

where n_i and n_s are the two refractive indices of the crystal for the directions of incidence and scattering. Since n_i and n_s can each have two values, there should be four pairs of values for (n_i, n_s) in Eq. (2). Further, for a given direction of elastic wave normal, there are three types of elastic waves, each of which can have a different velocity v_e. Thus from Eq. (2) it is easily seen that there are 12 possible values for Δv. In the case of a cubic crystal, the general Eq. (2) reduces to Eq. (1). The predictions of Chandrasekharan's theory could not be verified by using the experimental techniques available at that time.

During the period from 1952 to 1964, the only investigations on this subject were those of Fabelinskii in the P. N. Lebedev Physical Institute. The slackening of interest was mainly due to the serious limitations of the experimental techniques then available for such studies. With the advent of the laser as an intense source of monochromatic radiation for light scattering experiments, interest in Brillouin scattering has been revived, and a large number of publications have already appeared on the subject dealing with gases, liquids and solids. Special mention should be made to the work of groups headed by Benedek, Stoicheff, Rank, Fabelinskii, and Cummins. More accurate quantitative measurements of the shift, intensity (cross section) and width of the Brillouin components are being carried out. The use of very powerful lasers has made it possible to generate stimulated Brillouin scattering in gases, liquids and solids.

II. CLASSICAL THEORY OF THERMAL SCATTERING

Before dealing with the experimental results, it is desirable to give a brief account of the theoretical aspects of the thermal scattering of light, which are essential for interpreting the results to be presented in the succeeding sections. Liquids and solids will be treated separately. The four parameters which characterize the principal components of thermal scattering and which can be determined experimentally are (1) the spectral character (frequency shift), (2) intensity (cross section), (3) line width and (4) polarization. The theoretical treatment leads to expressions for these parameters in terms of the thermodynamical and optical properties of the medium.

A. Liquids and Compressed Gases

The classical derivation of the thermal scattering of light in a homogeneous medium was given by Brillouin (2). The main ideas of his theory are as follows: a homogeneous condensed medium at a certain temperature is in a constant state of vibration on account of thermal agitation. Consequently, the medium can be regarded as being traversed in all directions by elastic waves of all frequencies. In the case of liquids and compressed gases, these waves are compressional or longitudinal waves. Each wave will form alternate planes of compressions M_1, M_2, M_3, etc., and rarefactions N_1, N_2, etc., in the medium, making it optically inhomogeneous (see Fig. 2). When a beam of light of wavelength λ_i and frequency ν_i is incident in a direction AEA' making a glancing angle θ_i with the planes of compression of wavelength λ_e, it will be partially reflected or scattered along the direction EC at the layer at which there is change of refractive

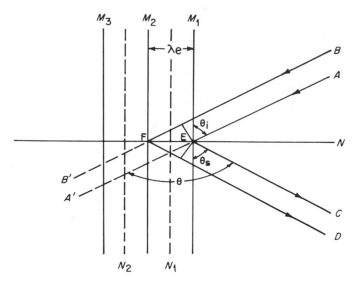

Fig. 2. Wave picture of scattering. Angle of scattering $= \theta = (\theta_i + \theta_s)$. θ_i, θ_s are the glancing angles of incidence and scattering.

index, i.e., at the plane M_1. EC makes an angle θ_s with the plane M_1, and EN is the normal to the same plane and the direction in which the sound waves are propagated. The reflections from successive layers M_1, M_2, etc., will reinforce if the Bragg relation

$$\lambda_i = 2\lambda_e \sin \theta_i \tag{3}$$

is satisfied. For given directions of incidence and observation between which the angle is $\theta = \theta_i + \theta_s$, only waves of wavelength given by Eq. (3) are operative in producing reflection or scattering of the incident light. Since the stratifications producing such a coherent reflection are moving along the normal EN with the velocity of sound v_e, the reflected light waves experience the Doppler effect resulting in a change of frequency given by the relation (1) where θ is the angle of scattering. This theory accounts for the observed Brillouin doublet appearing on either side of the unmodified or central component in thermal scattering. Equation (1), which indicates the spectral character of the Brillouin component, is applicable to optically isotropic media such as compressed gases and liquids.

On the basis of the theory of fluctuations (*18*), Einstein (*1*) derived an expression for the intensity of the light scattered by a homogeneous medium containing spherically symmetrical molecules. Brillouin (*2*) indicated that the total intensity of scattering given by the Einstein theory should be accounted for by the Brillouin doublet which should be perfectly polarized. Experimentally, one finds that the spectral character of the thermal scattering from a liquid is in the form of a triplet, two Brillouin (shifted) components, I_B and one Rayleigh (central) component I_C. The triplet structure was satisfactorily accounted for by Landau and Placzek (*19*) who analyzed the density fluctuations on the basis of the hole theory of the liquid state proposed by Frenkel (*20*). Fabelinskii (*21*) refined the theoretical treatment given by Landau and Placzek by avoiding some of their questionable assumptions. He also took into consideration the dispersion of the thermodynamical properties. Recently a generalized hydrodynamic theory of thermal scattering in a simple dispersive fluid has been outlined by Mountain (*22*), on the assumption that the internal vibrational degrees of freedom are weakly coupled to the translational degrees of freedom with a single relaxation time. He has used the linearized hydrodynamic equations of the irreversible thermodynamics to compute the relaxation time of the spontaneous density fluctuations in the fluid. From the theoretical analysis, it follows that the scattered light consists of (1) a central unmodified line with line shape the same as the exciting line, (2) two shifted Brillouin lines with broadened line shapes, and (3) a new unshifted line (since experimentally established), arising from a non-propagating mode due to density fluctuations associated with the energy exchange between internal vibrational modes and the translational modes. This new line is also broad. On the basis of Mountain's theory, the vibrational relaxation time can be evaluated from a knowledge of any of the following parameters which could be determined experimentally: (1) velocity dispersion in the hypersonic region, (2) breadth of the Brillouin lines due to excess absorption coefficient, and (3) the ratio of the intensities of the central lines to the Brillouin lines.

Cummins and Gammon (*23*) have modified the Landau–Placzek theory of light scattering in liquids by taking into consideration the effect of dispersion, and by neglecting the intrinsic temperature dependence of dielectric constant. The problem has also been considered from the theoretical point of view by O'Connor and Schlupf (24).

Intensity expressions for the thermal scattering of light in liquids have been derived here following the classical fluctuation theory of Smoluchowski (18) and Einstein (1). The total intensity I_s of light scattered by a volume element V of a homogeneous medium is given by the relation:

$$I_s = I_0 \frac{\pi^2}{r^2 \lambda_i^4} V^2 \langle (\Delta \varepsilon)^2 \rangle \tag{4}$$

where I_0 is the intensity of the incident radiation, r is the distance of the volume element from the point of observation, λ_i is the wavelength of the incident light and $\langle (\Delta \varepsilon)^2 \rangle$ is the mean square of the fluctuations in dielectric constant, ε, arising from fluctuations in density ρ, and temperature T. Since ε is a function of ρ and T

$$\langle (\Delta \varepsilon)^2 \rangle = \left(\frac{\partial \varepsilon}{\partial \rho} \right)_T^2 \langle (\Delta \rho)^2 \rangle + \left(\frac{\partial \varepsilon}{\partial T} \right)_\rho^2 \langle (\Delta T)^2 \rangle \tag{5}$$

From the theory of fluctuations we have (25)

$$\langle (\Delta \rho)^2 \rangle = \frac{\rho^2 k T \beta_T}{V} \tag{6}$$

$$\langle (\Delta T)^2 \rangle = \frac{k T^2}{C_V \rho V} \tag{7}$$

where k is the Boltzman constant, $\beta_T =$ the isothermal compressibility and $C_V =$ specific heat at constant volume. Combining Eqs. (4), (5), (6), and (7) we get

$$I_s = I_0 \frac{\pi^2 V}{r^2 \lambda_i^4} \left\{ k T \beta_T \left(\rho \frac{\partial \varepsilon}{\partial \rho} \right)_T^2 + \frac{k}{C_V \rho} \left(T \frac{\partial \varepsilon}{\partial T} \right)_\rho^2 \right\} \tag{8}$$

If it is assumed that the temperature fluctuations, $(\partial \varepsilon / \partial T)_\rho$ are small compared to density fluctuations $(\partial \varepsilon / \partial \rho)_T$, the second term on the right hand side of Eq. (8) is very small compared with the first term and therefore it can be neglected. The total intensity of thermal scattering is therefore given by

$$I_s = I_0 \frac{\pi^2 k T}{r^2 \lambda_i^4} \beta_T V \left(\rho \frac{\partial \varepsilon}{\partial \rho} \right)_T^2 \tag{9}$$

In the derivation of the above relation, it is assumed that the density fluctuations arc static and isothermal, and that no kind of phase relationship exists between the fluctuations in neighboring volume elements. Brillouin (2) obtained the same expression for the total intensity of scattering which (according to him) was distributed in the two shifted components. The main conclusions of this theory are the following:

(1) For incident plane polarized light, the intensity of Brillouin scattering is independent of the angle of scattering in the plane of observation which is perpendicular to the incident electric vector. The intensity varies as $\cos^2 \theta$ if the plane of observation is parallel to the incident electric vector. For incident unpolarized light, the intensity in either case varies as $(1 + \cos^2 \theta)$, where θ is the angle of scattering.

(2) The frequency shift varies as $\sin \theta/2$ where θ is the angle of scattering (see Eq. 1), being maximum for backward scattering ($\theta = 180°$) and minimum for forward scattering ($\theta = 0$). In the quantum picture, the Brillouin components arise from the interaction of the incident photon of frequency v_i and the acoustic phonon of frequency v_e in the medium. These acoustic waves lie in the hypersonic region $\sim 10^9$ cps. Thus by varying the angle of scattering θ, hypersonic waves of different frequencies become operative in giving rise to the Brillouin scattering.

(3) For incident unpolarized light, the components are perfectly polarized in the transverse direction, i.e., for $\theta = 90°$, while they are completely unpolarized in the forward and backward directions, i.e., for $\theta = 0°$ and $180°$.

Because of the fact that sound propagation is an adiabatic process, Landau and Placzek (19) decomposed the density fluctuations into two components, (1) pressure (P) fluctuations at constant entropy (adiabatic), and (2) entropy (S) fluctuations at constant pressure, which are not propagated in normal fluids and are coupled to the thermal conductivity. This decomposition is discussed in detail by Frenkel (20).

The frequency of the light scattered by the fluctuations at constant entropy (thermal sound waves or phonons) is shifted by an amount proportional to the velocity of the phonons. Energy and momentum considerations require that the proportionality constant be equal to the magnitude of the change in the wave vector of the scattered light. Two lines which are known as Brillouin lines are observed because scattering can occur from waves travelling in opposite directions but at the same speed. The dissipative processes which damp out the waves tend to broaden the Brillouin lines. The light scattered by entropy fluctuations at constant pressure is not shifted in frequency, although it is slightly broadened due to the thermal dissipative processes which damp out these fluctuations. By choosing ε as a function of a different set of thermodynamic parameters, namely S and P, Landau and Placzek (*19*) separated the components in the scattered radiation into $(2I_B)$ and (I_C). The mean square fluctuation in dielectric constant is given in terms of ΔP and ΔS as follows:

$$\langle (\Delta \varepsilon)^2 \rangle = \left(\frac{\partial \varepsilon}{\partial P} \right)_S^2 \langle (\Delta P)^2 \rangle + \left(\frac{\partial \varepsilon}{\partial S} \right)_P^2 \langle (\Delta S)^2 \rangle \tag{10}$$

$$\left(\frac{\partial \varepsilon}{\partial P} \right)_S^2 \langle (\Delta P)^2 \rangle = \left(\rho \frac{\partial \varepsilon}{\partial \rho} \right)_S^2 \frac{kT\beta_s}{V} \tag{11}$$

$$\left(\frac{\partial \varepsilon}{\partial S} \right)_P^2 \langle (\Delta S)^2 \rangle = \left(T \frac{\partial \varepsilon}{\partial T} \right)_P^2 \frac{k}{C_P \rho V} \tag{12}$$

where β_S is the adiabatic compressibility.

Combining Eqs. (4), (10), (11), and (12) we get for the total intensity of scattering

$$I_S = I_0 \frac{\pi^2 V}{r^2 \lambda_i^4} \left[kT\beta_s \left(\rho \frac{\partial \varepsilon}{\partial \rho} \right)_S^2 + \frac{k}{C_P \rho} \left(T \frac{\partial \varepsilon}{\partial T} \right)_P^2 \right] \tag{13}$$

The first term corresponds to the sum of the intensities $(2I_B)$ of the two Brillouin components, while the second term is the intensity (I_C) of the central Rayleigh component.

$$2I_B = I_0 \frac{\pi^2 V}{r^2 \lambda_i^4} kT\beta_s \left(\rho \frac{\partial \varepsilon}{\partial \rho} \right)_S^2 \tag{14}$$

$$I_C = I_0 \frac{\pi^2 V}{r^2 \lambda_i^4} \frac{k}{C_P \rho} \left(T \frac{\partial \varepsilon}{\partial T} \right)_P^2 \tag{15}$$

$$\left(\frac{\partial \varepsilon}{\partial T} \right)_P = \left(\frac{\partial \varepsilon}{\partial \rho} \right)_T \left(\frac{\partial \rho}{\partial T} \right)_P + \left(\frac{\partial \varepsilon}{\partial T} \right)_\rho \tag{16}$$

$$= \left(\rho \frac{\partial \varepsilon}{\partial \rho} \right)_T \alpha + \left(\frac{\partial \varepsilon}{\partial T} \right)_\rho \tag{17}$$

$$I_C = I_0 \frac{\pi^2 V k}{r^2 \lambda_i^4 C_P \rho} \left[T^2 \alpha^2 \left(\rho \frac{\partial \varepsilon}{\partial \rho} \right)_T^2 + T^2 \left(\frac{\partial \varepsilon}{\partial T} \right)_\rho^2 \right] \tag{18}$$

where α is the coefficient of cubic expansion. To a first approximation we can assume that the temperature dependence of dielectric constant is caused mainly by the density changes arising from thermal expansion and not by intrinsic temperature changes, that is ,

$$\left(\frac{\partial \varepsilon}{\partial T}\right)_\rho \ll \left(\frac{\partial \varepsilon}{\partial \rho}\right)_T \tag{19}$$

I_C can therefore be written as

$$I_C = I_0 \frac{\pi^2 V}{r^2 \lambda_i{}^4} \frac{kT^2\alpha^2}{C_P\rho}\left(\rho \frac{\partial \varepsilon}{\partial \rho}\right)_T^2 \tag{20}$$

In order to evaluate this quantity, a knowledge of $(\partial \varepsilon/\partial \rho)_T$ is required. On the assumption that I_s is the sum of $2I_B + I_C$, Landau and Placzek obtained an expression for I_C by subtracting $2I_B$ given by Eq. (14) from I_s given by Eq. (9)

$$I_C = I_s - 2I_B = I_0 \frac{\pi^2 V kT}{r^2 \lambda_i{}^4}\left[\left(\rho \frac{\partial \varepsilon}{\partial \rho}\right)_T^2 \beta_T - \left(\rho \frac{\partial \varepsilon}{\partial \rho}\right)_S^2 \beta_s\right] \tag{21}$$

They further assumed that $(\partial \varepsilon/\partial \rho)_T$ is nearly equal to $(\partial \varepsilon/\partial \rho)_S$ and obtained the ratio of the intensities, $I_C/2I_B$ as follows:

$$\frac{I_C}{2I_B} = \frac{\beta_T - \beta_s}{\beta_s} = \frac{C_P - C_V}{C_V} = \gamma - 1 \tag{22}$$

This is the well known relation derived by Landau and Placzek (*19,26*).

In deriving the above relation, Landau and Placzek did not take into consideration the fact that the Brillouin components arise from hypersonic waves of frequency $\sim 10^9$ cps, and the thermodynamical quantities involved should be appropriate to this very high frequency region and might therefore be different from the low frequency or static values because of dispersion. It is well known that some liquids exhibit appreciable dispersion of acoustic velocity with frequency, and in such cases Eq. (4) and (22) may not be valid. Fabelinskii (*21*) questioned the validity of the assumptions made by Landau and Placzek, and pointed out that what is important is not the inequality (19), but that the contribution from $(\partial \varepsilon/\partial T)_\rho$ is small compared with the contribution from $(\partial \varepsilon/\partial \rho)_T$ in the expression for I_C in Eq. (18). When α, the coefficient of cubic expansion is very small as for water near 4°C, the contribution from $(\partial \varepsilon/\partial \rho)_T$ becomes negligible in Eq. (16) and under these circumstances the contribution from $(\partial \varepsilon/\partial T)_\rho$, i.e. the intrinsic temperature dependence of the dielectric constant, even though small in magnitude, becomes appreciable. One has also to take into consideration the dispersion of the thermodynamical quantities in the hypersonic region. The undisplaced Rayleigh component I_C arises from slowly damped fluctuations, and the quantities involved in the expression for the intensity (I_C) correspond to the static values. The quantities involved in the expression for the intensity ($2I_B$) of the Brillouin components should be those appropriate to hypersonic waves, i.e., to frequencies of the order of $\sim 10^9$ cps. Cummins and Gammon (23) have considered the problem of dispersion and have derived the following expression for the intensity ratio

$$\frac{I_C}{2I_B} = \frac{\left[\left(\rho\frac{\partial\varepsilon}{\partial\rho}\right)_T^2 \alpha^2 T/\rho C_P\right]_{ST}}{\left[\left(\rho\frac{\partial\varepsilon}{\partial\rho}\right)_T^2 \beta_s\right]_{HS}} \tag{23}$$

ST means static case, HS means hypersonic case. The intensity of the central component can be correctly calculated by subtracting the Brillouin intensity (vide Eq. 14) from the total intensity (vide Eq. 9) evaluated using static values. The Landau–Placzek ratio becomes

$$\frac{I_C}{2I_B} = \frac{\left[\left(\rho\frac{\partial\varepsilon}{\partial\rho}\right)_T^2 (\beta_T - \beta_s)\right]_{ST}}{\left[\left(\rho\frac{\partial\varepsilon}{\partial\rho}\right)_T^2 \beta_s\right]_{HS}} \tag{24}$$

Taking thermal relaxation into consideration Mountain (22) derived the following expression for the intensity ratio assuming Eq. (19) to be valid.

$$\frac{I_C}{2I_B} = \frac{\left[(1-1/\gamma)\left\{\left(\frac{v_0}{v_e}\right)^4 + v_e^2 K_e^2 \tau^2\right\} + (v_\infty^2 - v_0^2)K_e^2\tau^2 - \left(\frac{v_e^2}{v_0^2} - 1\right)\right.}{\left.\times\left\{\left(\frac{v_0}{v_e}\right)^4 + v_0^2 K_e^2\tau^2\left(1 - \frac{1}{\gamma}\right)\right\}\right]}{\left[1 - \frac{v_0^2}{v_e^2}\left(1 - \frac{1}{\gamma}\right)\right]\left[v_e^2 K_e^2\tau^2 + \frac{v_0^2}{v_e^2}\right] - (v_\infty^2 - v_0^2)K_e^2\tau^2} \tag{25}$$

Where K_e is the acoustic wave vector which is related to the incident radiation vector K_i

$$K_e = 2nK_i \sin\theta/2, \tag{26}$$

v_∞ and v_0 are the limiting values of the acoustic velocity for the presence of and absence of relaxation states respectively; v_e is the acoustic velocity given by Eq. (1). In the absence of any relaxation process, $v_\infty = v_0 = v_e$ and the relaxation time $\tau = 0$ and Eq. (25) reduces to (22).

Absorption is always associated with dispersion, and hypersonic absorption has not been taken into consideration in deriving Eqs. (23)

and (24). If the absorption is large as in the case of viscous liquids, the pressure fluctuations are not truly reversible and damping terms have to be introduced which will increase the value of the ratio $I_C/2I_B$.

Due to the presence of thermal relaxation, the acoustic waves are damped with a characteristic life time $1/\Gamma(v_e)$ where $\Gamma(v_e)$ is the characteristic rate of decay of sound waves of frequency v_e. This gives rise to a finite width for the Brillouin components which have a Lorentzian line shape. The half width at half intensity is given by

$$\delta v_B = \frac{\Gamma(v_e)}{2\pi} \tag{27}$$

It is of the order of 50 to 1000 Mc/sec in the 2 to 6 Gc range. Thus the width of the Brillouin components is a measure of the damping of the sound waves. From the measured width δv_B, the amplitude absorption coefficient a for the sound waves is obtained from the relation

$$a = \frac{2\pi(\delta v_B)}{v_e} \tag{28}$$

Using the fact that the entropy fluctuations decay according to the heat diffusion equation, Leontowitsch (27) showed that the unmodified Rayleigh line should also be Lorentzian in shape, with half width (in cps) at half intensity given by the equation:

$$\delta v_C = \frac{2\pi\Lambda}{\rho C_P}|K_e|^2 \tag{29}$$

where Λ is the thermal conductivity and $\Lambda/\rho C_P$ is the thermal diffusivity; K_e is already defined by Eq. (26). The half width of the central line, δv_C is a function of the angle of scattering θ and has a maximum value for backward scattering. The typical half width of the central line for ordinary liquids is of the order of 3 to 50 Mc/sec. Thus the central line is much narrower than the Brillouin lines and optical heterodyne detection techniques have been developed to operate in the range of frequencies appropriate to the width of the central line. The determination of the width of the central line gives us a method of estimating the thermal diffusivity of any medium.

The existence of a fourth line called the thermal relaxation line has been envisaged in certain liquids according to the hydrodynamic theory of Mountain (22). Its origin is due to the frequency dependence of the specific heats. The width of this line is related to the relaxation time due to thermal conductivity, $\delta v_F = 1/2\pi\tau$. When the phonon frequency is far below the relaxation frequency, the new line is very weak, and when the phonon frequency is far above the relaxation frequency, the ratio of the intensity in the new mode to the intensity of the Brillouin components is a constant. The new mode does not propagate and is coupled to the thermal conductivity. In certain highly viscous liquids the fourth component arises from a structural relaxation process which is more prominent than thermal relaxation.

In the theory of the thermal scattering of light in fluids detailed above, the fluid is treated as a continuum and its internal structure is ignored. But the same considerations hold good if the molecular structure of the medium is taken into consideration provided the molecules are assumed to be spherically symmetrical. In any actual case, the fluid usually consists of nonspherical molecules which are optically anisotropic. In the classical theory, the total intensity of scattering in such a fluid consists of two parts: (1) the scattering due to fluctuations in density and (2) the scattering due to fluctuations in orientation (Ramanathan, 28). The density scattering I_d is completely polarized, while the anisotropic scattering I_a is depolarized to the extent of 6/7. For incident unpolarized light, the ratio I_a/I_d is shown to be equal to $13\rho/6-7\rho$ where ρ is the measured depolarization factor for the transversely scattered light. While the density scattering appears as the Brillouin components ($2I_B$) and the central component (I_C) (see Eq. 13), the anisotropic component appears on the central component and also as a background on either side.

B. Solids

It is a fact of observation that free and practically undamped propagation of elastic waves is possible in solids. It is also known that in transparent solids such waves give rise to Brillouin scattering, whose intensity is determined by their piezo-optic constants. Along any specific direction, there are in general three kinds of elastic waves with different velocities, one longitudinal and two transverse waves. As v_e in Eq. (1) can assume three values for a solid, one should observe three pairs of Brillouin components in the scattering by any solid which is crystalline, but not birefringent. In the case of an amorphous solid like glass, one observes only two independent pairs as the two transverse waves have the same velocity.

In a birefringent crystal the simple theory as developed by Brillouin had to be modified in order to take into consideration the variation of refractive index with direction and the state of polarization of the light beam in the medium. This was first pointed out by Chandrasekharan (*17*). The general treatment of scattering of light by a birefringent medium on the basis of the quantum theory is given below:

The scattering arises from the collision of the incident photon with the phonons present in the medium. In Fig. 3, let $I'OI$ be the direction of the incident light wave of frequency v_i and OS, the direction of scattered

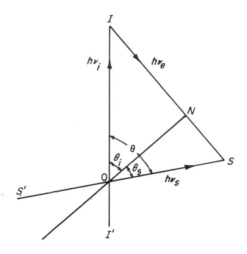

Fig. 3. Quantum picture of Brillouin scattering in crystals.

light wave of frequency v_s, θ is the angle of scattering. The elastic phonon of frequency v_e, responsible for scattering along OS, is along IS. Let ON be the normal to IS. θ_i and θ_s are the angles which the incident and scattered rays respectively make with the normal ON, the direction of the acoustic wave normal.

If the momenta of the incident and scattered photons and the elastic phonon are represented vectorially by **OI**, **OS** and **IS**, the conservation of momentum gives the relation

$$\mathbf{OI} + \mathbf{IS} = \mathbf{OS}$$

This vectorial equation is really equivalent to three conditions. First, all the three vectors lie in a plane. The other two conditions are that the momenta resolved (a) parallel and (b) perpendicular to IS must be conserved. We get

$$\frac{hv_i n_i \sin \theta_i}{c} + \frac{hv_s n_s \sin \theta_s}{c} = \frac{hv_e}{v_e} \tag{30}$$

$$\frac{hv_i n_i \cos \theta_i}{c} - \frac{hv_s n_s \cos \theta_s}{c} = 0 \tag{31}$$

where n_i and n_s are the refractive indices of the crystal for the incident and scattered directions, c is the velocity of light and v_e is the velocity of elastic waves inside the medium. The conservation of energy in the collision process gives

$$hv_s = hv_i \pm hv_e \tag{32}$$

The scattered light exhibits frequency shifts Δv given by

$$\Delta v = v_i - v_s = \pm v_e \tag{33}$$

Since v_e is very small compared to v_i, to a first approximation one can take

$$v_i = v_s \tag{34}$$

From Eqs. (30), (31), and (34) one gets the following scattering condition

$$\frac{v_e}{v_i} = \frac{v_e}{c} \sqrt{(n_i^2 + n_s^2 - 2n_i n_s \cos \theta)} \tag{35}$$

where

$$\theta = \theta_i + \theta_s \tag{36}$$

The frequency shift, Δv, of the Brillouin components is given by

$$\Delta v = \pm v_i \frac{v_e}{c} \sqrt{(n_i^2 + n_s^2 - 2n_i n_s \cos \theta)} \tag{37}$$

This is the same as Eq. (2). Equations (30), (31), (36), and (37) are the fundamental equations required to analyze the characteristics of the scattered radiation.

For given directions of incidence and scattering in a birefringent medium, and hence for a particular scattering angle θ, n_i and n_s can each take two values in general depending on the vibration direction. There would therefore be 4 pairs of values for (n_i, n_s) and hence from Eqs. (30), (31), and (36) there would be four sets of values for θ_i, θ_s and λ_e which satisfy Eq. (35). Therefore the wavelength as well as the direction of the elastic wave effective in scattering are fixed for any particular pair of values n_i and n_s. Along each direction there are three types of elastic waves with the same wavelength λ_e but with different velocities v_e and frequency v_e. Hence the frequency shift (Δv) given by Eq. (37) should have $2 \times 2 \times 3 = 12$ values. Therefore the light scattered by a birefringent crystal should consist of 12 pairs of Brillouin components when the incident light is unpolarized.

For given directions of incidence and of scattering, the unpolarized incident light wave can be taken to consist of two components with mutually perpendicular polarizations (for experimental convenience, vertical and horizontal, designated by V and H respectively), and the scattered light can also be split up into two components with vertical and horizontal polarizations designated by v and h respectively. Since V and H components of the incident light can each give rise to scattered components with polarizations v and h, the scattered radiation should consist of four species, I_{Vv}, I_{Vh}, I_{Hv}, and I_{Hh} each with distinctive polarization characteristics for the incident and corresponding scattered waves. For each species, I_{Hv}, a pair of values (n_i, n_s) is fixed and hence the direction of propagation and the wavelength of the elastic wave effective in giving rise to Brillouin scattering are also fixed. In general, both these quantities and the Brillouin shifts of frequency vary for the different species. Each species should consist of three pairs of Brillouin components due to the three different types of elastic waves. By using a suitably oriented polarizing device in the path of the incident light and another one in the path of the scattered light, each species of three pairs of Brillouin components could be isolated and investigated separately.

For each species, the direction of the normal of the elastic wave effective in scattering and hence the wave front ON (Fig. 3) is uniquely determined. In certain circumstances the number of species observed will be very much reduced, due either to some of them having the same frequency shifts or to some of them having zero intensity; let us consider some special cases:

Case I: In the forward scattering $\theta = 0$, the shifts for I_{Vv} and I_{Hh} are zero since $n_i = n_s$ for these species. The shifts for corresponding components of I_{Hv} and I_{Vh} species are the same and in consequence one would observe only 3 distinct pairs of components in the scattered light even when the incident light is unpolarized.

Case II: For backward scattering $\theta = 180°$

$$\Delta v = \pm v_i \frac{v_e}{c} (n_i + n_s) \tag{38}$$

and the effective elastic wave normals coincide with that of the incident direction. For the species I_{Vv}, Eq. (39a), and for I_{Hh}, Eq. (39b):

$$\Delta v = \pm v_i \frac{v_e}{c} 2n_1 \tag{39a}$$

$$\Delta v = \pm v_i \frac{v_e}{c} 2n_2 \tag{39b}$$

and for the corresponding components I_{Vh} and I_{Hv} the shifts have the same value. Therefore

$$\Delta v = \pm v_i \frac{v_e}{c} (n_1 + n_2) \tag{40}$$

where n_1 and n_2 are the two principal refractive indices. There will thus be nine pairs of Doppler components.

In the case of a singly refracting medium (e.g. a cubic crystal) $n_i = n_s = n$ and therefore Eq. (37) reduces to the original Eq. (1) given by Brillouin. The effective elastic wave front (ON in Fig. 3) bisects the internal angle between the incident and scattered directions and the scattering process in such a case may be regarded as specular reflection.

In the theoretical treatment outlined above, the small change in frequency of the scattered radiation is implicitly ignored in the equation for conservation of momentum. Equation (34) is assumed to be valid in deriving Eq. (35). In a recent paper Chandrasekharan (29) took into consideration the small difference between v_i and v_s and derived the exact equation for Brillouin shifts in the case of an anisotropic crystal; his treatment is given below. Let

$$\beta_i = \frac{n_i v_e}{c}$$

$$\beta_s = \frac{n_s v_e}{c} \tag{41}$$

From Eqs. (30), (31) and (41), one gets

$$v_e^2 = \beta_i^2 v_i^2 + \beta_s^2 v_s^2 - 2\beta_i \beta_s v_i v_s \cos \theta \tag{42}$$

Combining Eqs. (33) and (42), the exact equation for the Brillouin shifts is obtained.

$$\frac{\Delta v}{v_i} = \frac{\beta_s^2 - \beta_s \beta_i \cos \theta \pm \sqrt{[4\beta_s \beta_i \sin^2 \theta/2 + (\beta_s - \beta_i)^2 - \beta_s^2 \beta_i^2 \sin^2 \theta]}}{(1 - \beta_s)^2}$$

$$\tag{43}$$

Ignoring terms of order higher than β^2, Eq. (43) reduces to

$$\frac{v_s - v_i}{v_i} = \frac{\Delta v}{v_i} = \beta_s{}^2 - \beta_s\beta_i \cos\theta \pm \sqrt{[(\beta_s - \beta_i)^2 + 4\beta_s\beta_i \sin^2\theta/2]} \quad (44)$$

since $\beta_s \ll 1$. The additional features in this equation are the anisotropic effect for birefringent crystals and the quadratic terms. The first two terms on the RHS of Eq. (44) are the quadratic terms which arise from the fact that v_s is not equal to v_i. If these terms are neglected, Eq. (44) reduces to

$$\frac{\Delta v}{v_i} = \pm\sqrt{(\beta_i{}^2 + \beta_s{}^2 - 2\beta_i\beta_s \cos\theta)} \quad (45)$$

Combining Eq. (41) and (45) one gets the original Eq. (37) of Chandrasekharan.

In the absence of birefringence, i.e., in cubic crystals and glasses, $\beta_i \approx \beta_s$ and the exact equation is given by

$$\frac{\Delta v}{v_i} = \pm 2\beta_i \sin\frac{\theta}{2} + 2\beta_i{}^2 \sin^2\frac{\theta}{2}\left(1 + \frac{v_i}{n_i}\frac{dn}{dv}\right) \quad (46)$$

The effect of the quadratic terms in Eq. (44) and (46) is to give rise to unequal frequency shifts for the Stokes and anti-Stokes Brillouin components. This is an important result; because of the high value of the elastic constants of diamond, it is one of the most favourable cases for observing this difference. For backward scattering along the [111] direction in diamond, the shifts to be expected from Eq. (46) for longitudinal components are for 2537 Å, $\Delta v_S = -12.79370$ cm^{-1}, $\Delta v_{AS} = +12.79887$ cm^{-1}. The difference is of the order of 0.005 cm^{-1}. For the helium-neon laser line, 6328 Å, the corresponding shifts are $\Delta v_S = -4.7164$ cm^{-1} and $\Delta v_{AS} = +4.7178$ cm^{-1}. The difference is of the order of 0.0014 cm^{-1} or 42 Mc. With the use of a single mode laser having a very narrow line width (<0.001 cm^{-1}) and optical heterodyne techniques of frequency measurements employed for Brillouin scattering studies, it may be possible to detect this small but finite difference in the frequency shifts of the anti-Stokes and Stokes Brillouin components predicted by Chandrasekharan.

Let us now pass on to the problem of the intensity of scattering in a birefringent crystal. The thermal scattering of light in crystals was considered from the theoretical stand point by Leontowitsch and Mandelstam (30), Tamm (31), Theimer (32), and Chandrasekharan (33). A good account of the microscopic calculations of the Brillouin scattering is given by Born and Huang (*34*). From the stand point of the quantum theory, the Brillouin scattering in a crystal is simply the first order Raman scattering associated with the transitions in the vibrational states of the acoustic vibrations and is generally restricted to the lower reaches of the phonon branches, i.e., regions of low K (wave vector). Since the energy of these elastic waves is very small compared to kT at practically any temperature; the quantum mechanical treatment should give the same result as the classical treatment. For deriving expressions for the intensity of Brillouin scattering in a crystal, the classical procedure followed by Chandrasekharan (*33*) is outlined here.

A long wavelength acoustic phonon produces elastic deformation in a crystal, which in turn introduces photoelastic effects. A strain e_{ij} in the lattice produces a change in the component $\varepsilon_{\mu\nu}$ of the optical dielectric constant tensor ε given by

$$\delta\varepsilon_{\mu\nu} = -\sum_{\rho,\sigma} \varepsilon_{\mu\rho} p_{\rho\sigma,ij} \varepsilon_{\sigma\nu} e_{ij} \tag{47}$$

where $p_{\rho\sigma,ij}$ is an elasto-optic coefficient (Loudon, *35*). The components of the dielectric constant tensor oscillate with the same frequency as the phonon frequency (v_e) and consequently light is scattered with the frequencies ($v_i \pm v_e$) and appears as Brillouin components. The intensity of the Brillouin components in a crystal should therefore depend on its elastic (c_{ij}) and photoelastic constants (p_{ij}) and refractive indices. Leaving out a constant factor $\pi^2 kT/2\lambda_i^4$, the intensities of the four species of Brillouin components arising from the same acoustic branch j are given by

$$\begin{aligned} I_{Vv} &= (\mathbf{v}[\Delta\varepsilon]_V^v \mathbf{V})^2/q_{1e} \\ I_{Vh} &= (\mathbf{h}[\Delta\varepsilon]_V^h \mathbf{V})^2/q_{2e} \\ I_{Hv} &= (\mathbf{v}[\Delta\varepsilon]_H^v \mathbf{H})^2/q_{3e} \\ I_{Hh} &= (\mathbf{h}[\Delta\varepsilon]_H^h \mathbf{H})^2/q_{4e} \end{aligned} \tag{48}$$

where $\mathbf{V}$ and $\mathbf{H}$ are two mutually perpendicular unit vectors parallel to the vertical and horizontal directions of vibration of the incident wave, and similarly $\mathbf{v}$ and $\mathbf{h}$ are two mutually perpendicular unit vectors parallel to the vertical and horizontal directions of vibration of the scattered wave, the plane of scattering being horizontal. There are three acoustic branches, one longitudinal and two transverse, and each branch is associated with four equations of type (48); q_{1e}, q_{2e}, q_{3e}, and q_{4e} are the stiffness coefficients along the concerned wave normals inside the medium, and are given by

$$v_e = \sqrt{\left(\frac{q_e}{\rho}\right)} \tag{49}$$

where ρ is the density and v_e is the velocity of the acoustic wave. The values of q_e's can be evaluated using Christoffel's equation (36) for the propagation of plane elastic waves in any desired direction. Using the known elastic and photoelastic constants of quartz and calcite, Chandrasekharan (33) evaluated the intensities of the 12 pairs of Brillouin components for specific crystal orientations and for incident unpolarized light. As already indicated in the first part of this section, for specific values of the angle of scattering and for specific directions along the crystallographic axes, the number of distinct components will be less than twelve.

In the case of cubic crystals, all the four components given by Eq. (48) have the same frequency shift and appear as one pair of components for each acoustic wave even when the incident light is unpolarized. Whereas the velocities of the elastic waves and consequently the shifts of the Brillouin components depend only on the direction of the elastic wave normal and angle of scattering θ, the intensity of light scattered depends also on the plane of scattering in a cubic crystal. If the direction of incidence and of scattering are parallel to any two cubic directions, for unpolarized incident light, the intensities of the pair of components for the three acoustic phonons are

$$I_B(t_1) = \frac{\pi^2 k T n^8}{2\lambda_i{}^4} \left[\frac{p_{44}^2}{c_{44}} \right] \tag{50}$$

$$I_B(t_2) = 0$$

$$I_B(l) = \frac{\pi^2 k T n^8}{2\lambda_i{}^4} \left[\frac{2(p_{44}^2 + p_{12}^2)}{c_{11} + c_{12} + 2c_{44}} \right] \tag{51}$$

where t_1 and t_2 represent the transverse waves and l the longitudinal wave. The sum of the intensities of the Brillouin components due to the elastic wave traversing a specific direction, when observed in mutually perpendicular planes, is not the same even though the frequency shift is the same in both cases. All these results arise from the fact that the intensity of Brillouin scattering depends on two fourth order tensors, viz., elastic and elasto-optic tensors:

$$I_{Hv} = I_{Vh} = \tfrac{1}{2} I_B(t_1) = \frac{\pi^2 k T n^8}{4\lambda_i{}^4} \left[\frac{p_{44}^2}{c_{44}} \right] \tag{52}$$

$$I_{Vv} = \frac{\pi^2 k T n^8}{2\lambda_i{}^4} \left[\frac{2p_{12}^2}{c_{11} + c_{12} + 2c_{44}} \right] \tag{53}$$

$$I_{Hh} = \frac{\pi^2 k T n^8}{2\lambda_i{}^4} \left[\frac{2p_{44}^2}{c_{11} + c_{12} + 2c_{44}} \right] \tag{54}$$

In the case of an amorphous solid for which $c_{11} - c_{12} = 2c_{44}$, while Eq. (50) and (52) are unaffected, Eq. (51), (53), and (54) are simplified, and we get

$$I_B(l) = I_{Vv} + I_{Hh} = \frac{\pi^2 kTn^8}{2\lambda_i{}^4}\left[\frac{p_{12}^2}{c_{11}} + \frac{p_{44}^2}{c_{11}}\right] \tag{55}$$

The treatment given above is applicable to an ideal harmonic crystal, and the entire scattering appears as Brillouin components, and there are no hydrodynamic modes at all unlike the case of a liquid. In any real crystal the situation may be different. An undisplaced component may be present due to anharmonicity and the presence of impurities and defects in the crystal. A thermal diffusion mode in solids due to mosaicity, similar to the one predicted by Landau and Placzek for liquids, scatters light very weakly and the intensity of the central line arising from the thermal diffusion mode may be less than 10% of the intensities of the Brillouin components. This will be completely masked by the presence of diffuse reflections of unmodified radiation from the sides of the crystal specimens and macroscopic inclusions inside the crystal.

III. EXPERIMENTAL TECHNIQUES

The study of Brillouin scattering in any medium is beset with numerous difficulties and demands exacting optical conditions. The intensity of scattering is usually small and one has to take extra precautions in order to eliminate all the parasitic illuminations arising from the diffuse reflections from the walls of the container or from the sides and inclusions usually present in the case of crystals. The change of wavelength to be expected is only of the order of 0.2 Å or less and the separation between the components arising from the two transverse elastic waves in the case of a crystal is very much smaller than 0.05 Å. This extremely small separation of the Brillouin components from the unmodified line necessitates the use of instruments of high resolving power such as the Fabry Perot etalon, Lummer Gehrcke plate, or Michelson echelon. These interferometers having very poor luminosity will considerably weaken the scattered light passing through them and thereby lead to long exposure times or require very sensitive photoelectric detection.

The most commonly used source of illumination in the earlier experiments was the mercury arc, though it had its limitations. In the very first investigations 4046 Å and 4358 Å radiations of Hg were used. These lines suffer from the disadvantage that they are accompanied by intense hyperfine structure satellites which make their appearance in the scattered light and thereby make it difficult to identify the Brillouin components. 4358 Å is particularly unsuited as the principal maxima themselves are excessively broad, while 4078 Å is comparatively more satisfactory as the hfs components are of relatively low intensity. In order to reduce the intrinsic width of the exciting line specially designed low density, cathode-cooled mercury vapor lamps were used by Rao (8). The experimental technique used by Rao is shown in Fig. 4.

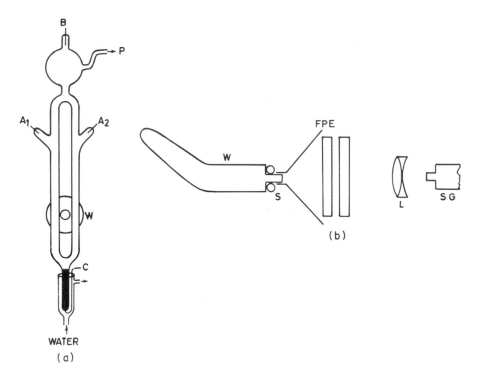

Fig. 4. Experimental arrangement employed by Rao (8) for recording Brillouin scattering in liquids in the backward direction ($\theta = 180°$). (a) The specially designed mercury vapour lamp with the vertical cross section of the Wood's tube (W) in the background. The lamp has two vertical branches with a common water cooled mercury cathode C and two tungsten anodes A_1 and A_2. The additional tungsten anode B is for initiating the discharge by means of an induction coil. (b) Experimental arrangement in the path of the scattered light. FPE = Fabry-Perot Echelon, L = condensing lens, and SG = Spectrograph.

Ramm (5) was the first to use the 4680 Å of the zinc arc which was free from satellites. Later Venkateswaren (9) developed the zinc mercury amalgam arc giving sharp, highly monochromatic, and intense radiations (4680 Å, 4722 Å, and 4810 Å, possessing only very weak satellites), and used it successfully for investigating the frequency shifts, intensity and polarization characteristics of Brillouin scattering in liquids and liquid mixtures.

The techniques described above could not be used successfully in the case of those substances where the unmodified line appears with very much enhanced intensity due to extraneous circumstances. The 2537 Å radiation from a water-cooled, magnet-controlled mercury arc is an ideal source for such cases as was pointed out by the author (Krishnan, 14). The main advantages of using this technique are the following: (1) The mercury resonance radiation is more intense compared to the other radiations emitted. (2) It can be very efficiently filtered out from the scattered light by mercury vapor itself, so that the fogging effect arising from the undisplaced component consisting mainly of bogus radiation and its wings can be successfully eliminated. (3) Being in the ultraviolet region, the scattering power is very much enhanced due to λ^{-4} law, and the frequency shift of the Brillouin components are correspondingly increased. (4) The Brillouin components could be recorded, well separated from the unmodified line, with the aid of high dispersion quartz spectrographs with reasonable exposure times without the use of interferometers.

Unfortunately 2537 Å also has its own limitations. The radiation coming out of an ordinary arc consists of five closely spaced components giving an overall width of 0.5 cm^{-1}. Hence it is not an ideal source for quantitative studies of the width of Brillouin scattering. This difficulty could be partly eliminated by working with a single isotope mercury (Hg^{198}) lamp. Such lamps are, however, costly and have limited life and therefore they have not been widely used so far for studies on Brillouin scattering. Finally, many substances are not transparent to the 2537 Å radiation and some decompose on exposure to this radiation; in such cases this technique cannot be used.

The mercury sources are generally extended sources and there is always some ambiguity in defining the value of θ appearing in Eq. (1). The θ will always have a finite range of values, and consequently the Brillouin components would be broadened and quantitative measurements on dispersion, absorption and relaxation phenomena are not possible.

All these difficulties are eliminated by the use of the highly monochromatic, intense, and parallel beam of light obtainable from a modern laser source. Numerous investigations have already been reported in the literature in recent years using the 6328 Å of He–Ne gas laser; 4880 Å radiation of the ionized argon laser has also been used. The 6943 Å of the ruby laser has also been employed for investigating the stimulated Brillouin effect. Whenever extremely narrow spectral width is desired, low power, single mode, helium-neon lasers are used. The width of the exciting line in such cases would be less than 1 Mc or 3×10^{-5} cm^{-1}.

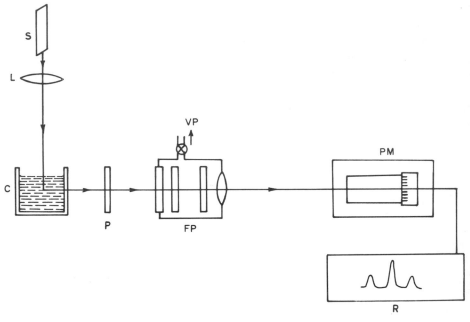

Fig. 5. Experimental arrangement for recording the Brillouin spectra, using a laser source and pressure scanned dielectric coated Fabry-Perot interferometer: S = single mode helium-neon laser; L = condensing lens; C = cell containing the scattering sample; P = polaroid. FP = Fabry-Perot interferometer; VM = Vacuum pump and controlled leak; PM = Photomultiplier tube assembly; R = Pen recorder.

All the three interferometers namely Michelson, Fabry Perot, and Lummer Gehrcke combined with photographic recording were used in the experiments with the visible radiations of the mercury and zinc arcs. No interferometer was necessary for 2537 Å excitation. A high dispersion quartz or grating spectrograph will serve the purpose. The Hilger three metre quartz spectrograph (having a dispersion of 1 Å/mm in 2537 Å region) was used by the author and Chandrasekharan in their experiments.

The very first investigations on Brillouin scattering with the laser source were carried out using a conventional high dispersion grating spectrograph having a fairly high resolving power in combination with photoelectric recording. The modern technique is to use a frequency stabilized single mode laser, a high resolution, temperature-controlled Fabry–Perot interferometer and a photomultiplier detecting system (see Fig. 5). The mirrors of the interferometer are dielectric coated with a reflection coefficient ranging from 90–99% depending on the required resolution. The spacing is adjusted so as to cover the required free spectral range. The interferometer has been used in two ways, one as a variable pressure instrument and the other as a variable spacing instrument. In the first technique (37,38) which is more frequently employed, the interferometer assembly is kept inside the temperature-controlled optical chamber, which is evacuated, and air, hydrogen, or carbon dioxide is slowly leaked in, and the scanning over the spectral region is carried out as the pressure is slowly increased.

In the second type, the pressure of gas is between the interferometer plates is kept constant and the scanning is carried out as the distance between the plates is varied. This technique is used by S. J. Fray et al. at the Royal Radar Establishment, Great Malvern, England (unpublished work). In this technique one of the interferometer mirrors is firmly fixed to the supporting box, while the second mirror is capable of small movement in a direction parallel to the axis of the interferometer, the two mirrors maintaining parallelism throughout. A piezoelectric modulator is attached to the movable mirror, and as it is made to vibrate piezo-electrically, the interferometer distance is altered in a periodic way with the frequency of the transducer, the variation being directly proportional to the amplitude of oscillation. The emergent beam is scanned over each cycle of oscillation and its intensity is plotted as a function of time. Even Raman lines with frequency shifts extending up to 100 cm^{-1} could be recorded using this technique.

In both these arrangements, the ring pattern of the interferometer is focussed centrally on a very small aperture kept immediately in front of a photomultiplier tube, the output of which is amplified and fed on to a recorder or a cathode ray oscillograph. The intensity of the central spot is recorded as a function of pressure or time as the case may be.

When the width of the laser radiation is extremely small, as is the case with single mode, low power, helium-neon lasers, optical heterodyne techniques (Forrester, 39) capable of detecting exceedingly small changes in frequency or width of the scattered line have been used (Cummins et al. *40*). The technique consists in splitting the laser radiation into two beams, one entering the scattering medium and the other passing through an acoustical Bragg-reflection-modulator which introduces a frequency difference of a few Mcs. The two beams are again brought together and allowed to fall on a photomultiplier tube whose output signal is then scanned with a suitable wave analyser which decomposes the fluctuations in the photocurrent into their spectral components.

In a self beating spectrometer adopted by Lastovka and Benedek (*41*), the Brillouin scattering and the light scattered by dust particles on the cell window which acts as a local oscillator are mixed on the surface of a photomultiplier tube. The two wave fronts are made to be accurately collinear over the photo surface. The resulting photo current contains beat notes between all the spectral components of the two fields. The power spectrum of the photo current, which is identical with the power spectrum of the scattered light, is examined with the aid of a wave analyzer, and the output gives the root mean square photo-current in a small range of frequencies around the central frequency to which the analyzer is tuned. This technique is specially useful for determining the width of unmodified lines after scattering.

IV. STUDIES IN GASES

According to the hydrodynamical theory of Mountain, in the case of gases at one atmosphere pressure, the mean free path becomes equal to or larger than the wavelength of the scattering fluctuations, and consequently no Brillouin components may be expected to appear in thermal scattering. But the situation is altered when the pressure is increased to a higher value. Venkateswaran (*42*) was the first to examine spectroscopically the light scattered in the backward direction by hydrogen, nitrogen, oxygen, and carbon dioxide at a pressure of 100 atm. He employed a Fabry–Perot interferometer and 4047 Å radiation as exciter. In his experiments long exposures were used, and the Fabry–Perot interferometer was neither temperature nor pressure controlled. As was expected, none of the gases showed displaced components similar to the ones observed in liquids. The pattern obtained with hydrogen showed a broadening and the half width of the line was found to be of the order to be expected from Maxwellian distribution of velocities. In the other three gases, the Doppler broadening was too small to be observed. Fabelinskii (*43*) was, however, of the view that the observed broadening in the case of hydrogen was not due to the

Doppler effect, but to splitting of the lines which were not resolved because of the finite width of the incident radiation and due to pressure variations.

Using a helium-neon laser Eastman, Wiggins, and Rank (44) observed the spontaneous Brillouin scattering in CO_2 and N_2 at high pressures. Ranson et al. (45) who used a helium-neon laser operating at 6328 Å with a line width of 550 Mc and a power of 5 mW, a pressure scanned Fabry–Perot interferometer, and photoelectric recording, observed only a broadening of the unmodified line in the case of argon and helium at 1 atm pressure. When the pressure of the sample gas was raised, they succeeded in recording Brillouin components in all the gases. The range of pressures used was from 80–160 atm in the case of oxygen and nitrogen, from 45–175 atm in the case of argon, and from 35–130 atm in the case of methane. The lowest pressure at which the Brillouin components could be recorded was determined by the signal to noise ratio. They reported that the three components had roughly the same half width as the incident laser line. In the case of argon, oxygen, and nitrogen, the triplet was not completely resolved. The ratio of the peak intensity of the central component I_C to twice the peak intensity of the Brillouin components ($2I_B$) was equal to $\gamma - 1$ in accordance with the Landau Placzek Eq. (22), for an ideal fluid. With increase in the pressure of the gas and hence its density, a noticeable decrease in intensity of the Brillouin components relative to the central component was observed, indicating thereby that there was a corresponding increase in the ratio of specific heats. Using Eq. (1) Ranson et al. have evaluated the velocity of sound and its variation with density in Ar, CH_4, N_2, and O_2 from the measured frequency shifts. In all the gases studied except in CH_4, the values of the velocity obtained thereby agreed well with the adiabatic values reported in the literature from ultrasonic measurements. In the case of CH_4, the calculated value was nearer to the isothermal value than the adiabatic value. This anomaly has been attributed to viscosity, thermal conductivity and relaxation phenomena.

Almost simultaneously, Greytek and Benedek (46) reported the observation of a well resolved triplet in the scattered spectra of argon, xenon, nitrogen, carbon dioxide, and methane even at one atmosphere pressure but only at small scattering angles of the order of 10° or less. They used a frequency stabilized, lower power, single mode helium-neon laser, a high resolution Fabry–Perot interferometer, a photomultiplier tube (ITT FW 130) of very low dark current, and a pulse height discriminator; the spread in the scattering angle was of the order of 10^{-3} rad. The scattering towards the forward direction was analyzed with a spherical Fabry–Perot interferometer of 750 Mc/sec free spectral range and an instrumental profile of 28 Mc/sec full width at half height. When the scattering angle was increased to 20°, the three components partially overlapped. When θ was 150°, only a broad line appeared with broad shoulders on either side indicative of the existence of weak Brillouin peaks associated with sound waves. Thus when the scattering angle was changed from the forward to the backward direction, they observed a change from a hydrodynamic to a kinetic character of the fluctuations in the gaseous medium. The negative result obtained by Ranson et al. (45) in gases at 1 atm pressure for the transversely scattered light ($\theta = 90°$) is therefore understandable on the basis of the above results.

Table 1 gives the observed Brillouin shift, the calculated velocity of hypersonic waves, and the low frequency sound velocity for the five gases studied by Greytek and Benedek (44) at an angle of 10.6°. The values of the hypersonic velocities calculated from the observed Brillouin shifts for $\theta = 10.6°$ were found to be slightly lower than the corresponding ultrasonic values for the five gases investigated by Greytek and Benedek (44). In the case of xenon and carbon dioxide, the observed ratio of the intensities of the Rayleigh line to that of the Brillouin lines is found to be equal to $\gamma - 1$ in accordance with the Landau Placzek relation (22).

TABLE 1

Brillouin Shifts and Velocities for Scattering at an Angle of 10.6°

Gas	Pressure (mmHg)	Temperature (°C)	Δv (Mc/s)	Hypersonic velocity (m/sec)	Ultrasonic velocity (m/sec)
Ar	770	28	93.0	318	323
Xe	795	25.2	50.8	174	178
N_2	770	28.0	100.5	344	354
CO_2	770	24.9	81.5	279	281
CH_4	777	24.7	129.0	442	454

V. STUDIES IN LIQUIDS

A. Main Results

Fairly extensive quantitative investigations have been carried out on Brillouin scattering in a large number of liquids and liquid mixtures. In

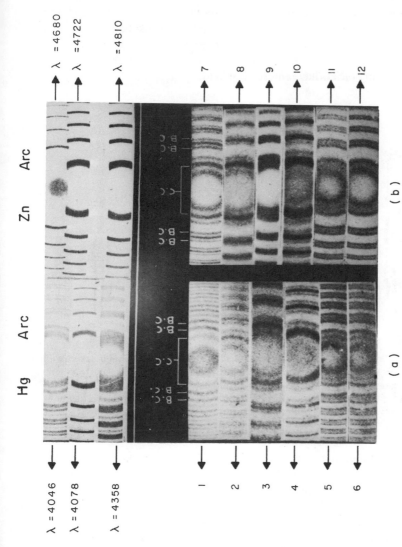

Fig. 6. Fabry-Perot interference patterns of Brillouin scattering in liquids taken with zinc arc excitation by Venkateswaran (9) for backward scattering: FP plate separation = 5 mm; A. Top left side picture—FP pattern of Hg arc, B. Top right side picture—FP pattern of zinc arc. (1) Water 30°C; (2) cyclohexane 30°; (3) carbon tetrachloride 25°; (4) Benzene 28°; (5) ethyl alcohol 25°; (6) ethyl alcohol 65°; (7) acetone 28°; (8) acetone 54°; (9) ether 30°; (10) tetralin 30°; (11) Isobutyric acid 25°; and (12) isobutyric acid 54°. The interferograms 1–12 were taken with λ 4810 Å excitation.

liquids, it is fairly easy to prepare the medium completely free from dust particles and the scattered light could therefore be made free of bogus illumination by proper optical alignment. Rao (*8*), Venkateswaran (*9*), and Sunanda Bai (*10*) were the earlier pioneers who investigated the Brillouin scattering in liquids and liquid mixtures using conventional mercury and zinc arc sources, and obtained quantitative results; they were followed by Rank (*16*) and Fabelinskii (*21,47*). With the advent of the laser, many others have entered the field.

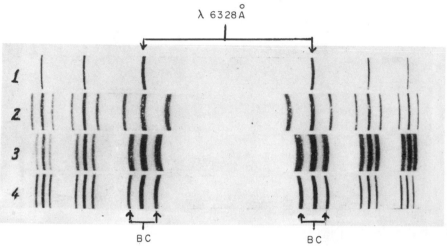

Fig. 7. Fabry-Perot interference patterns of Brillouin scattering in liquids taken with laser excitation by Mash et al. (*48*) for $\theta = 90°$. Separation of the FP plates = 8 mm. (1) Direct laser radiation λ 6328 Å; (2) Scattered spectrum from benzene—$\Delta v = 0.164 \, cm^{-1}$; (3) Scattered spectrum from carbon tetrachloride—$\Delta v = 0.110 \, cm^{-1}$; (4) Scattered spectrum from chloroform—$\Delta v = 0.113 \, cm^{-1}$.

The very first investigations in liquids using lasers were those of Benedek et al. (*37*), Chiao and Stoicheff (*38*), and Mash et al. (*48*). These groups carried out their investigations independently and simultaneously. Their work has been followed by extensive investigations in liquids with lasers in many laboratories (*49–53, 23* and *24*). Fabry–Perot patterns of thermal scattering in typical liquids taken with ordinary sources are reproduced in Fig. 6 and those taken with a laser are reproduced in Figs. 7 and 8. A schematic diagram of the intensity distribution in the scattered spectrum as shown in Fig. 9.

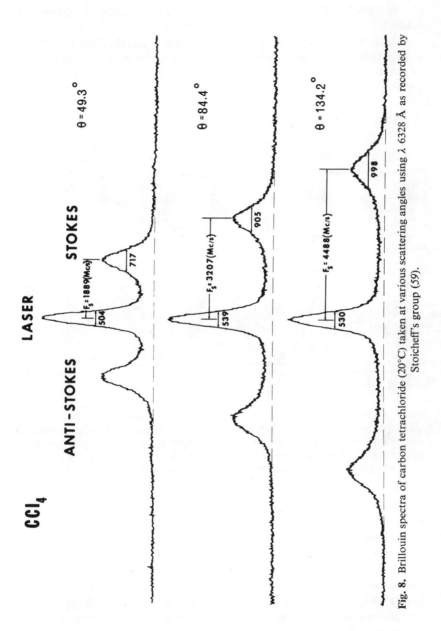

Fig. 8. Brillouin spectra of carbon tetrachloride (20°C) taken at various scattering angles using λ 6328 Å as recorded by Stoicheff's group (59).

The main results obtained with liquids can be broadly summarized as follows:

1. The scattered radiation in all liquids is generally found to exhibit mainly three components; a central component (called the Rayleigh line) of the same frequency as the original radiation, and the other two components called Brillouin components, symmetrically placed on either side of the undisplaced line with a shift of frequency in accordance with Brillouin's formula (1).

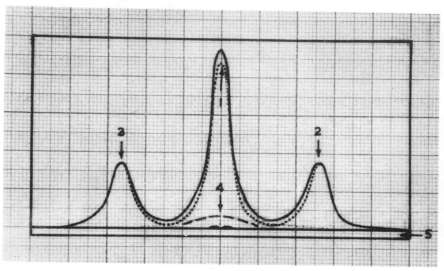

Fig. 9. Schematic representation of the spectrum of the scattered light from a liquid: (1) Central undisplaced or Rayleigh component; (2, 3) Stokes and anti-Stokes Brillouin components; (4) Non-propagating fourth component (Mountain, 22); (5) Anisotropic background. Dotted line indicates the profile of each component, while the continuous line indicates the aggregate intensity distribution in the scattered spectrum.

2. At room temperature all these three components are sharp and have Lorentzian line shapes with half widths significantly greater than that of the incident radiation. The half width of either of the Brillouin components is greater than that of the central component.

3. The Brillouin components which arise from density fluctuations are strongly polarized for scattering in the transverse direction, while the Rayleigh component is only partially polarized. The depolarization of the central component is found to depend on the temperature and viscosity of the liquid and the anisotropy of the molecules.

4. There is a fourth component which is fairly broad and less intense than the other three components and is due to thermal conductivity. This appears as a background which extends on either side of the central component to the Brillouin components producing an asymmetry in the intensity profiles of the Brillouin lines. (See Fig. 8 and also the schematic diagram, Fig. 9.) This fourth component is polarized in the same plane as the Brillouin components.

5. There is a general background superposed over the entire interferogram. This is the depolarized component known as the Rayleigh "wing." This depolarized component is centered at zero frequency and extends over 100 cm^{-1}. The intensity of the background scattering is greater with either higher depolarization of the total scattering of the liquid or higher anisotropy of the molecules contained in the liquid.

6. The relative intensities of the various spectral components of scattering are found to depend on temperature, viscosity, ratio of specific heats, thermal conductivity, and optical anisotropy.

We shall discuss the experimental results on frequency shift, intensity, and width of the lines separately.

B. Frequency Shift and Hypersonic Velocity

The frequency shifts of the Brillouin components have been very accurately measured in more than forty liquids using laser excitation and the frequencies of the corresponding hypersonic waves have been evaluated. From the measured frequency shifts, the velocities of the hypersonic waves have been evaluated using Eq. (1). The accuracy achieved in the velocity determination is of the order of $\pm 0.3\%$. When the angle of scattering θ is varied from 20°–170°, the frequency of the hypersonic waves varies from about 1 Gc/s (1×10^9 cycles/sec) to 6 Gc/s in most liquids. Thus by measuring the frequency shifts of the Brillouin components as θ is varied from a low value to the limiting value, the corresponding velocities of the hypersonic waves have been estimated as a function of frequency. In Table 2 are collected the most reliable data for 33 liquids; most of them have been taken from the paper by Wiggins et al. (54). The temperature of the medium and the frequency of the hypersonic waves at which velocity data are taken are also included in Table 2 as are the acoustic velocities for ultrasonic waves of frequency ~1 Mc/s taken from the literature. The values of $\Delta V/V_u$, the dispersion factor for the velocity, is given in the last column. A perusal of the values given in Table 2 shows that con-

TABLE 2

Velocity of Sound in Various Liquids

No.	Substance	Temp. (°C)	Hypersonic Range Freq. (Gc/s)	V_{HS} (m/s)	Ultrasonic V_u (m/sec) Freq. $\sim$ 1 Mc.	$\frac{\Delta V}{V_u} = \frac{V_{HS} - V_u}{V_u}$ (%)
1.	Acetic acid	20	4.56	1190	1180	1.0
2.	Acetone	20	4.62	1205	1192	1.0
3.	Aniline	20	7.77	1733	1656	4.6
4.	Benzene	20	6.33	1511	1326	14.0
5.	Benzaldehyde	20	6.72	1546	1479	4.5
6.	Carbon disulphide	20	5.82	1275	1158	10.1
7.	Carbon tetrachloride	20	4.38	1069	938	14.0
8.	Chloroform	20	4.44	1083	1005	7.5
9.	Cyclohexane	20	5.40	1341	1284	4.4
10.	Ethyl acetate	24	3.90	1273.5	1176	8.3
11.	Ethyl alcohol	20	3.54	1160	1150	0
12.	Ethylene glycol	20	5.42	1740	1616	7.7
13.	Ethyl ether	20	3.03	1003	985	1.8
14.	Formic acid	20	4.07	1331	1287	3.4
15.	Furan	20	6.3	1272	1124	13.0
16.	Glycerine	20	11.6	2851	1923	48.2
17.	n-Heptane	20	3.67	1186	1180	0.5
18.	n-Hexane	20	3.42	1110	1083	2.5
19.	Methyl acetate	23	4.48	1173	1164	0
20.	Methyl alcohol	20	4.26	1124	1123	0
21.	Methylene bromide	24	5.5	1099	971	13.0
22.	Methylene chloride	20	3.53	1113	1079	3.0
23.	Methylene iodide	25	4.98	1014	977	4.0
24.	Nitrobenzene	20	6.84	1563	1473	6.1
25.	m-Nitrobenzene	26	6.87	1553	1489	4.3
26.	o-Nitrotoluene	26	6.51	1471	1432	2.7
27.	Octane	20	5.82	1434	1197	20.0
28.	1-Octyl alcohol	20	4.41	1390	1358	2.3
29.	Pyridine	20	6.78	1600	1445	10.7
30.	Quinoline	70	5.69	1572	1360	15.5
31.	Toluene	20	5.79	1389	1328	4.6
32.	Water	27	5.91	1544	1500	3.0
33.	p-Xylene	20	5.97	1408	1330	5.8

siderable dispersion of sound velocity is exhibited by benzene, carbon disulphide, carbon tetrachloride, chloroform, ethyl acetate, ethylene glycol, furan, glycerine, methylene bromide, octane, pyridine, quinoline, and p-xylene. The dispersion is maximum for the highly viscous liquid glycerine. Many have reported absence of dispersion in the case of water in the range of temperature 0°–50°C (24). But the recent measurements of Wiggins and others (54) quoted in Table 2 indicate a definite though small dispersion. In many cases the velocity increase takes place over a narrow range of frequencies in the hypersonic region.

The temperature variation of the hypersonic velocity has been measured in many liquids by Venkateswaran (9), by Pesin and Fabelinskii (47), by Chiao and Stoicheff (38), by O'Connor and Schlupf (24,55), by Rank et al. (56), and by Fleury and Chiao (53). In the case of viscous liquids the decrease of velocity with increase of temperature is proportionately large. In the case of nonviscous liquids the decrease of velocity with increase of temperature ($\Delta V/\Delta T$) is of the order of -0.5% per degree. The proportional decrease is the same as that reported for the ultrasonic region in the same liquids. In water, as the temperature is raised the velocity increases by about 1.6% per °C in the region 4° to 50°C (24).

C. Intensity

In many nonviscous liquids, the sum of the intensities of the Brillouin components is found to be greater than the intensity of the central component at ordinary temperatures. When the temperature is raised, the intensity of the Brillouin components remains either unaffected or decreases, while the intensity of the central component increases. Many attempts have been made in the past to test the validity of the Landau–Placzek relation (22). In order to estimate the ratio $I_C/2I_B$ experimentally, some have determined the aggregate intensity of the lines integrated over the entire width, while some others have obtained the total intensity by multiplying the peak intensity of each line with its full width at half intensity. In this connection reference should be made to the work of Venkateswaran (9), Sunanda Bai (10), Rank et al. (16), Fabelinskii et al. (21), Cummins and Gammon (23), and O'Connor and Schlupf (24). Venkateswaran (9) was the first to demonstrate the failure of the simple Landau–Placzek relation in some liquids. Later the discrepancy between theory and experiment has been attributed to dispersion of acoustic velocity, and also to the dispersion of other thermodynamic properties of the medium. Cummins and Gammon (23) examined this problem thoroughly and have given most reliable values for the ratio $I_C/2I_B$ for eleven liquids. The values are given in Table 3. The experimental values of the ratio $I_C/2I_B$ are in good agreement with the Landau–Placzek formula in the case of liquids which do not exhibit any dispersion except in the case of acetic acid, which is a highly associated liquid. In those cases where there is appreciable dispersion, the $I_C/2I_B$ ratio given by the dispersion corrected Eq. (24) is in better agreement with the observed value. Even

TABLE 3

Intensity Ratio in Liquids

No.	Substance	Freq. (Gc/s)	V_{HS} (m/sec)	Velocity Disper- sion (%)	$I_C/2I_B$ Experi- mental	$I_C/2I_B$ L-P formula $(\gamma-1)$	$I_C/2I_B$ After dispersion correction from Eq. (24)
1.	Acetic acid	3.57	1160	1.0	0.41	0.21	0.28
2.	Acetone	3.60	1190	1.0	0.44	0.39	0.47
3.	Benzene	5.01	1500	14.0	0.84	0.43	0.66
4.	Carbon disulphide	4.53	1250	10.1	0.71	0.55	0.79
5.	Carbon tetra- chloride	3.27	1000	14.0	0.72	0.45	0.62
6.	Ethyl alcohol	3.54	1160	0.0	0.23	0.18	0.24
7.	Ethyl ether	3.03	1000	1.8	0.35	0.37	0.36
8.	n-Hexane	3.42	1110	2.5	0.35	0.28	0.34
9.	Methyl alcohol	3.30	1110	0.0	0.26	0.21	0.27
10.	Toluene	4.50	1350	4.6	0.42	0.36	0.41
11.	Water	4.41	1480	3.0	0.02	0.007	0.008

in this category, the agreement is not so good for benzene and carbon tetrachloride. O'Connor and Schlupf (55) have calculated the $I_C/2I_B$ ratio using Mountain's Eq. (25) and compared the calculated values with the experimental values of the ratio for benzene. There was agreement between the two over the temperature range 10°–50°C. But in the case of carbon tetrachloride even Mountain's formula (25) is not valid. The breakdown in the case of carbon tetrachloride may be due to the existence of more than one relaxation time. In every case where there is disagreement between the observed and calculated values of $I_C/2I_B$, the observed value is always higher than the theoretical one.

Water has been studied in detail by O'Connor and Schlupf (24) over the temperature range 4°–50°C. Since the thermal expansion coefficient is zero for water at 4°C, from Eq. (23), I_C should vanish and the ratio should become zero. As is to be expected there is no trace of the central component in the case of water at 4°C. Over the range 4°–50°C, the ratio of $I_C/2I_B$ is given by the exact expression without neglecting terms like $(\delta\varepsilon/\delta T)_\rho$ in Eq. (18). Water is an ideal liquid without any relaxation time, and the observed ratio $I_C/2I_B$ even at room temperature is much less than 0.02.

D. Width

Dispersion of hypersonic waves is the direct result of absorption and relaxation mechanism which produces a broadening of the Brillouin components. A direct measurement of the width of these components enables one to determine the amplitude absorption coefficient and the corresponding relaxation time using Eq. (27) and (28). Under the high resolution available with a low power, helium-neon laser and a pressure scanned Fabry–Perot interferometer, quantitative measurements of the width of the Brillouin components have been made by Chiao and Stoicheff (47), by Fabelinskii's group (48,52), by Fleury and Chiao (53), by O'Connor and Schlupf (55), and by Hanes et al. (57). The widths of the central and Brillouin components and their variation with scattering angle θ for carbon tetrachloride are beautifully illustrated in Fig. 8.

In ordinary liquids the width δv_B is of the order of 5×10^{-3} cm^{-1}, (150 Mc/sec), and the relaxation time is of the order of 1.2×10^{-10} sec. The value of the amplitude coefficient of hypersonic attenuation a has a value of about 3.10×10^3 cm^{-1}. In the case of formic acid, ethyl acetate, and acetic acid the half width is of the order 50×10^{-3} cm^{-1}. Relaxation processes have been observed in CS_2, CCl_4, C_6H_{14}, $C_6H_5CH_3$, CH_3COOH, and $C_6H_5NO_2$ by Fleury and Chiao (53). The width of the Brillouin components in CS_2 and CCl_4 is very small (of the order of 2×10^{-3} cm^{-1}), although they exhibit high dispersion of hypersonic velocity. The graph showing the variation of a/f^2 with frequency exhibits a sudden drop in value in CS_2, CCl_4, C_6H_{12}, and $C_6H_5CH_3$ in the range 0.5 to 5 Gc/sec. In the case of C_6H_6, CS_2, and CCl_4, O'Connor and Schlupf (55) report that the relaxation time calculated from measurements of line width is in very good agreement with that calculated from velocity dispersion measurement using Mountain's equation. These values, however, do not agree with the value for τ calculated from excess sound absorption in ultrasonic measurements. As already mentioned in Section 2, the width of the central component is very much less compared to that of the Brillouin components. Using a heterodyne beating technique, Lastovka and Benedek (41) measured the width of the central component and its dependence on angle of scattering in the case of toluene; the line shape was accurately Lorentzian. Its half width for backward scattering is equal to 10.5 Mc/sec (3.5×10^{-4} cm^{-1}) at a temperature of 20°C. The magnitude and the (scattering) angular dependence of the line width are in accordance with the Leontowitsch–Landau–Placzek theory vide Eq. (26) and (29), showing thereby that the heat flow equations accurately describe both the temporal and spatial behavior of entropy fluctuations. From the measured value of the width of the central line, one can evaluate the thermal diffusivity.

E. Polarization of Scattered Light

From the theoretical stand point, the Brillouin and central components should be completely polarized. Cummins and Gammon (58) measured the degree of polarization of the different components and of the background scattering in benzene and toluene. The Brillouin and central components were highly polarized with ρ_v (depolarization factor for vertically polarized incident light) less than 3 % for both. The depolarization of the background was $\rho_v = 59\%$ and $\rho_u = 74\%$. They were able to satisfactorily account for the bulk depolarization by adding the depolarization of the background to the depolarization of the polarized components, and taking their respective intensities into consideration.

F. Fourth Component (I_F)

The fourth component envisaged in Mountain's theory (22) has been identified by Stoicheff's group in the scattered spectra of carbon tetrachloride (59) and of glycerine (60) (see Figs. 8, 9, and 10). In carbon tetrachloride, the intensity and breadth of the fourth component are found by Gornall et al. (59) to be independent of temperature in the range 15°–75°C and the component is polarized in the same plane as the exciting laser light. It accounts for an appreciable part (about 20%) of the total intensity in these spectra. In the case of CCl$_4$, it is due to the thermal relaxation process occuring in the frequency range 1.6 to 4.7 Gc/sec. The relaxation time τ obtained by Gornall et al. (59) is equal to

6.42×10^{-11} sec. As the fourth component is mainly superimposed over the central component, the measured ratio of $I_C/2I_B$ will always be higher than the theoretical value even after applying correction for dispersion (see the values given in Table 3 for CCl_4).

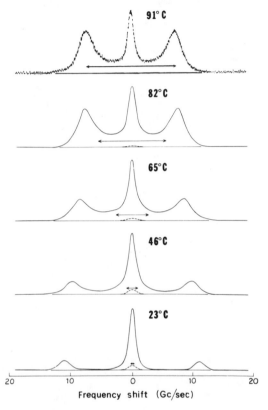

Fig. 10. Brillouin scattering at 113° in glycerine at five different temperatures taken by Stoicheff's group (60). The solid curves show the total scattered intensity (i.e., polarized and depolarized). The dashed curves show the intensity of the depolarized light. The width at half intensity of the fourth component is indicated by the extent of the arrows.

In the case of glycerine, there is molecular association which leads to high viscosity and consequently structural relaxation $[(\Delta T)_V = 0]$ is mainly responsible for the fourth component (60). At 23°C the fourth component of glycerine is as narrow as the central component. When the temperature is raised, its intensity and width increase very rapidly. Over the range 23–91°C the change in width is nearly twenty times. In both the liquids (carbon tetrachloride and glycerine), the observed spectral intensity distribution and the width of the fourth component at any temperature are found to be in good agreement with the theoretical predictions of Mountain's theory.

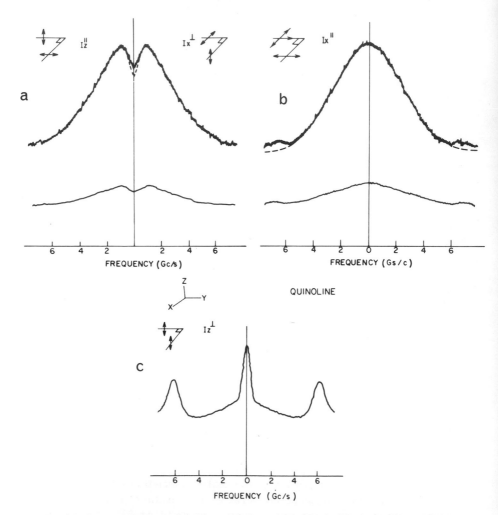

Fig. 11. Spectra of liquid quinoline at 20°C taken by Stoicheff's group (*63*). Scattering angle = 90°. (a) and (b) are the spectra of depolarized scattered light, with planes of polarization as indicated; (c) is the corresponding spectrum of isotropic scattering.

G. Anisotropic Scattering in Liquids

As already mentioned, there is a depolarized spectrum superimposed over the central and Brillouin components arising from the anisotropy of molecules in the liquid. This can be split up into two portions, one portion adjacent to the central component and extending up to 10 cm^{-1} and the second portion which extends from 10 cm^{-1} to more than 100 cm^{-1}. The first part of the depolarized spectrum from a number of liquids has been studied in detail under high dispersion using a laser source (61–63). Starunov, Tiganov, and Fabelinskii (61,62) reported that in many liquids the depolarized scattered spectrum in the low frequency shift region consists of a doublet with an intensity minimum at the exciting frequency and with a peak separation of 1 to 3 Gc/sec, depending on the nature of the liquid. This observation has been confirmed by Stegeman and Stoicheff (63). The depolarized spectrum of liquid quinoline taken by these authors is reproduced in Fig. 11.

The doublet separation was found to depend on the K vector and hence the depolarized spectrum has its origin in the scattering by thermally excited shear waves. A phenomenological theory of the scattering of light in liquids due to temperature and stress fluctuations was given by Rytov (64). Many of the features predicted by this theory have been confirmed by Stegeman and Stoicheff. The value of ω_T, the frequency of the transverse shear waves in quinoline is 0.91 ± 0.04 Gc/sec and relaxation time $\tau = 3.7 \times 10^{-11}$ sec. From the parameters ω_T and τ a transverse sound velocity of 415 m/sec, a high frequency shear modulus of 1.88×10^9 dyne/cm^2, and a shear relaxation time of 4.0×10^{-11} sec were estimated by Stegeman and Stoicheff (63) for liquid quinoline at 20°C.

H. Influence of Temperature

When the temperature of the liquid is increased, the Brillouin components become broader and shift towards the central line as a consequence of the decrease in the hypersonic velocity. In nonviscous liquids, the peak intensity of the Brillouin components does not appreciably change with temperature, whereas in highly viscous liquids, the Brillouin components not only broaden but also increase in intensity as the temperature is raised.

When the temperature of the liquid approaches the critical temperature T_c, the intensity of the central component increases rapidly and the

Brillouin components become very much weaker and get lost in the background. Mountain (22) has theoretically analyzed the spectral distribution of the light scattered by CO_2 in the super critical region. Using the well known properties of CO_2, he has calculated $I_C/2I_B$ and the distribution of frequency of the scattered light in the super critical region and also away from the critical point. As already mentioned in Section 2, the thermal conductivity of the medium could be estimated from a knowledge of the width of the central component. It is difficult to directly measure the former very near T_c, but measurements of the width of the central line near T_c can be carried out for determining the thermal conductivity.

Ford and Benedek (65) were the first to investigate the dependence of the half width of the central component in SF_6 in the neighborhood of its T_c (both above and below). This has been followed by Alpert et al. (66) in the case of CO_2. A very detailed investigation of the frequency shift, intensity and width of the spectral components of the light scattered by CO_2 was carried out recently by Gammon et al. (67). Their observations cover the range of temperature from 0.2–6.0°C above T_c in the gaseous phase, and a range from 0.1–8°C below T_c both in the liquid and gaseous phase. When $T_c - T = 1.12°C$ the intensity of the central component I_C has the same value in the liquid and vapor phases. As T_c is approached, I_C increases rapidly and its width becomes very small, showing that the entropy fluctuations decay very slowly in the critical region. I_B approaches a nonzero value as $T \rightarrow T_c$, and the Brillouin components are practically lost in the instrumental wings of the central line. The hypersonic velocity V_{HS} is found to be higher than the thermodynamic value near T_c due to the existence of additional structural relaxation (as in the case of viscous liquids) arising from cluster formation associated with critical fluctuations (68). Very near T_c, V_{HS} is about 180 meters/sec. When $T = T_c - 8°C$, V_{HS} is about 335 meters/sec in the liquid phase and is only ~ 205 meters/sec. in the vapor phase; δv_B is about twice the instrumental width. At 0.5°C below T_c, the Brillouin shifts are equal for the two phases, while δv_B for the liquid is greater than that for the gas by 25 Mc/sec.

Near T_c, $C_p \gg C_v$, and the observed $I_C/2I_B$ ratio fits in with the ratio $C_p/C_v - C'$ in the neighborhood of T_c where C' is the vibrational contribution to the low frequency specific heat. Far away from T_c, I_B is found to be proportional to C_v. Alpert et al., found that δv_c was a linear function of $\sin^2 \theta/2$ and $T - T_c$. The coefficient of thermal conductivity was estimated to be 5.7×10^{-7} cm^2/sec at $T - T_c = 0.002°C$. The thermal diffusivity diverges quite differently above and below T_c.

I. Viscous Liquids

Venkateswaran (9,69), investigated the fine structure of the thermal scattering in a number of viscous liquids, including glycerine and castor oil. He reported the existence of very weak Brillouin components in glycerine at 0°C having a viscosity of 120.4 poise contrary to the predictions of Leontowitsch's theory (27). Later more detailed investigations were carried out by Pesin and Fabelinskii (70) on glycerine and triacetin, and by Rank et al. (56) on glycerine, ethylene glycol and octyl alcohol over a very wide range of temperature and hence viscosity. Recently, Knapp et al. (60) have examined the scattering in glycerine in some detail. The interferograms of the spectrum of the light scattered by glycerine at five different temperatures taken by Knapp et al. (60) are reproduced in Fig. 10. The main results are summarized as follows:

1. Even at low temperatures and at very high viscosities Brillouin components are present; but their intensity is very low.

2. As the temperature increases, there is a rapid increase in the intensity of the Brillouin components as compared with that of the central component.

3. As the temperature increases there is a rapid increase in the intensity of the fourth component in the region between the central and Brillouin components.

4. The sound velocities of glycerine at four different temperatures are given in Table 4.

TABLE 4

Sound Velocity in Glycerine

Temperature (°C)	−70	−21	23	91
Hypersonic velocity V_{HS} (m/s at 10 Gc/sec)	3665	3200	2890	1910
Ultrasonic velocity V_U (m/s at 1 Mc/sec)	3675	2100	1940	1800

There is considerable increase in the dispersion of hypersonic velocity as the viscosity increases, except at very low temperatures. With increase of temperature the Brillouin components progressively move towards the central line and the width of all the components also increases.

5. In the temperature range from −21°C to 115°C the ratio $I_c/2I_B$ varies from about 5 to 0.23. The extrapolated value of $I_c/2I_B$ to zero viscosity agrees with the Landau Placzek relation (Eq. 22).

. The appearance of the Brillouin components in viscous liquids corresponding to frequencies of more than 10 Gc/sec provides an experimental proof for the solid-like behavior of liquids towards hypersonic waves; it also confirms the forecast of the relaxation theory. In order to quantitatively account for the observed results, it is necessary to assume that there is more than one relaxation time with different distribution functions.

VI. STUDIES IN SOLIDS

Solids can be divided into two categories, amorphous solids like glass and crystalline solids. The case of amorphous solids will be considered first.

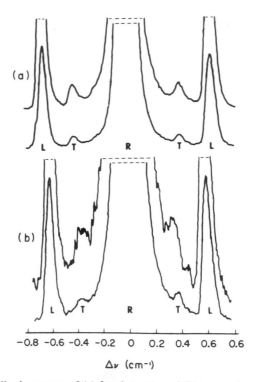

Fig. 12. The Brillouin spectra of (a) fused quartz and (b) pyrex glass taken with laser 6328 Å excitation at two different gains by Cummins' group (72). L, T, and R are respectively the longitudinal, the transverse and the Rayleigh components. The relatively high intensity of the central Rayleigh component is clearly seen in the picture. This phenomenon is characteristic of amorphous substances (15).

A. Amorphous Solids

The author (*15*) succeeded for the first time in photographing the Brillouin components of an amorphous solid, namely fused quartz using 2536 Å excitation; only the longitudinal components were recorded. The observed frequency shift was in general agreement with those calculated from the known elastic constants of fused quartz. The transverse components could not be recorded as they were very weak and were also absorbed by the mercury vapor filter. The total intensity of the Brillouin components was found to be one thirtieth of the intensity of Rayleigh scattering. The author's results were confirmed by Flubacher et al. (*71*) using a lamp operating on an isotope of mercury Hg^{198}. They were able to record both the transverse (very weak) and longitudinal components. The values of the velocities of the longitudinal and transverse hypersonic waves calculated from the observed shifts are 5910 and 3840 M/sec respectively. Recently Shapiro et al. (*72*) have recorded the Brillouin scattering spectra of fused quartz and pyrex glass. At room temperature the lines were quite sharp and the attenuation coefficient a of both longitudinal and transverse phonons at 10 to 20 Gc/sec was less than 10^3 cm^{-1} (see Fig. 12).

B. Crystalline Media

The very first experimental observation with crystals was that of Gross (*11*). This was followed by Raman and Venkateswaran (*12*) in gypsum and by Sibaiya (*13*) in Rochelle salt. Using 2537 Å Hg radiation as exciter, systematic quantitative investigations were carried out by the author (*14,73–76*) and by Chandrasekharan (*77*) in diamond, quartz, alumina and a few alkali halides. The studies with diamond and quartz have been very thorough and the results are therefore briefly reviewed here.

1. DIAMOND (*14,75,77*)

The best specimen of diamond used by the author was in the form of a rectangular plate ($10 \times 6 \times 1.3$ mm) with faces and edges well polished. The length, breadth and the thickness of the specimen were parallel to [011], [111] and [211] directions respectively. Photographs of the Brillouin components in diamond for various settings are reproduced in Fig. 13 (*a, b, c*). They were taken with a high dispersion spectrograph without any interferometer. Only two pairs of components are recorded on either side for all the orientations, one due to longitudinal waves and the other due to the two transverse waves which have nearly the same velocity for the orientations used. The l or longitudinal component has a shift of ~ 8.5 cm^{-1} while the t or transverse components have a shift of ~ 5.5 cm^{-1}. Using Eq. (1), one finds that for such a large shift, the velocity of longitudinal sound in diamond reaches a value $\sim 18,000$ M/sec, while that

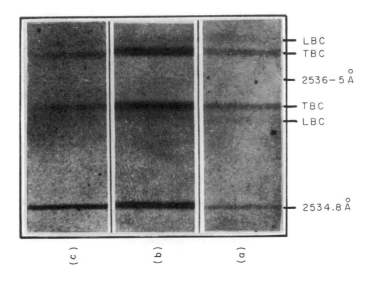

Fig. 13. The Brillouin spectrum of diamond for three different orientations for scattering at 90° taken by Chandrasekharan (77) with 2537 Å excitation. The unmodified line is absent due to absorption by mercury vapor filter. *LBC* = Longitudinal Brillouin Component, *TBC* = Transverse Brillouin Components.

of the transverse sound a value $\sim 11,000$ M/sec; the l component is less intense than the t components. This surprising result follows from Eq . (50) and (51) when one substitutes the known values of the piezo-optic and elastic constants of diamond. The calculated ratio of the intensity of the longitudinal components to that of the transverse components is 1:4, which is supported by the experimental results. The sum of the intensities of the Brillouin components is found to be less than a tenth of the intensity of the 1332 Raman line at room temperature (see Fig. 14). The intensity

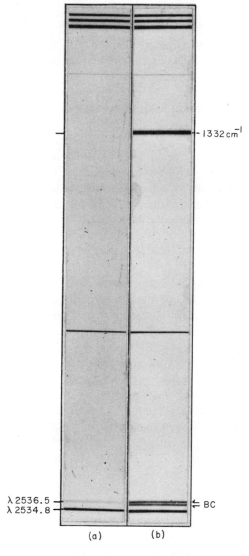

Fig. 14. (b) Raman spectrum of diamond showing the Brillouin components and the 1332 cm⁻¹ Raman line taken with 2537 Å excitation and a Hilger E1 quartz spectragraph, (dispersion = 40 cm⁻¹/mm), by the author *(14)*. (a) A comparison spectrum of the mercury arc. In (a) and (b) the exciting radiation is suppressed by mercury vapor filter.

of the Brillouin components is found to be very much temperature dependent over the range from 87°K to 570°K, while the intensity of the Raman line is practically unaffected by temperature over the same range (*14*). At 570°K the components are as intense as the Raman line, while at 87°K the components are very weak. The dependence of the frequency shifts on the orientation of the crystal with reference to the incident and scattered directions has been verified for five settings. The observed shifts were in very good agreement with the values calculated from the known elastic constants.

Chandrasekharan (*77*) worked out general expressions for the intensities of Brillouin components for 11 specific orientations of cubic crystals belonging to the T_d, O_h, and O classes and for 6 orientations of T and T_d crystal classes. He evaluated the intensities in the case of diamond and other cubic crystals. The results obtained for diamond compared well with our experimental data.

2. CRYSTALLINE QUARTZ

Using 2537 Å mercury resonance radiation as exciter, Krishnan and Chandrasekharan (*73*) recorded the longitudinal Brillouin components in a single crystal of quartz for different orientations. The transverse components were very weak and could not be recorded with the 2537 Å excitation. The observed frequency shift for the longitudinal components is in very good agreement with the value calculated from the known elastic constants. The dependence of frequency shift on orientation has been quantitatively verified for seven different settings of the crystal. For specific orientations, the intensities of the Brillouin components in quartz have been evaluated by Chandrasekharan (*33*).

Crystalline quartz has recently been investigated by Shapiro et al. (*72*) using a helium-neon laser. Only one orientation in which the optic axis of the crystal was perpendicular to the plane of scattering was studied. Three pairs of Brillouin components were recorded by them, an intense longitudinal pair and two weak transverse ones (see Fig. 15). The central component is as intense as the more intense transverse component. Shapiro and others found that the longitudinal pair and the weaker transverse pair are completely plane polarized, while the stronger transverse pair was depolarized to the extent of 50%. There was practically no broadening of the lines, indicating thereby that the absorption coefficient a is less than 10^3 cm^{-1}. The hypersonic velocities obtained by Shapiro and others are given in Table 5.

Shapiro and Cummins (*78*) investigated the temperature dependence of Brillouin scattering by crystalline quartz for acoustic phonons propagating in the (100), (010), (001) and (110) directions. They found that the frequency of the longitudinal component exhibited a temperature hysteresis in the α–β transition region, with a sharp discontinuity on heating and a gradual change on cooling. The central undisplaced component which was normally less intense than the Brillouin lines suddenly increased in intensity by a factor of $\sim 10^4$ at the transition temperature.

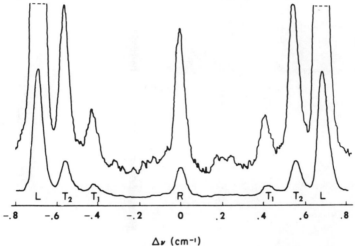

Fig. 15. Brillouin spectrum of crystalline quartz at two different gains taken with the laser 6328 Å excitation by Cummins' group (*72*). The spectrum shows the two transverse components (T_1 and T_2) in addition to the very much more intense longitudinal component (L). R is the central Rayleigh component.

TABLE 5

Brillouin Scattering Data for Quartz

Substance	Brillouin component	Hypersonic frequency (Gc/sec)	Hypersonic velocity (m/sec)
Crystalline quartz	L	20.4	5860
	T_1	16.4	4720
	T_2	12.4	3570
Fused quartz	L	19.4	5940
	T	12.2	3740

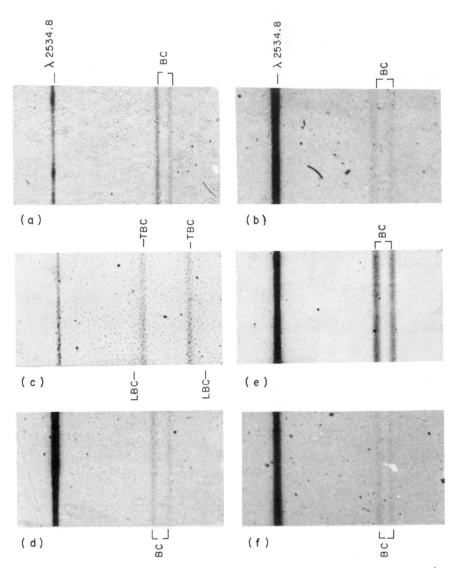

Fig. 16. Brillouin spectra of some typical crystals taken by the author (76) with 2537 Å excitation and a Hilger three metre quartz spectrograph (dispersion = 14 cm⁻¹/mm). (a) Rock salt, (b) diamond, (c) barite, (d) calcite, (e) quartz and (f) gypsum. Except in the case of diamond, only the longitudinal components have been recorded since the transverse ones are very weak. The unmodified line in the scattered light is completely suppressed by mercury vapor filter.

3. CUBIC AND OTHER CRYSTALS

The author made a preliminary study of the Brillouin scattering in LiF, NaCl, KCl, calcite, alumina, and barite (74,76) (see Fig. 16). In every case only the longitudinal pair was recorded. The method of evaluating the elastic constants of crystals from the observed frequency shifts of the Brillouin components was indicated by the author (76). Benedek et al. (37) investigated the Brillouin scattering in CsI, KI and TiO_2 using a helium-neon laser and estimated the hypersonic velocities in these crystals. Later, detailed investigations were carried out on KCl, KI, and RbCl by Benedek and Fritsch (79). From the observed frequency shifts of the Brillouin components, the elastic constants c_{11}, c_{12}, and c_{44} were very accurately evaluated at the hypersonic range of frequencies 8–15 Gc/sec. These values were in very good agreement with the values obtained from ultrasonic measurements at 10 Mc/sec indicating thereby that there is no dispersion of sound velocity over three orders of magnitude change in the sound wave frequency, and that the elastic constants are also independent of frequency. These workers have also worked out the theory of thermal scattering of light in cubic crystals and obtained expressions for the intensity, polarization and spectral distribution of the scattered light as a function of the incident and scattered directions in the crystal. They have also obtained expressions for the temperature dependence of the scattering valid at very low temperatures. According to their theoretical analysis, the longitudinal and the mixed mode acoustic components will be considerably more intense than the components from the purely transverse waves; their experimental results confirmed the theoretical predictions.

Kaiser and Zurek (80) measured the intensity of scattering and frequency shift of the Brillouin component of $SrTiO_3$ as a function of temperature from 300°K to 80°K. The $SrTiO_3$ has a transition temperature at ~110°K at which the structure changes from a cubic to lower symmetry. They noticed a sharp maximum in the intensity of scattering and a minimum in the frequency shift and hence a minimum in the acoustic velocity near the transition temperature. This suggests that the phase transition is of order > 1. They have also observed a new additional Brillouin doublet in the noncubic phase well below 110°K.

The Brillouin scattering of triglycine sulphate (TGS) which has a ferroelectric transition temperature ($T_c = 49°C$) has been investigated by Gammon and Cummins (81) in the temperature range 34–54°C. They found an anomalous change in the shifts of both the L and T Brillouin components (see Fig. 17). The frequency shift versus temperature curves for the different components exhibited an abrupt increase in value when the specimen passed through the transition temperature. This abrupt change was produced by the relaxation dispersion of the hypersonic velocity. The magnitude of the dispersion was found to depend strongly on crystal orientation with reference to the directions of incidence and scattering. For certain orientations of the crystal, dispersion was observed.

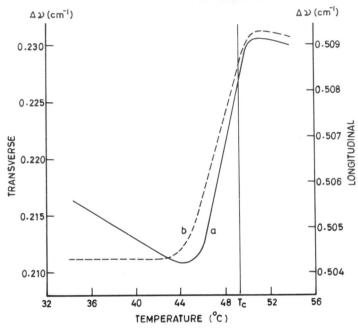

Fig. 17. Variation of frequency shift of Brillouin components with temperature in triglycine sulphate through the ferroelectric transition point $T_c = 49.2°C$. The continuous curve (a) is for transverse component, while the dashed curve (b) is for longitudinal components. The data are collected from the paper by Gammon and Cummins (81) and refer to scattering at 90°.

The relaxation dispersion of transverse phonons is 10 times greater than that of longitudinal phonons. Near the center of resonance, a marked broadening of the transverse components was also observed. From the measurements of the intensities and shifts of the Brillouin components coming under the species I_{Vv}, I_{Vh}, I_{Hv}, and I_{Hh} for different orientations of TGS, its photoelastic constants have been evaluated by Cummins and Gammon. This is the first time Brillouin scattering has been used for the determination of the photoelastic constants of a crystal.

Recently studies on Brillouin scattering in KH_2PO_4, NH_4Cl, and $LiNbO_3$ have been carried out, and the preliminary results were presented at the International Conference on Light Scattering Spectra of Solids held in September 1968 (78).

Griffiin (82) has recently given a theoretical review of the Brillouin scattering arising from the hydrodynamic collective modes of crystals. The intensity and spectral distribution of the scattered light have been expressed in terms of the Fourier transform of the displacement-displacement correlation function which is the spectral weight of the phonon propagator. Following the recent work of Loudon (35), the problem has been treated quantum mechanically. Griffin has derived expressions for the velocity and damping of the collective modes and has drawn attention to the occurrence of "second sound" or thermal diffusion modes in crystals which gives rise to an undisplaced or central component. In crystals it is not so easy to isolate pure unmodified scattering since the latter is usually mixed up with bogus scattering arising from impurities, surface and volume defects, etc. The optical conditions for the detection of the central component have therefore been reviewed. From a measurement of the intensity and width of the pure intrinsic central component, one can get information about the second sound. Griffin has also referred to the scattering arising from additional modes due to atomic diffusion, crystal surfaces, and phase transitions. Brillouin scattering is a very direct way of studying the dispersion relation of the surface oscillations or Rayleigh waves.

VII. STIMULATED BRILLOUIN SCATTERING

Using a very high power ruby laser as a source of excitation, Chiao, Townes and Stoicheff (83) demonstrated for the first time the appearance of stimulated Brillouin scattering in quartz and sapphire. The effect is similar to the stimulated Raman scattering except that the optical phonon of the lattice spectrum is replaced by the acoustic phonon. Unlike the stimulated Raman scattering, where the maximum Stokes output is in the forward direction, in stimulated Brillouin scattering the maximum effect is observed in the backward direction, i.e. $\theta = 180°$. Similar effects were observed in liquids by Garmire and Townes (84) and by Brewer and Rieckhoff (85), in amorphous solids and supercooled liquids by Mash et al. (86), and in gases by Hagenlocker and Rado (87), Mash et al. (88), and by Rank et al. (89).

The main condition for the appearance of the stimulated Brillouin scattering is that the power of the incident radiation should be above a threshold value which depends on the sample under investigation and is generally higher than that required for stimulated Raman scattering, except in the case of self-focussing fluids where the two thresholds are equal. The relation between the frequency, the direction of the scattered light, and the frequency of the associated phonon frequency is given by Eq. (1). In the process of producing stimulated Brillouin scattering, very intense hypersonic waves are generated in the medium which often cause severe damage to solid specimens. Multiple components due to several orders of the successively scattered light waves appear on either side of the exciting line, more on the Stokes side than on the other side. Intensities of most of the components are comparable with that of the incident light. Stimulated Brillouin scattering can also be observed in a direction perpendicular to the incident laser beam. The intensity of the stimulated scattering increases nonlinearly with increase in the linear dimensions of the scattering volume in the direction of observation of the scattered light. Because of the high directionality of the stimulated Brillouin components, their extreme sharpness and the many orders that are recorded, stimulated Brillouin scattering can be used for measuring hypersonic velocities to a high degree of accuracy.

When a beam from an intense laser source is focussed inside any medium, enormous electrostrictive pressures are developed in the medium which vary as E^2 where E is the electric field. The interaction between the light wave of the laser, the elastic wave or the pressure wave produced by electrostriction, and the polarization wave that is produced in terms of the pressure wave, gives rise to the phenomenon of stimulated Brillouin scattering. During this process, response of the medium at one point is effected by the response at neighboring points as well as by the response in an entire region with dimensions comparable to the acoustic decay length. A large number of papers has already appeared on this subject and some of the important results will be briefly reviewed here; stimulated Brillouin scattering will be denoted by its shortened form "SBS."

A. Solids

Chiao et al. (83) worked out the threshold power required for observing stimulated Brillouin scattering in quartz and sapphire. It was found to be of the order of 10^4 MW/cm^2. They used a ruby laser of 50 MW power and of 30 nsec pulse duration in their experiments on stimulated scattering in quartz and sapphire. Intense hypersonic waves of frequency 3×10^{10} cps were generated in the medium with the maximum power of 1 KW, which finally resulted in the destruction of the specimens. Hsu and Kavage (90) working on the SBS of crystalline quartz with laser powers well below the destruction point were able to excite not only the hypersonic phonons of frequency ~ 25.6 Gc/sec, but also the low frequency phonons (75 Mc/sec) corresponding to the forward scattering. The low frequency phonons are generated at lower threshold power. Krivokhizha et al. (91) and Tannenwald and Thaxter (92) investigated the SBS in single crystals of quartz in the range 2.1° to 293°K. The velocity of longitudinal sound has been calculated from the Brillouin shifts at various temperatures. Tannenwald and Thaxter used only 3–10 MW of power inside the specimen so as not to damage the same. Krivokhizha et al. reported that a quartz crystal kept at 80°K was not damaged by SBS and could therefore be used as a phonon generator for frequency of 3×10^{10} cps and for power levels of 50 kW. By suitable acoustic contact, the hypersonic waves could be transmitted into any other medium.

Brewer (93) found that crystals of LiF, NaCl and MgO were destroyed by the focussed laser beam before the appearance of stimulated Brillouin scattering. Martini (94) observed a very low threshold value for the appearance of SBS in ferroelectric crystals. It is of the order of 1 MW for Rochelle salt and twice that value for triglycine sulphate. The application of an electric field brings about an abrupt change in the threshold near T_c. Heinische and Winterling (95) measured the threshold power for the production of SBS in quartz over the range 5°–300°K; the dependence of threshold power on temperature was found to be very small. They carried out threshold measurements in ten different substances and came to the conclusion that the threshold power depended on the photoelastic properties of the substance under study. Absorption of sound also controls the threshold value of flux required to initiate SBS (96).

Mash et al. (86) reported the SBS in fused quartz and silicate glasses. Ordinary and stimulated Brillouin scattering form an effective method for the study of the acoustic properties of supercooled liquids. Ordinary sound waves could not be used for such studies as they induce crystallization in the supercooled liquid.

B. Liquids

Garmire and Townes (84) investigated the SBS in a few common liquids and found that the threshold power varied from liquid to liquid.

For CS_2 the threshold power was 30 MW/cm^2, for benzene it was 1200 MW/cm^2 and it was higher still for nitrobenzene. The threshold for the stimulated Raman effect was found to be lower than the same for SBS in CS_2, $C_6H_5NO_2$, $C_6H_5CH_3$, C_6H_6, and CH_3COCH_3. Unlike solids, liquids are not damaged by SBS which usually produces only cavitation (85). Brewer (97) who studied the SBS in liquids, discovered that the hypersonic waves that arise in the process of SBS possess a nonlinear character, and he was able to detect the existence of a second harmonic of the hypersound in the medium excited as the result of the nonlinearity. The SBS in CS_2 was excited by Takuma and Jennings (98) with an off axis resonator, the angle of scattering amounting to $\sim 2.5°$.

Rank and his collaborators (54,89,99) made a detailed investigation of the SBS in 23 liquids and 2 glasses using a high resolution grating spectrograph and a giant laser. In all cases, they observed a large number of Stokes and anti-Stokes components arising from repeated SBS, the frequency shifts being exact multiples of the first Brillouin component. Eighty percent of the polarized light incident on the liquids is back scattered as SBS. In liquids like CS_2, 30 Stokes, and 15 anti-Stokes components were recorded. Although the observations were made along the forward direction ($\theta = 0°$), the frequency shifts corresponded to backward scattering ($\theta = 180°$). They found that absolutely none of the laser light was transmitted without being modified. The laser frequency appears in the spectrum but both it and the modified components are completely depolarized, while the incident light is completely polarized. Back scattered Brillouin components are found to be polarized. Several liquids exhibited a continuum on the Stokes side due to the rotational wing. The number and the intensities of components in glycerine are practically unaffected by temperature, unlike the spontaneous Brillouin scattering. Wiggins and others (54) have determined very accurately the hypersonic velocities in 23 liquids based on measurements of SBS frequency shifts.

C. Gases

With the use of giant lasers as a source of excitation, SBS was observed in compressed gases by various workers (87–89); H_2, O_2, N_2, A, CO_2, and CH_4 are some of the gases examined. The SBS has also been reported near T_c of CO_2; as T_c is approached the SBS components shift towards the central line. Rank and others (89) could not observe any SBS with helium.

In the case of H_2 and N_2, contrary to theoretical expectations, the values of V_{IIS} are close to the isothermal V_U. Mink et al. (87) have obtained SBS in deuterium at pure rotational frequencies.

On the theoretical side, a large number of papers have appeared on stimulated Brillouin scattering. In this connection special mention should be made of the theoretical work of K. Grob (100).

VIII. FUTURE TRENDS

Quantitative determination of the intensity, width and depolarization of the Brillouin components has yet to be carried out in many crystals. The existence of a genuine central component in crystals and its dependence on the properties of the crystals have yet to be established. Studies of Brillouin scattering in crystals which have phase transitions will be helpful in understanding the nature of such transitions. Scattering experiments on single crystals near the melting point, in mixed crystals, and in molten salts would also be very useful in getting an insight into the process of mixing and also of melting.

Concerning liquids, detailed studies on the intensity and width of the four components near the critical temperature in the case of simple liquids and near the critical solution temperature in the case of liquid mixtures would also be very useful. Studies of the Brillouin scattering in high polymers and glasses will give us information on the nature of polymerization and on the glassy state. With the development of more and more sophisticated lasers one may expect to see a very commendable increase in activity in the field of both spontaneous and stimulated Brillouin scattering.

Acknowledgment

The author wishes to express his sincere thanks to Prof. B. P. Stoicheff, University of Toronto, for kindly placing at his disposal the original spectra reproduced in Figs. 8, 10, 11, and 13.

BIBLIOGRAPHY OF GENERAL ARTICLES ON BRILLOUIN SCATTERING

1. G. Bruhat, *Optique*, (A. Kastler, ed.), Masson & Cie Editeurs, Paris, 1954, p. 280.
2. P. L. Kelley, B. Lax, and P. E. Tannenwald, *Physics of Quantum Electronics*, McGraw-Hill Book Co., New York, 1956.

3. Proceedings of the 1966 International Quantum Electronics Conference, *IEEE Journal of Quantum Electronics*, Vol. 8, 190–298 and 337–637 (1966).

4. I. L. Fabelinskii, *Molecular Scattering of Light*, Translated from Russian by R. T. Bayer, Plenum Press, New York, 1968.

REFERENCES

1. A. Einstein, *Ann. Physik*, **33,** 1275 (1910).

2. L. Brillouin, *Ann. Phys.* (*Paris*), **88,** 17, (1922).

3. E. Gross, *Z. Physik*, **63,** 685 (1930).

4. E. H. L. Meyer and W. Ramm, *Phys. Z.*, **33,** 270 (1932).

5. W. Ramm, *Phys. Z.*, **35,** 11, 756 (1934).

6. K. Birus, *Physik Z.* **39,** 80 (1933).

7. Rafalowski, *Nature*, **128,** 495 (1931).

8. B. V. R. Rao, *Proc. Indian Acad. Sci.*, **A1,** 261, 473, 765 (1934). *Proc. Indian Acad. Sci.*, **A2,** 236 (1935).

9. C. S. Venkateswaran, *Proc. Indian Acad. Sci.*, **A15,** 322, 362, 371 (1942).

10. K. Sunanda Bai, *Proc. Indian Acad. Sci.*, **A15,** 349, 357 (1942).

11. E. Gross, *Nature*, **126,** 211 (1930).

12. C. V. Raman and C. S. Venkateswaran, *Nature*, **142,** 280 (1938).

13. L. Sibaiya, *Proc. Indian Acad. Sci.*, **A8,** 393 (1938).

14. R. S. Krishnan, *Nature*, **159,** 740 (1947). *Proc. Indian Acad. Sci.*, **A22,** 329 (1945); **A26,** 399 (1947).

15. R. S. Krishnan, *Nature*, **165,** 934 (1950). *Proc. Indian Acad. Sci.*, **A37,** 377 (1953).

16. D. H. Rank, J. S. McCartney, and G. J. Szask, *J. Opt. Soc. Amer.*, **38,** 287 (1948).

17. V. Chandrasekharan, *Current Sci. India*, **19,** 371 (1951). *Proc. Indian Acad. Sci.*, **A33,** 183 (1951).

18. M. Smoluchowski, *Ann. Physik*, **25,** 205 (1908).

19. L. D. Landau and G. Placzek, *Phys. Z. Sowjet Union*, **5,** 172 (1934).

20. J. Frenkel, *Kinetic theory of Liquids*, Oxford, (1946).

21. I. L. Fabelinskii, *Dokl. Akad. Nauk, SSSR*, **17,** 538 (1953).

22. R. D. Mountain, *Rev. Mod. Phys.*, **38,** 205 (1966). *J. National Bureau Standards*, **70A,** 207 (1966). *J. Chem. Phys.*, **44,** 832 (1966).

23. H. Z. Cummins and R. W. Gammon, *J. Chem. Phys.*, **44,** 2785 (1966).

24. C. L. O'Connor and J. P. Schlupf, *J. Chem. Phys.*, **47,** 31 (1967).

25. L. D. Landau and E. M. Lifshitz, *Statistical Physics*, Pergamon, New York, 352 (1959).

26. L. D. Landau and E. M. Lifshitz, *Electrodynamics of Continuous Media*, Addison-Wesley, (1960).

27. M. Leontowitsch, *Z. Physik*, **72,** 247 (1931).

28. K. R. Ramanathan, *Indian J. Phys.*, **1,** 413 (1927).

29. V. Chandrasekharan, *J. Phys.*, **26,** 655 (1965).

30. M. Leontowitsch and L. Mandelstam, *Phys. Zeits. Sowjet.*, **1,** 317 (1931). *Z. Physik*, **75,** 350 (1932).

31. I. Tamm, *Z. Physik*, **60,** 345 (1930).

32. O. Theimer, *Proc. Phys. Soc.*, **64,** 1012, (1951). *Proc. Phys. Soc.*, **65,** 38 (1952).

33. V. Chandrasekharan, *Proc. Nat. Inst. Sci.* (*India*), **19,** 547 (1953).

34. M. Born and K. Huang, *Dynamical Theory of Crystal Lattices*, Oxford, (1954).
35. R. Loudon, *Adv. Phys.*, **13**, 459 (1964).
36. R. E. S. Hearmon, *An Introduction to Applied Anisotropic Elasticity*, Oxford, p. 68, 1961.
37. G. B. Benedek, J. B. Lastova, K. Fritsch, and T. J. Greytek, *J. Opt. Soc. Amer.*, **54**, 1284 (1964).
38. R. Y. Chiao and B. P. Stoicheff, *J. Opt. Soc. Amer.*, **54**, 1286 (1964).
39. A. T. Forrester, *J. Opt. Soc. Amer.*, **51**, 253 (1961).
40. H. Z. Cummins, N. Knable, and Y. Yeh, *Phys. Rev. Letters*, **12**, 150 (1964).
41. J. B. Lastovka and G. B. Benedek, *Phys. Rev. Letters*, **17**, 1039 (1966).
42. C. S. Venkateswaran, *Proc. Indian Acad. Sci.*, **A15**, 316 (1942).
43. I. L. Fabelinskii, *J. Theor. Fiz. Akad.*, USSR, 254 (1959).
44. D. P. Eastman, T. A. Wiggins, and D. H. Rank, *Appl. Opt.* **5**, 879 (1966).
45. E. G. Ranson, E. H. Hara, A. D. May, and H. L. Welsh, *J. Opt. Soc. Amer.*, **56**, 1403 (1966).
46. T. J. Greytek and G. B. Benedek, *Phys. Rev. Letters*, **17**, 179 (1966).
47. M. S. Pesin and I. L. Fabelinskii, *Dokl. Akad. Nauk. SSSR.*, **122**, 575 (1958). *Sov. Phys. Dok.*, **3**, 974 (1958).
47a. I. L. Fabelinskii, *Uspekhi Fiz. Nauk.*, **77**, 644 (1962). *Sov. Phys. Uspheki*, **5**, 667 (1963).
48. D. I. Mash, V. S. Starunov, and I. L. Fabelinskii, *J. Exptl. Theor. Phys. USSR.*, **47**, 783 (1964).
49. D. H. Rank, E. M. Kiess, W. Fink and T. A. Wiggins, *J. Opt. Soc. Amer.*, **55**, 925 (1965).
50. G. B. Benedek and T. J. Greytek, *Proc. IEEE.*, **53**, 1623 (1965).
51. E. M. Kiess, Ph.D., Thesis Pennsylvania State University (1966).
52. D. L. Mash, V. I. Starunov, E. V. Tiganov, and I. L. Fabelinskii, *J. Exptl. Theor. Phys. USSR*, **49**, 1764 (1965).
53. P. A. Fleury and R. Y. Chiao, *J. Acous. Soc. Amer.*, **39**, 751 (1966).
54. T. A. Wiggins, R. W. Wick, N. D. Foltz, C. W. Cho, and D. H. Rank, *J. Opt. Soc. Amer.*, **57**, 661 (1967).
55. C. L. O'Connor and J. P. Schlupf, *J. Acous. Soc. Amer.*, **40**, 663 (1966).
56. D. H. Rank, E. M. Kiess, and W. Fink, *J. Opt. Soc. Amer.*, **56**, 163 (1966).
57. G. R. Hanes, R. Turner, and J. B. Piercy, *J. Acous. Soc. Amer.*, **38**, 1057 (1965).
58. H. Z. Cummins and R. W. Gammon, *Appl. Phys. Letters*, **6**, 171 (1965).
59. W. S. Gornall, G. I. A. Stegeman, B. P. Stoicheff, R. H. Stolen, and V. Volterra, *Phys. Rev. Letters*, **17**, 297 (1966).
60. K. F. P. Knapp, W. S. Gornall, and B. P. Stoicheff, *Phys. Rev.*, **166**, 139 (1968).
61. V. S. Starunov, E. V. Tiganov, and I. L. Fabelinskii, *JETP.*, **5**, 260 (1967).
62. I. L. Fabelinskii and V. S. Starunov, *Appl. Opt.*, **6**, 1793 (1967).
63. G. I. A. Stegeman and B. P. Stoicheff, *Phys. Rev. Letters*, **21**, 202 (1968).
64. S. M. Rytov, *Sov. Phys.*, *JETP.*, **6**, 401, 513 (1958).
65. N. C. Ford and G. B. Benedek, *Phys. Rev. Letters*, **15**, 649 (1965).
66. S. S. Alpert, D. Balzarini, R. Novick, L. Liegel, and Y. Yeh, *Proc. Conf. Phys. Quantum Electronics*, (1965), Puerto Rico.
67. R. W. Gammon, H. L. Swinney, and H. Z. Cummins, *Phys. Rev. Letters*, **19**, 1467 (1967).
67a. H. Z. Cummins and H. L. Swinney, *J. Chem. Phys.*, **45**, 4438 (1966).

67b. H. L. Swinney and H. Z. Cummins, *Phys. Rev.*, **171**, 152 (1968).
68. R. S. Krishnan, *Proc. Indian Acad. Sci.*, **A1**, 211, 915 (1934).
69. C. V. Raman and C. S. Venkateswaran, *Nature*, **142**, 791 (1938). *Nature*, **143**, 798 (1939).
70. M. S. Pesin and I. L. Fabelinskii, *Dokl. Akad. Nauk. SSSR*, **129**, 299 (1959). *Soviet Phys. Dokl.*, **4**, 1264 (1960).
   M. S. Pesin and I. L. Fabelinskii, *Dokl. Akad. Nauk.*, *SSSR*, **135**, 1114 (1960).
71. P. Flubacher, A. J. Leadbetter, J. A. Morrison, and B. P. Stoicheff, *Int. J. Phys. Chem. Solid*, **12**, 53 (1960).
72. S. M. Shapiro, R. W. Gammon, and H. Z. Cummins, *Appl. Phys. Letters*, **9**, 157 (1966).
73. R. S. Krishnan and V. Chandrasekharan, *Proc. Indian Acad. Sci.*, **A31**, 427 (1950).
74. R. S. Krishnan, *Proc. Indian Acad. Sei.*, **A26**, 450 (1947).
75. R. S. Krishnan, V. Chandrasekharan, and E. S. Rajagopal, *Nature*, **182**, 318 (1958).
76. R. S. Krishnan, *Proc. Indian Acad. Sci.*, **A41**, 91 (1955).
77. V. Chandrasekharan, *Proc. Ind. Acad. Sci.*, **A32**, 379 (1950). *J. Indian Inst. Sci.*, **34** 269 (1952).
78. S. M. Shapiro and H. Z. Cummins, *Proc. of the International Conference on Light Scattering Spectra of Crystals*, Springer-Verlag, New York, 1968. 705.
79. G. B. Benedek and K. Fritsch, *Phys. Rev.*, **149**, 647 (1966).
80. W. Kaiser and R. Zurek, *Phys. Letters*, **23**, 668 (1966).
81. R. W. Gammon and H. Z. Cummins, *Phys. Rev. Letters*, **17**, 193 (1966).
82. A. Griffin, *Rev. Mod. Phys.*, **40**, 167 (1968).
83. R. Y. Chiao, C. H. Townes, and B. P. Stoicheff, *Phys. Rev. Letters*, **12**, 592 (1964).
84. E. Garmire and C. H. Townes, *Appl. Phys. Letters*, **5**, 84 (1964).
85. R. G. Brewer and K. E. Rieckhoff, *Phys. Rev. Letters*, **13**, 334 (1964).
86. D. I. Mash, V. V. Morozov, V. S. Starunov, E. V. Tiganov, and I. L. Fabelinskii, *Zh. Eko. i. Theor. Fiz. Pisma*, **2**, 246 (1965). *JETP Letters*, **2**, 157 (1965).
87. E. E. Hagenlocker and W. G. Rado, *Appl. Phys. Letters*, **7**, 236 (1965). R. W. Mink, E. E. Hagenlocker, and W. G. Rado, *Phys. Rev. Letters*, **17**, 229 (1966).
88. D. I. Mash, V. V. Morozov, V. S. Starunov, and I. L. Fabelinskii, *Zh. Eko. i. Teo. Fiz. Pisma*, **2**, 349 (1965).
89. D. H. Rank, J. A. Wiggins, R. V. Wick, D. P. Eastman, and A. H. Guenther, *J. Opt. Soc. Amer.*, **56**, 174 (1966).
90. H. Hsu and W. Kavage, *Phys. Letters*, **15**, 207 (1965).
91. V. S. Krivokhizha, D. I. Mash, V. V. Morozov, V. S. Starunov, and I. L. Fabelinskii, *Zh. Eks. i. Theor. Fiz. Pisma*, **3**, 245 (1966).
92. P. E. Tannenwald and J. B. Thaxter, *Science*, **154**, 1319 (1966).
93. R. G. Brewer, *Phys. Rev.*, **140A**, 800 (1965).
94. F. De Martini, *App. Phys. Letters*, **9**, 31 (1966).
95. W. Heinische and G. Winterling, *App. Phys. Letters*, **11**, 231 (1967).
96. R. L. Gordon, *J. App. Phys.*, **39**, 306 (1968).
97. R. G. Brewer, *App. Phys. Letters*, **8**, 165 (1965).
98. H. Takuma and D. A. Jennings, *App. Phys. Letters*, **5**, 241 (1964).
99. R. V. Wick, D. H. Rank, and T. A. Wiggins, *Phys. Rev. Letters*, **17**, 466 (1966).
100. K. Grob, *Z. Physik.*, **201**, 59 (1967).